TENSORS
Mathematics of Differential Geometry and Relativity

TENSORS
Mathematics of Differential Geometry and Relativity

ZAFAR AHSAN

Former Professor
Department of Mathematics
Aligarh Muslim University
Aligarh

PHI Learning Private Limited

Delhi-110092
2018

TENSORS: Mathematics of Differential Geometry and Relativity
Zafar Ahsan

ISBN-978-81-203-5088-5

Second Printing · · · December, 2017

Published by Asoke K. Ghosh, PHI Learning Private Limited, Rimjhim House, 111, Patparganj Industrial Estate, Delhi-110092 and Printed by Mudrak, 30-A, Patparganj, Delhi-110091.

Contents

Preface

The principal aim of tensor analysis is to investigate the relations which remain valid when we change from one coordinate system to any other. The laws of physics cannot depend on the frame of reference which the physicist chooses for the description of such laws. Accordingly it is aesthetically desirable and sometime convenient to utilise tensors as the mathematical background in which these laws can be formulated. Albert Einstein (1879–1955) found it an excellent tool for the presentation of his general theory of relativity and as a result, tensors came into great prominence. Now it has applications in most branches of theoretical physics and engineering, such as mechanics, fluid mechanics, elasticity, plasticity and electromagnetism, etc.

The present book is intended to serve as a text for the postgraduate students of mathematics, physics and engineering. It is ideally suited for the students and teachers who are engaged in research in general theory of relativity and differential geometry. The book is self contained and requires only a knowledge of elementary calculus, differential equations and classical mechanics as pre-requisites. It comprises six chapters, and each chapter contains a large number of solved examples. Each chapter ends up with a carefully selected set of unsolved problems, and the answers and hints for the solution of these problems are given at the end of the book.

Chapter 1 deals with an introduction of tensors and their algebra. The symmetry properties of the tensors have also been discussed here. In Chapter 2, the notion of the Riemannian space is defined which lead to the concept of fundamental tensors. Relative, absolute and Levi-Civita tensors are also defined and discussed here along with related results. Christoffel symbols, covariant and intrinsic differentiations and related results form the contents of Chapter 3 along with the equation of a geodesic and affine parameter. In Chapter 4, a detailed account of the Riemann curvature tensor and its properties is discussed. The integrability condition and uniqueness of the Riemann tensor along with the Ricci and Einstein tensors, the flatness of the space, the Einstein spaces and the spaces of constant curvature have also been discussed in this chapter. Chapter 5 deals with some advanced topics like equation of geodesic deviation, the decomposition of Riemann tensor, its invariants and the classification of gravitational fields. This chapter also covers a detailed discussion of Lie derivative and related results.

The final chapter deals with the applications of tensors to relativity theory and differential geometry. The book concludes with a list of references. Mathematical equations appearing in the book have been numbered serially in each chapter. If, for example, Eq. (12) of Chapter 1 is used in any subsequent chapter, it will represented by Eq. (1.12).

While preparing the manuscript of this book, I have consulted many standard works. I am indebted to the authors of these works. I am thankful to my publisher, PHI Learning, in particular, the editorial and production teams for their nice efforts in bringing out the book. Finally, I wish to thank my family members for the encouragement and patience they have shown during the preparation of the manuscript.

Any suggestions or comments for improving the contents will be warmly appreciated.

Zafar Ahsan

CHAPTER 1

Tensors and Their Algebra

1.1 Introduction

In many areas of mathematical, physical and engineering sciences, it is often necessary to consider two types of quantities. First, those which have magnitude only. Such quantities are known as *scalars*. Mass, length, volume, density, work, electric charge, time, temperature, etc. are the examples of scalars. The second type are those which have both magnitude and direction. These are known as *vectors*. Some of the examples of vectors are velocity, acceleration, force, momentum, etc.

Quite often the notion of vector is not sufficient to represent a physical quantity. What happens when we need to keep the track of two (or more) pieces of information for a given physical quantity? For such situation, we need a tensor. A tensor contains the information about the directions and the magnitudes in those directions. Thus, for example, the stress at a point depends upon two directions; one normal to the surface and the other that represents the force creating stress and thus stress cannot be described by a vector quantity. As another example, the measurement of charge density will depend upon the four velocity of the observer and thus can be represented by a vector, while the measurement of electric field strength in some direction will not only depend upon this direction but also on the four velocity of the observer and thus such measurement cannot be described by a vector quantity alone. These and similar other examples led to the generalization of a vector quantity to a quantity known as *tensor*.

Life would have been miserable without tensors as we cannot walk across a room without using a tensor (the pressure tensor), it is impossible to align the wheels on our car without using a tensor (the inertia tensor) and definitely one cannot understand Einstein's theory of gravity without using tensors. The word "tensor" itself was introduced in 1846 by William Rowan Hamilton to describe something different from what is now meant by a tensor. The contemporary usage was brought in by Woldemar Voigt in 1898. The word *tensor* is derived from the Latin word *tensus* meaning *stress* or *tension*. In anatomy the word tensor means a muscle that stretches or tightens some part of the body.

The concept of tensors has its origin in the development of differential geometry by Gauss, Riemann and Christoffel. The tensor calculus (also

1

known as absolute calculus) was developed around 1890 by Gregorio Ricci-Curbastro and originally presented by Ricci in 1892. It was made accessible to many mathematicians by the publication of Ricci and his pupil Tullio Levi-Civita's classic text *"Methodes de calcul diffrentiel absolu et leurs applications"* (Methods of absolute differential calculus and their applications) [Mathematische Annalen Vol. 54 (1901)]. In the 20th century, the subject came to be known as tensor analysis, and became popular when Albert Einstein used it in his general theory of relativity around 1915. General relativity is formulated completely in the language of tensors. In Einstein's general relativity, using Riemannian geometry, gravity-inhabited space is analysed. The mass manifests as curvature in the spacetime geometry. Riemannian geometry (geometry of the curved space), until that time, was thought to be an abstract mathematical structure with no physical use. With the tools of Riemannian geometry, Einstein was able to formulate a theory that predicts the behaviour of objects in the presence of gravity, electromagnetic and other forces.

Einstein had learned about tensors, with great difficulty, from the geometer Marcel Grossmann. Levi-Civita then initiated a correspondence with Einstein to correct mistakes Einstein had made in his use of tensor analysis. The correspondence lasted 1915–17, and was characterized by mutual respect:

> *I admire the elegance of your method of computation; it must be nice*
> *to ride through these fields upon the horse of true mathematics while*
> *the like of us have to make our way laboriously on foot.*
>
> —ALBERT EINSTEIN

Tensors were also found to be useful in other fields such as continuum mechanics. Some well-known examples of tensors in differential geometry are quadratic forms such as metric tensors, and the Riemann curvature tensor. The exterior algebra of Hermann Grassmann, from the middle of the 19th century, is itself a tensor theory and highly geometric; but it was some time before it was seen, with the theory of differential forms, as naturally unified with tensor calculus. The work of Elie Cartan made differential forms one of the basic kinds of tensors used in mathematics. From about the 1920s onwards, it was realised that tensors play a basic role in algebraic topology. There are different types of tensor concepts that frequently occur in many branches of abstract algebra, particularly in homological algebra and representation theory. Multilinear algebra can be developed in greater generality than for scalars coming from a field, but the theory is then certainly less geometric, and computations are more technical and less algorithmic. Tensors are generalized within category theory by means of the concept of monoidal category, from the 1960s.

Nowadays tensors have many applications in most of the branches of theoretical physics and engineering, such as mechanics, fluid mechanics, elasticity, plasticity and electromagnetism, etc.

1.2   Transformation of Coordinates

The fundamental notion involved in tensor analysis is that of a geometrical point which is defined by means of its coordinates. Thus, in plane Euclidean geometry, a point is specified by its two Cartesian coordinates (X, Y) or, its polar coordinates (r, θ). All the points which together constitute the plane are said to form a two-dimensional manifold of points, the number of dimensions of the manifold being equal to the number of independent coordinates required to specify a point on it. In a similar way, ordinary three-dimensional Euclidean space forms a three-dimensional manifold of points, where three coordinates are required to specify each point completely. Therefore, a n-dimensional manifold of points is that for which n independent real numbers $(x^1, x^2, ... x^n)$ are required to specify every point completely. These n numbers are denoted collectively by x^i and are called the *coordinates* of the point.

Essentially, the coordinates are the names which we give to the events in the universe; in the first instant they have nothing to do with the physical properties.   For this reason all coordinate systems are also in principle equivalent, and a choice of a particular coordinate system is purely a question of expediency. Just as in three-dimensional space for a problem with spherical symmetry one would use spherical coordinate.   The description of a point by means of coordinates may be changed and one of the aims of tensor analysis is to investigate what consequential changes are produced by a simultaneous alteration of the coordinates of the points of the manifold. The operation by means of which the coordinates x^i of every point in the manifold are changed to x'^i is called a *coordinate transformation.*

Consider two set of variables $(x^1, x^2 \ldots x^n)$ and $(x'^1, x'^2 \ldots x'^n)$ which determine the coordinates of a point in a n-dimensional space in two different frames of reference. These two set of variables are related to each other by means of equation

$$x'^i \; = \; f^i(x^1, x^2, \ldots, x^n), \quad i = 1, 2, \ldots, n \qquad (1.1)$$

where the functions f^i are single-valued, continuous differentiable functions of the coordinates. They are also independent.

Differentiating Eq. (1.1) with respect to each of the coordinates x^j, we get $n \times n$ transformation matrix of coefficients

$$\frac{\partial x'^i}{\partial x^j} = \begin{bmatrix} \dfrac{\partial x'^1}{\partial x^1} & \dfrac{\partial x'^1}{\partial x^2} & \cdots & \dfrac{\partial x'^1}{\partial x^n} \\[2mm] \dfrac{\partial x'^2}{\partial x^1} & \dfrac{\partial x'^2}{\partial x^2} & \cdots & \dfrac{\partial x'^2}{\partial x^n} \\[1mm] \vdots & \vdots & \vdots & \vdots \\[1mm] \dfrac{\partial x'^n}{\partial x^1} & \dfrac{\partial x'^n}{\partial x^2} & \cdots & \dfrac{\partial x'^n}{\partial x^n} \end{bmatrix} \qquad (1.2)$$

The determinant J' of this matrix is called the *Jacobian* of the transformation:

$$J' = \left| \frac{\partial x'^i}{\partial x^j} \right| \tag{1.3}$$

We shall assume that this is non-zero for some range of coordinates x^j so that we can solve Eq. (1.1) for the coordinates x^j and we have

$$x^i = F^i(x'^1, x'^2, \ldots, x'^n), \quad i = 1, 2, \ldots, n \tag{1.4}$$

If we denote the Jacobian of the inverse transformation by

$$J = \left| \frac{\partial x^i}{\partial x'^j} \right| \tag{1.5}$$

then from the product rule for determinants it follows that $J = \dfrac{1}{J'}$. Equations (1.1) and (1.4) are said to define a *coordinate transformation*.

We shall now consider two simple examples of coordinate transformations. In the two-dimensional Euclidean space, the transformation from Cartesian coordinates $x = x^1, y = x^2$ to polar coordinates $r = x'^1, \theta = x'^2$ is given by the equation

$$x^1 = x'^1 \cos x'^2, \quad x^2 = x'^1 \sin x'^2 \tag{1.6}$$

While in a three-dimensional Euclidean space, the transformation from Cartesian coordinates $x = x^1, y = x^2, z = x^3$ to spherical polar coordinates $r = x'^1, \theta = x'^2, \phi = x'^3$ is

$$x^1 = x'^1 \sin x'^2 \cos x'^3$$

$$x^2 = x'^1 \sin x'^2 x'^3 \tag{1.7}$$

$$x^3 = x'^1 \cos x'^2$$

The set of Eqs. (1.6) and (1.7) can be solved for x'^i; for example, Eq. (1.6) can lead to

$$x'^1 = [(x^1)^2 + (x^2)^2]^{1/2}, \quad x'^2 = \tan^{-1}\left(\frac{x^2}{x^1}\right)$$

If we take the differential of Eq. (1.1), then

$$dx'^i = \frac{\partial x'^i}{\partial x^1} dx^1 + \frac{\partial x'^i}{\partial x^2} dx^2 + \cdots + \frac{\partial x'^i}{\partial x^n} dx^n$$

$$= \sum_{j=1}^{n} \frac{\partial x'^i}{\partial x^j} dx^j, \quad (i = 1, 2, \ldots, n) \tag{1.8}$$

while the differential of Eq. (1.4) is

$$dx^i = \sum_{j=1}^{n} \frac{\partial x^i}{\partial x'^j} dx'^j, \quad (i = 1, 2, \ldots, n) \tag{1.9}$$

1.3   Summation Convention

If any index in a term is repeated, then a summation with respect to that index over the range $1, 2, \ldots, n$ is implied. This convention is known as *Einstein summation convention*.

According to this convention, instead of the expression $\sum\limits_{i=1}^{n} a_i x^i$, we simply write $a_i x^i$ and Eqs. (1.8) and (1.9) with this convention may, respectively, be expressed as

$$dx'^i = \frac{\partial x'^i}{\partial x^j} dx^j \quad \text{and} \quad dx^i = \frac{\partial x^i}{\partial x'^j} dx'^j$$

Thus, summation convention means the drop of summation symbol for the index appearing twice in the term.

If a suffix (index) occurs twice in a term, once in the upper position and once in the lower position, then that suffix (index) is called a *dummy suffix (index)*; for example, j is a dummy suffix in Eq. (1.8). Also

$$a_i^k x^i = a_1^k x^1 + a_2^k x^2 + \cdots + a_n^k x^n$$

and

$$a_j^k x^j = a_1^k x^1 + a_2^k x^2 + \cdots + a_n^k x^n$$

Thus, $a_i^k x^i = a_j^k x^j$ which shows that a dummy suffix can be replaced by another dummy suffix not already appearing in the expression.

A suffix (index) which is not repeated is called a *real suffix (index)*. For example, k is a real suffix in $a_i^k x^i$. A real suffix cannot be replaced by another real suffix as $a_i^k x^i \neq a_i^p x^i$.

1.4   Kronecker Delta

The symbol *Kronecker delta* δ_j^i (named after 19th century German mathematician Leopold Kronecker) is defined by

$$\delta_j^i = \begin{cases} 1, & \text{for } i = j \\ 0, & \text{for } i \neq j \end{cases}$$

It has the following properties:

(i) If $x^1, x^2, \ldots, x^n$ are independent varaiables, then

$$\frac{\partial x^i}{\partial x^j} = \delta_j^i.$$

(ii) $\delta_k^i A^k = A^i$.

(iii) In n dimensions, $\delta_i^i = n$.

(iv) $\delta_j^i \delta_k^j = \delta_k^i$ and $\dfrac{\partial x^i}{\partial x'^j} \dfrac{\partial x'^j}{\partial x^k} = \delta_k^i.$

The generalization of the Kronecker delta can be done as follows:

(a) the subscript and the superscript can have any value from 1 to n,

(b) if either at least two subscripts have the same value or, the subscripts are not the same set as the superscript, then the generalized Kronecker delta is zero. For example

$$\delta^{ikk}_{jnl} = \delta^{ijk}_{lmm} = \delta^{ijk}_{klm} = 0.$$

(c) if all the subscripts are separately different and the subscripts are the same set of numbers as the superscripts, then the generalized Kronecker delta has the value $+1$ or -1, according whether it requires an even or odd number of permutations to arrange the superscripts in the same order as subscripts. For example

$$\delta^{ij}_{kl} = \begin{cases} +1, & i \neq j . ij = kl \\ -1, & i \neq j . ij = lk \\ 0, & \text{otherwise} \end{cases}$$

$$\delta^{ijk}_{lmn} = \begin{cases} +1, & i \neq j \neq k, ijk \text{ is an even permutation of } lmn \\ -1, & i \neq j \neq k, ijk \text{ is an odd permutation of } lmn \\ 0, & \text{otherwise} \end{cases}$$

and a similar expression for δ^{ijkl}_{mnop}.

We thus have

$$\delta^{ij}_{kl} = \begin{vmatrix} \delta^i_k & \delta^j_k \\ \delta^i_l & \delta^j_l \end{vmatrix} \tag{1.10}$$

$$\delta^{ijk}_{lmn} = \begin{vmatrix} \delta^i_l & \delta^j_l & \delta^k_l \\ \delta^i_m & \delta^j_m & \delta^k_m \\ \delta^i_n & \delta^j_n & \delta^k_n \end{vmatrix} \tag{1.11}$$

$$\delta^{ijkl}_{mnop} = \begin{vmatrix} \delta^i_m & \delta^j_m & \delta^k_m & \delta^l_m \\ \delta^i_n & \delta^j_n & \delta^k_n & \delta^l_n \\ \delta^i_o & \delta^j_o & \delta^k_o & \delta^l_o \\ \delta^i_p & \delta^j_p & \delta^k_p & \delta^l_p \end{vmatrix} \tag{1.12}$$

EXAMPLE 1.1 In 4-dimensions, prove that $\delta_{lmk}^{ijk} = 2\delta_{lm}^{ij}$.

Solution From Eq. (1.11), we have

$$\delta_{lmk}^{ijk} = \begin{vmatrix} \delta_l^i & \delta_l^j & \delta_l^k \\ \delta_m^i & \delta_m^j & \delta_m^k \\ \delta_k^i & \delta_k^j & \delta_k^k \end{vmatrix}$$

$$= 3(\delta_l^i \delta_m^j - \delta_l^j \delta_m^i) - (\delta_l^i \delta_m^j - \delta_l^j \delta_m^i)$$

$$= \begin{vmatrix} \delta_l^i & \delta_l^j \\ \delta_m^i & \delta_m^j \end{vmatrix}$$

$$= 2\delta_{lm}^{ij}$$

[from Eq. (1.10)].

1.5 Scalar, Contravariant and Covariant Vectors

In the study of a physical theory we are concerned with geometrical objects—a collective name for all objects whose components ξ^i transform under a given transformation in such a way that the new components ξ'^i are unique functions of the old ones, of the transformation matrix J' [cf., Eq. (1.2)] and of its derivatives. These objects may be classified as

Scalar (invariant or tensor of rank zero).

Vector (tensor of rank one).

Tensor (of second and higher ranks).

Scalar Two functions $\phi(x)$ and $\phi'(x')$ are said to define a *scalar* (or an invariant) if they are reducible to each other by a coordinate transformation, where $\phi(x)$ is the value of the scalar in one coordinate system and $\phi'(x')$ is its value in another coordinate system. Thus, a scalar does not change under coordinate transformation. Its value at a point remains constant even if the coordinates of this point are changed. For example, the interval ds of two points is a scalar. Another typical scalar (invariant) is a time-dependent temperature distribution function which assigns a number, the temperature, to each space point.

Vectors A set of n quantities A^i, which transform like the coordinate differentials [cf., Eq. (1.8)]

$$A'^i = \frac{\partial x'^i}{\partial x^j} A^j, \quad i, j = 1, 2, \ldots, n \tag{1.13}$$

are called the components of a *contravariant vector* (*contravariant tensor of rank one*).

A set of n quantities A_i are called the components of a *covariant vector* (*covariant tensor of rank one*), if they transform like

$$A_i' = \frac{\partial x^j}{\partial x'^i} A_j, \quad i, j = 1, 2, \ldots, n \tag{1.14}$$

EXAMPLE 1.2 Show that the tangent vector of a smooth curve transforms as a contravariant tensor of rank one.

Solution Let C be a smooth curve parametrically represented in x^i-coordinate system by

$$x^i = x^i(t), \quad a \le t \le b$$

The tangent vector T^i is defined by

$$T^i = \frac{dx^i}{dt}$$

Under the change of coordinate system given by Eq. (1.1), the equation of the curve in x'^i-coordinate system is

$$x'^i = x'^i(t), \quad a \le t \le b$$

and the tangent vector for the curve C in x'^i-coordinate system has the components

$$T'^i = \frac{dx'^i}{dt}$$

But from the chain rule, we have

$$T'^i = \frac{\partial x'^i}{\partial x^j} \frac{dx^j}{dt} = \frac{\partial x'^i}{\partial x^j} T^j$$

which shows that the tangent vector transforms like the components of a contravariant tensor of rank one (see also Section 2.4).

EXAMPLE 1.3 Show that the gradient of an arbitrary differentiable function is a covariant vector.

Solution Let $f(x)$ denote a differentiable scalar field defined in x^i-coordinate system. The gradient of f is defined as

$$\nabla f = \frac{\partial f}{\partial x^i}$$

In x'^i-coordinate system, the gradient is $\nabla' f' = \dfrac{\partial f'}{\partial x'^i}$, where $f'(x') = f \circ x(x')$. Using Eq. (1.4), the chain rule for partial differentiation yields

$$\frac{\partial f'}{\partial x'^i} = \frac{\partial f}{\partial x^j} \frac{\partial x^j}{\partial x'^i}$$

which is simply Eq. (1.14) as $A'_i = \dfrac{\partial f'}{\partial x'^i}$, $A_i = \dfrac{\partial f}{\partial x^i}$. Thus, the gradient of an arbitrary differentiable function is a covariant tensor of rank one (see also Chapter 3).

Remarks

1. If we interchange the two system of axes (coordinates) and change the suffices in Eqs. (1.13) and (1.14), we get

$$A^j = \frac{\partial x^j}{\partial x'^i} A'^i \tag{1.13a}$$

$$A_j = \frac{\partial x'^i}{\partial x^j} A'_i \tag{1.14a}$$

2. Covariant and contravariant components describe the same vector, the difference between them being typical of non-orthogonal coordinates.

3. Figure 1.1 shows how in $x^1 x^2$-plane we obtain the contravariant components by parallel projection onto and the covariant components by dropping perpendiculars onto, the coordinate axes of a non-orthogonal Cartesian system.

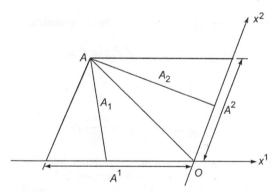

Figure 1.1 Contravariant and covariant components of a vector.

The transformation Eqs. (1.13) and (1.14) suggest the question: what is the relationship of these quantities which we have defined as contravariant and covariant vectors with the conventional physical vectors with which we are familiar, such as velocity, force, electric and magnetic fields, etc.? How can we know whether a given physical vector should be transformed as a contravariant or covariant vector? Before proceeding to answer these questions, we must first observe that in the (1+3)-coordinate spacetime continuum, the vectors A^i and A_i necessarily possess four components in contrast to the physical vectors (mentioned above) which are three component vectors, defined in three-dimensional space of ordinary experiance. In order to treat the physical vectors as contravariant or covariant tensors of rank one in four dimensions they must be extended by the addition of a fourth component in some suitable manner. Unfortunately, no general prescription for making this extension can be given, and particular cases must be dealt with individually on the basis of what is known about the physical quantity. We shall find in some cases, notably that of electromagnetic fields, that the physical vectors can be redefined as members of a two-dimensional array which is a tensor of rank two.

The terms contravariant and covariant as applied to vectors should preferably be modified to specify the contravariant and covariant components of the physical vectors. In fact, we can transform from one set of components of a given vector to another by means of the metric tensor, as we shall see in Chapter 2.

EXAMPLE 1.4 In a Cartesian coordinate system, show that there is no difference between the contravariant and covariant vectors.

Solution   Let (x, y) and (x', y') be the coordinates of a point with respect to the Cartesian coordinate axes X, Y and X', Y', respectively. Also, if l_1, m_1 and l_2, m_2 are the direction cosines of X' and Y', respectively, then

$$x' = l_1 x + m_1 y, \quad y' = l_2 x + m_2 y \tag{1.15}$$

which leads to

$$x = l_1 x' + l_2 y', \quad y = m_1 x' + m_2 y' \tag{1.16}$$

Let $x^1 = x, x^2 = y$ and $x'^1 = x', x'^2 = y'$, then from Eq. (1.13), we have

$$A'^1 = \frac{\partial x'}{\partial x} A^1 + \frac{\partial x'}{\partial y} A^2$$

$$A'^2 = \frac{\partial y'}{\partial x} A^1 + \frac{\partial y'}{\partial y} A^2$$

From Eq. (1.15), these equations lead to

$$A'^1 = l_1 A^1 + m_1 A^2, \quad A'^2 = l_2 A^1 + m_2 A^2 \tag{1.17}$$

Now, consider the transformation law (1.14) for a covariant vector and proceed in the same way as above to get

$$A'_1 = l_1 A_1 + m_1 A_2, \quad A'_2 = l_2 A_1 + m_2 A_2 \tag{1.18}$$

Comparing Eqs. (1.17) and (1.18) we see that there is no difference between the contravariant and covariant vectors as far as the Cartesian coordinates are concerned.

EXAMPLE 1.5 Find the components of a vector in polar coordinate system whose components in Cartesian coordinate sysytem are $\dot{x}, \dot{y}$ and $\ddot{x}, \ddot{y}$.

Solution   Given that $x^1 = x, x^2 = y$ and $x'^1 = r, x'^2 = \theta; A^1 = \dot{x}, A^2 = \dot{y}$ and $A^1 = \ddot{x}, A^2 = \ddot{y}$, then we have to find A'^1 and A'^2.

It is known that $x = r \cos \theta, y = r \sin \theta, r^2 = x^2 + y^2$ and $\theta = \tan^{-1}(y/x)$, which gives

$$\frac{\partial r}{\partial x} = \frac{x}{r}, \ \frac{\partial r}{\partial y} = \frac{y}{r}, \ \frac{\partial \theta}{\partial x} = -\frac{y}{r^2}, \ \frac{\partial \theta}{\partial y} = \frac{x}{r^2}, \ r\dot{r} = x\dot{x} + y\dot{y}, \ \dot{\theta} = \frac{x\dot{y} - y\dot{x}}{r^2}$$

Thus, from Eq. (1.13), we have

$$A'^1 = \frac{\partial x'^1}{\partial x^1} A^1 + \frac{\partial x'^1}{\partial x^2} A^2 = \frac{\partial r}{\partial x}\dot{x} + \frac{\partial r}{\partial y}\dot{y} = \dot{r}$$

$$A'^2 = \frac{\partial x'^2}{\partial x^1} A^1 + \frac{\partial x'^2}{\partial x^2} A^2 = \frac{\partial \theta}{\partial x}\dot{x} + \frac{\partial \theta}{\partial y}\dot{y} = \dot{\theta}$$

and therefore $\dot{r}$ and $\dot{\theta}$ are the components of the vector in polar coordinates when its components in Cartesian coordinates are $\dot{x}$ and $\dot{y}$.

Similarly, the components of a vector in polar coordinates are $\dfrac{r\ddot{r} - r^2\dot{\theta}^2}{r}, \ddot{\theta} + \dfrac{2\dot{r}\dot{\theta}}{r}$ when its components in Cartesian coordinates are $\ddot{x}, \ddot{y}$.

1.6 Tensors of Higher Rank

Scalars, contravariant and covariant vectors are the special cases of a class of quantities which transform with a law of transformation under the coordinate transformations given by (1.1) and (1.4). Such quantities are called *tensors* and accordingly a scalar is a tensor of rank (order) zero and a vector is a tensor of rank one. Since there are two types of vectors, viz. contravariant and covariant, there are three types of tensors of rank two which are defined as follows.

Consider a set of n^2 quantities $A^{kl}(k, l = 1, 2, \ldots, n)$ in coordinate system x^i and let these quantities have the values A'^{ij} in another coordinate system x'^i. If these quantities obey the law

$$A'^{ij} = \frac{\partial x'^i}{\partial x^k} \frac{\partial x'^j}{\partial x^l} A^{kl} \qquad (1.19)$$

then the quantities A^{kl} are said to be the components of a *contravariant tensor of rank two*. Similarly, the quantities A_{kl} are said to be the components of a *covariant tensor of rank two* if

$$A'_{ij} = \frac{\partial x^k}{\partial x'^i} \frac{\partial x^l}{\partial x'^j} A_{kl} \qquad (1.20)$$

If the n^2 quantities A^k_l and A'^i_j in the coordinate systems x^i and x'^i, respectively, are related to each other by the transformation law

$$A'^i_j = \frac{\partial x'^i}{\partial x^k} \frac{\partial x^l}{\partial x'^j} A^k_l \qquad (1.21)$$

then the quantities A_l^k are said to be the components of a *mixed tensor of rank two*.

It may be noted that a mixed tensor A_l^k transforms like a covariant vector with respect to the index l and like a contravariant vector with respect to the index k. Thus, the Kronecker delta is a mixed tensor due to the transformation property

$$\frac{\partial x'^i}{\partial x^a} \frac{\partial x^b}{\partial x'^j} \delta_b^a = \frac{\partial x'^i}{\partial x^a} \frac{\partial x^a}{\partial x'^j} \delta_a^a = \frac{\partial x'^i}{\partial x'^j} = \delta_j'^i$$

Moreover, by interchanging the systems of coordinates and changing the suffixes in Eqs. (1.19)–(1.21), we have

$$A^{kl} = \frac{\partial x^k}{\partial x'^i} \frac{\partial x^l}{\partial x'^j} A'^{ij} \tag{1.19a}$$

$$A_{kl} = \frac{\partial x'^i}{\partial x^k} \frac{\partial x'^j}{\partial x^l} A'_{ij} \tag{1.20a}$$

$$A_l^k = \frac{\partial x^k}{\partial x'^i} \frac{\partial x'^j}{\partial x^l} A'^i_j \tag{1.21a}$$

Second rank tensors have a number of useful applications. We illustrate below a physical example of such a tensor.

Beam carrying a load. Consider a beam carrying a load; there are stresses and strains in the material of the beam. If we imagine cutting the beam in two parts by a plane perpendicular to the x-direction, we realize that there is a force per unit area exerted *by* the material on one side of our imaginary cut *on* the material on the other side. This is a vector having three components P_{xx}, P_{xy}, P_{xz}, where the first subscript denotes the force across a plane perpendicular to the x-direction. Similarly, if we consider a plane perpendicular to the y-direction, there is a force per unit area across this plane with components P_{yx}, P_{yy}, P_{yz}; and finally across a plane perpendicular to the z-direction there is a force with components P_{zx}, P_{zy}, P_{zz}.

We then have a set of nine quantities at a point in the beam. These quantities can be expressed as the matrix

$$\begin{bmatrix} P_{xx} & P_{xy} & P_{xz} \\ P_{yx} & P_{yy} & P_{yz} \\ P_{zx} & P_{zy} & P_{zz} \end{bmatrix}$$

This is a second rank tensor known as *stress tensor*. The forces (per unit area) P_{xx}, P_{yy}, P_{zz} are *pressures* or *tensions* (*principal stresses*); the others are *shear forces* (per unit area). For example, P_{zy} is a force per unit area in the y-direction acting across a plane perpendicular to the z-direction; this force tends to shear the beam.

Remarks

1. Upper index of a tensor denotes the contravariant nature while the lower index indicates the covariant character of the tensor. The total number of upper and lower indices of a tensor is called the *rank* or *order* of the tensor. The rank of a tensor when raised as power to the number of dimensions gives the number of components of the tensor. Thus, *a tensor of rank r in n dimensions has n^r components.*

2. A tensor of rank zero (scalar) has magnitude only and has only one component; and a tensor of rank zero is sufficient to represent a single temperature or a temperature field across a surface, for example, an aircraft compressor blade. A tensor of rank one (vector) has magnitude and one direction as well, it has three components (in three dimensions). A rank one tensor is required to represent the electric field surrounding a point charge in space or the gravitational field of a massive object. While a rank two tensor has nine components in three dimensions, a magnitude and two directions are asociated with it; and is necessary to represent a magnetic permeability in complex materials, or the stress in a material object or in a field, and so on.

We can define the tensors of much higher rank as follows:

A set of quantities $A^{i_1 i_2 \cdots i_r}$ in a coordinate system x^i are said to be the components of a *contravariant tensor of rank r* if they satisfy the transformation law

$$A'^{j_1 j_2 \cdots j_r} = \frac{\partial x'^{j_1}}{\partial x^{i_1}} \frac{\partial x'^{j_2}}{\partial x^{i_2}} \cdots \frac{\partial x'^{j_r}}{\partial x^{i_r}} A^{i_1 i_2 \cdots i_r} \tag{1.22}$$

where $A'^{j_1 j_2 \cdots j_r}$ are the quantities in x'^i coordinate system.

Similarly, the quantities $A_{i_1 i_2 \cdots i_r}$ obeying the law

$$A'_{j_1 j_2 \cdots j_r} = \frac{\partial x^{i_1}}{\partial x'^{j_1}} \frac{\partial x^{i_2}}{\partial x'^{j_2}} \cdots \frac{\partial x^{i_r}}{\partial x'^{j_r}} A_{i_1 i_2 \cdots i_r} \tag{1.23}$$

are said to form the components of a *covariant tensor of rank r.*

While, the quantities $A^{i_1 i_2 \cdots i_r}_{j_1 j_2 \cdots j_s}$ satisfying the law

$$A'^{l_1 l_2 \cdots l_r}_{m_1 m_2 \cdots m_s} = \left(\frac{\partial x'^{l_1}}{\partial x^{i_1}} \frac{\partial x'^{l_2}}{\partial x^{i_2}} \cdots \frac{\partial x'^{l_r}}{\partial x^{i_r}} \right) \left(\frac{\partial x^{j_1}}{\partial x'^{m_1}} \frac{\partial x^{j_2}}{\partial x'^{m_2}} \cdots \frac{\partial x^{j_s}}{\partial x'^{m_s}} \right) A^{i_1 i_2 \cdots i_r}_{j_1 j_2 \cdots j_s} \tag{1.24}$$

are the components of a *mixed tensor of rank $(r + s)$.*

If $A^{i_1 i_2 \cdots i_r}_{j_1 j_2 \cdots j_s} = 0$ then from Eq. (1.24) it follows that

$$A'^{l_1 l_2 \cdots l_r}_{m_1 m_2 \cdots m_s} = 0$$

and we have

Theorem 1.1 If all the components of a tensor vanish in one coordinate system, then they necessarily vanish in every coordinate system.

Thus, for example, if a tensor equation $A^i_{jkl} - \alpha B^I_{jkl} = 0$ (where α is a scalar) is true in x^i-coordinate system then it is true in all coordinate system.

1.7   Symmetry of Tensors

The interchange of some of the indices of a tensor leads to an important property of a tensor, viz. its symmetry/skew-symmetry property.

If two indices of a tensor, either covariant or contravariant, are interchanged and the resulting tensor remains the same, the tensor is then said to be *symmetric* with respect to these two indices.

For example, if

$$A^{ij} = A^{ji} \quad \text{or} \quad A_{ij} = A_{ji} \tag{1.25}$$

then the second rank contravariant tensor A^{ij} or the second rank covariant tensor A_{ij} is symmetric. A rank three tensor A^{ij}_k is symmetric with respect to the indices i and j if $A^{ij}_k = A^{ji}_k$.

Now, if a tensor A^{ijk}_l is symmetric with respect to the indices i and j, then

$$A^{ijk}_l = A^{jik}_l \tag{1.26}$$

Moreover, A^{ijk}_l transforms as

$$
\begin{aligned}
A'^{abc}_d &= \frac{\partial x'^a}{\partial x^i} \frac{\partial x'^b}{\partial x^j} \frac{\partial x'^c}{\partial x^k} \frac{\partial x^l}{\partial x'^d} A^{ijk}_l \\
&= \frac{\partial x'^a}{\partial x^i} \frac{\partial x'^b}{\partial x^j} \frac{\partial x'^c}{\partial x^k} \frac{\partial x^l}{\partial x'^d} A^{jik}_l \quad \text{[from Eq. (1.26)]} \\
&= \frac{\partial x'^a}{\partial x^j} \frac{\partial x'^b}{\partial x^i} \frac{\partial x'^c}{\partial x^k} \frac{\partial x^l}{\partial x'^d} A^{ijk}_l
\end{aligned}
$$

which shows that the given tensor is symmetric in this new coordinate system. This result can also be proved when the covariant indices of the tensor A^i_{jkl} are considered. We thus have

Theorem 1.2   The symmetry property of a tensor is independent of the coordinate system.

Now consider the tensor A^{ijk}_l which is symmetric with respect two indices i and l, i.e. one contravariant and other covariant, respectively, then we have

$$A^{ijk}_l = A^{ljk}_i \tag{1.27}$$

and

$$
\begin{aligned}
A'^{abc}_d &= \frac{\partial x'^a}{\partial x^i} \frac{\partial x'^b}{\partial x^j} \frac{\partial x'^c}{\partial x^k} \frac{\partial x^l}{\partial x'^d} A^{ijk}_l \\
&= \frac{\partial x'^a}{\partial x^i} \frac{\partial x'^b}{\partial x^j} \frac{\partial x'^c}{\partial x^k} \frac{\partial x^l}{\partial x'^d} A^{ljk}_i \quad \text{[from Eq. (1.27)]} \\
&= \frac{\partial x'^a}{\partial x^l} \frac{\partial x'^b}{\partial x^j} \frac{\partial x'^c}{\partial x^k} \frac{\partial x^i}{\partial x'^d} A^{ljk}_i \\
&= \frac{\partial x^i}{\partial x'^d} \frac{\partial x'^b}{\partial x^j} \frac{\partial x'^c}{\partial x^k} \frac{\partial x'^a}{\partial x^l} A^{ljk}_i \tag{1.28}
\end{aligned}
$$

But according to transformation law for tensors

$$A_a'^{dbc} = \frac{\partial x'^d}{\partial x^i} \frac{\partial x'^b}{\partial x^j} \frac{\partial x'^c}{\partial x^k} \frac{\partial x^l}{\partial x'^a} A_l^{ijk} \qquad (1.29)$$

From Eqs. (1.28) and (1.29), we now have

$$A_d'^{abc} \neq A_a'^{dbc}$$

and the symmetry is not preserved after a change of coordinate system. We thus have

Theorem 1.3 The symmetry property of a tensor is defined only when the indices are of the same type, i.e., both indices are either covariant or contravariant.

On the other hand, when two contravariant or covariant indices are interchanged and the resulting tensor changes its sign without changing its magnitude, then the tensor is said to be *skew symmetric*. Thus, for example, if $A^{ij} = -A^{ji}$ (or $A_{ij} = -A_{ji}$) then the tensor A^{ij} (or A_{ij}) is skew symmetric. Also, if $A_l^{ijk} = -A_l^{jik}$ then A_l^{ijk} is skew-symmetric with respect to the indices i and j.

It can easily be verified that Theorems 1.2 and 1.3 hold for skew-symmetric case also.

Remarks

1. *A second rank symmetric tensor has $\frac{1}{2}n(n+1)$ components in n dimensions* which can be seen as follows:

   The total number of components of rank two tensor in n dimensions is n^2. Since the tensor is symmetric, out of these n^2, all the n diagonal terms are different and the rest $(n^2 - n)$ are equal in pairs. The number of pairs are $(n^2 - n)/2$. Therefore, the total number of independent components of a second rank symmetric tensor is

   $$n + \frac{n^2 - n}{2} = \frac{n(n+1)}{2}.$$

   In a similar way, a rank three symmetric tensor has $\frac{n(n+1)}{2}n = \frac{n^2(n+1)}{2}$ independent components.

2. We know that the total number of components of a second rank tensor in n dimensions are n^2. Out of this n^2, if the tensor A_{ij} is skew symmetric, all the diagonal terms are zero as $A_{ii} = 0$. The rest $(n^2 - n)$ are equal in pairs. The number of pairs are $\frac{n^2 - n}{2}$. Therefore, *the total number of independent components of a second rank skew symmetric tensor are* $\frac{n(n-1)}{2}$.

   In general, the number of independent components of a rank r skew symmetric tensor in n dimensions are

   $$^nC_r = \frac{n!}{r!(n-r)!}$$

If the rank of a skew symmetric tensor is same as that of the dimension of the space then the tensor has only one independent component. It may be noted that skew symmetric tensor, whose rank is higher than the dimension of the space, is identically zero.

From any second rank covariant tensor T_{ij} we can construct its symmetric part S_{ij} and skew symmetric part A_{ij}. These parts are uniquely determined as

$$S_{ij} = \frac{1}{2}(T_{ij} + T_{ji}) = T_{(ij)}, \quad A_{ij} = \frac{1}{2}(T_{ij} - T_{ji}) = T_{[ij]} \qquad (1.30)$$

Thus

$$T_{ij} = T_{(ij)} + T_{[ij]} = S_{ij} + A_{ij}$$

The same proceedure can be adapted for a second rank contravariant tensor. Thus, for a second rank contravariant tensor, we have

$$C^{ij} = \frac{1}{2}(C^{ij} + C^{ji}) + \frac{1}{2}(C^{ij} - C^{ji}) = S^{ij} + A^{ij} \qquad (1.31)$$

From Eq. (1.30) and the transformation law for a second rank tensor we can find the transformed symmetric and skew symmetric parts $T'_{(ij)}$ and $T'_{[ij]}$ of a tensor T_{ij} from its transformed component T'_{ij}. For instance

$$\begin{aligned}
T'_{(ij)} &= \frac{1}{2}(T'_{ij} + T'_{ji}) \\
&= \frac{1}{2}\left\{ \frac{\partial x^k}{\partial x'^i} \frac{\partial x^l}{\partial x'^j} T_{kl} + \frac{\partial x^l}{\partial x'^j} \frac{\partial x^k}{\partial x'^i} T_{lk} \right\} \\
&= \frac{1}{2} \frac{\partial x^k}{\partial x'^i} \frac{\partial x^l}{\partial x'^j} (T_{kl} + T_{lk}) \\
&= \frac{\partial x^k}{\partial x'^i} \frac{\partial x^l}{\partial x'^j} T_{(kl)}
\end{aligned}$$

Similarly

$$T'_{[ij]} = \frac{\partial x^k}{\partial x'^i} \frac{\partial x^l}{\partial x'^j} T_{[kl]}$$

The meanings of round and square brackets enclosing a set of indices (or the process of symmetrization and skew symmetrization for tensors of higher rank) are defined as follows:

$$T_{(i_1 \ldots i_p)} \equiv \frac{1}{p!} \sum T_{i_{\pi_1} \ldots i_{\pi_p}}, \quad T_{[i_1 \ldots i_p]} \equiv \frac{1}{p!} \sum (-1)^\pi T_{i_{\pi_1} \ldots i_{\pi_p}} \qquad (1.32)$$

In these expressions, the sum is taken over all permutations π of the numbers $1, 2, \ldots, p$ and $(-1)^\pi$ is $+1$ or -1 according to the permutation is even or odd. The quantity T may have other indices, not shown here, apart from the set of p indices $i_1, i_2, \ldots, i_p$, but only this set of indices is affected by the operation mentioned here. The numbers $\pi_1, \pi_2, \ldots, \pi_p$ are the numbers $1, 2, \ldots, p$ rearranged according to the permutation π.

Equation (1.32) can also be expressed as

$$T_{(i_1 i_2 \ldots i_p)} = \frac{1}{p!} \text{ (sum over all permutation of the indices } i_1 \text{ to } i_p)$$

$$T_{[i_1 i_2 \ldots i_p]} = \frac{1}{p!} \text{ (alternating sum over all permutation of the indices } i_1 \text{ to } i_p)$$

(This may be remembered by noting that the positive terms are obtained by cycling the indices to the right and the negative terms by flipping the last two indices.)

If S and A, respectively, are the symmetric and skew symmetric parts of a tensor then the above definition leads to

$$S_{[ij]} = 0, \quad A_{(ij)} = 0, \quad S_{(ij)} = S_{ij}, \quad A_{[ij]} = A_{ij}$$

$$S_{(ijk)} = \frac{1}{3}(S_{ijk} + S_{ikj} + S_{jki}), \quad A_{[ijk]} = \frac{1}{3}(A_{ijk} + A_{kij} + A_{jki})$$

A *totally (completely) symmetric tensor* is defined to be one equal to its symmetric part, and a *totally skew symmetric tensor* is one equal to its skew symmetric part. Thus

$$T_{(ijk)} = \frac{1}{3!}(T_{ijk} + T_{jki} + T_{kij} + T_{jik} + T_{ikj} + T_{kji}) \tag{1.33}$$

$$T_{[ijk]} = \frac{1}{3!}(T_{ijk} + T_{jki} + T_{kij} - T_{jik} - T_{ikj} - T_{kji}) \tag{1.34}$$

are, respectively, completely symmetric and skew symmetric tensors under interchange of any two of its three indices.

Moreover, if a tensor S_{ijk} is itself completely symmetric, then

$$S_{(ijk)} = S_{ijk}$$

while if a tensor A_{ijk} is itself completely skew symmetric, then

$$A_{[ijk]} = A_{ijk}$$

From the definition, we also have

$$C_{ij} = C_{[ij]} + C_{(ij)} = C_{[ij]} + \left\{ C_{(ij)} - \frac{1}{4} A_k^k g_{ij} \right\} + \frac{1}{4} A_k^k g_{ij}$$

and thus the symmetric part in this equation can be decomposed into a trace-free term and a term proportional to a tensor g_{ij}.

Remark The physically important second rank tensor often belong to one of the symmetry classes, or at least their constituent parts have different physical meaning. For example, the electromagnetic field tensor is skew symmetric, the energy-momentum tensor of electromagnetic field is symmetric and trace-free and the general energy-momentum tensor is symmetric (cf., Example 1.10 and Chapter 6).

EXAMPLE 1.6 If A_i are the components of a covariant vector, show that $B_{ij} = A_i A_j - A_j A_i$ are the components of a skew symmetric covariant tensor of rank two.

Solution Here

$$B_{ij} = A_i A_j - A_j A_i = -(A_j A_i - A_i A_j) = -B_{ij}$$

which shows that B_{ij} is skew symmetric. Moreover, from the transformation law for A_i, we have

$$A_i' A_j' - A_j' A_i' = \left(\frac{\partial x^k}{\partial x'^i} A_k\right)\left(\frac{\partial x^l}{\partial x'^j} A_l\right) - \left(\frac{\partial x^l}{\partial x'^j} A_l\right)\left(\frac{\partial x^k}{\partial x'^i} A_k\right)$$

$$= \frac{\partial x^k}{\partial x'^i}\frac{\partial x^l}{\partial x'^j} A_k A_l - \frac{\partial x^l}{\partial x'^j}\frac{\partial x^k}{\partial x'^i} A_l A_k$$

$$= \frac{\partial x^k}{\partial x'^i}\frac{\partial x^l}{\partial x'^j} (A_k A_l - A_l A_k)$$

Thus

$$B_{ij}' = \frac{\partial x^k}{\partial x'^i}\frac{\partial x^l}{\partial x'^j} B_{kl}$$

which shows that B_{ij} transforms like the components of a covariant tensor of rank two.

EXAMPLE 1.7 If A^{ij} is a symmetric tensor and B_{ij} is a skew symmetric tensor, show that $B_{ij} A^{ij} = 0$ and also for any arbitrary tensor C^{ij} shows that

$$C^{ij} B_{ij} = \frac{1}{2}(C^{ij} - C^{ji})B_{ij}, \quad C^{ij} A_{ij} = \frac{1}{2}(C^{ij} + C^{ji})A_{ij}$$

Solution From the given symmetries $B_{ij} A^{ij} = -B_{ji} A^{ji}$. Since i and j are dummy indices, we can interchange i and j to get

$$B_{ij} A^{ij} = -B_{ji} A^{ij} = -B_{ij} A^{ij}$$

and thus

$$B_{ij} A^{ij} = 0$$

Moreover, we know that any tensor C_{ij} can be written as the sum of its symmetric part $\tilde{C}_{ij} = \frac{1}{2}(C_{ij} + C_{ji})$ and its skew symmetric part $\bar{C}_{ij} = \frac{1}{2}(C_{ij} - C_{ji})$, thus

$$C^{ij} B_{ij} = \tilde{C}^{ij} B_{ij} + \bar{C}^{ij} B_{ij} = \bar{C}^{ij} B_{ij} = \frac{1}{2}(C^{ij} - C^{ji})B_{ij}$$

$$C^{ij} A_{ij} = \tilde{C}^{ij} A_{ij} + \bar{C}^{ij} A_{ij} = \tilde{C}^{ij} A_{ij} = \frac{1}{2}(C^{ij} + C^{ji}) A_{ij}$$

EXAMPLE 1.8 Show that in general

$$B_{ijk} \neq B_{(ijk)} + B_{[ijk]}$$

Solution If a relation similar to Eq. (1.31)

$$B_{ijk} = B_{(ijk)} + B_{[ijk]} \tag{1.35}$$

were true for a tensor of rank three, we would then have

$$B_{jik} = B_{(jik)} + B_{[jik]} = B_{(ijk)} - B_{[ijk]}$$

$$B_{jki} = B_{(kji)} + B_{[kji]} = B_{(ijk)} + B_{[ijk]} = B_{ijk} \tag{1.36}$$

Since B_{ijk} does not in general have the symmetry properties implied by Eq. (1.36) and thus the decomposition (1.35) cannot be true.

EXAMPLE 1.9 If B_{abcd} is a fourth rank tensor, show that

$$B_{a[[bc]d]} = B_{a[bcd]}$$

Solution We have

$$B_{a[[bc]d]} = \frac{1}{6}\{B_{a[bc]d} + B_{a[cd]b} + B_{a[db]c} - B_{a[cb]d} - B_{a[bd]c} - B_{a[dc]b}\}$$

$$= \frac{1}{12}\{B_{abcd} - B_{acbd} + B_{acdb} - B_{adcb} + B_{adbc} - B_{abdc}$$

$$- B_{acbd} + B_{abcd} - B_{abdc} + B_{adbc} - B_{adcb} + B_{acdb}\}$$

$$= B_{a[bcd]}$$

EXAMPLE 1.10 Show that the energy-momentum tensor

$$T_{ij} = \frac{1}{4\pi}\left(-F_{ik}F_{jl}g^{kl} + \frac{1}{4}g_{ij}F_{pq}F^{pq}\right)$$

for the electromagnetic field is symmetric and $T_i^i = 0$.

Solution Given that

$$T_{ij} = \frac{1}{4\pi}\left(-F_{ik}F_{jl}g^{kl} + \frac{1}{4}g_{ij}F_{pq}F^{pq}\right)$$

which can be written as

$$T_{ij} = -\frac{1}{4\pi}\left(F_{ik}F_j^k - \frac{1}{4}g_{ij}F_{pq}F^{pq}\right)$$

Thus

$$T_{ji} = -\frac{1}{4\pi}\left(F_{jk}F_i^k - \frac{1}{4}g_{ji}F_{pq}F^{pq}\right)$$

$$= -\frac{1}{4\pi}\left(F_i^k F_{jk} - \frac{1}{4}g_{ji}F_{pq}F^{pq}\right)$$

$$= -\frac{1}{4\pi}\left(F_{ik}F_j^k - \frac{1}{4}g_{ij}F_{pq}F^{pq}\right)$$

$$= T_{ij}$$

(by raising/lowering of indices) which shows that T_{ij} is symmetric. Moreover,

$$g^{ij}T_{ij} = T_k^k = T$$

$$= -\frac{1}{4\pi}\left(g^{ij}F_{ik}F_j^k - \frac{1}{4}g^{ij}g_{ij}F_{pq}F^{pq}\right)$$

$$= -\frac{1}{4\pi}\left(F_{ik}F^{ik} - F_{pq}F^{pq}\right)$$

$$= 0$$

EXAMPLE 1.11 If P^i and Q^i are the components of contravariant vectors and S_{ij} and T_{ij} are symmetric tensors such that $(S_{ij} - \alpha T_{ij})P^i = 0$, $(S_{ij} - \beta T_{ij})Q^i = 0$, for $i, j = 1, 2, ..., n$ and $\alpha \neq \beta$, prove that

$$S_{ij}P^iQ^j = 0, \quad T_{ij}P^iQ^j = 0 \quad \text{and} \quad \alpha = \frac{S_{ij}P^iQ^j}{T_{ij}P^iQ^j}$$

Solution Multiplying first given equation by Q^j and the second by P^j, we get

$$(S_{ij} - \alpha T_{ij})P^iQ^j = 0 \tag{1.37}$$

$$(S_{ij} - \beta T_{ij})P^jQ^i = 0 \tag{1.38}$$

As S_{ij} and T_{ij} are symmetric tensors, Eq. (1.38), after changing the dummy indices, leads to

$$(S_{ij} - \beta T_{ij})P^iQ^j = 0 \tag{1.39}$$

As $\alpha \neq \beta$, subtraction of Eqs. (1.39) and (1.37) yields $T_{ij}P^iQ^j = 0$ and therefore $S_{ij}P^iQ^j = 0$. Moreover, from the given condition $(S_{ij} - \alpha T_{ij})P^i = 0$, we have $\alpha T_{ij}P^i = S_{ij}P^i$ which leads to

$$\alpha = \frac{S_{ij}P^iQ^j}{T_{ij}P^iQ^j}$$

1.8 Algebra of Tensors

In tensor algebra only those operations are allowed which when performed on tensors give rise to new tensors. Some of the algebraic operations on tensors are discussed as follows.

(a) Addition and subtraction A linear combination of tensors of same type and same rank is a tensor of same type and same rank.

Thus, if A_{ij} and B_{ij} are second rank covariant tensors and α and β are scalars, then

$$C_{ij} = \alpha A_{ij} + \beta B_{ij}$$

is also a second rank covariant tensor. This can be seen as follows:

$$C'_{ij} = \alpha A'_{ij} + \beta B'_{ij}$$

$$= \alpha \frac{\partial x^k}{\partial x'^i} \frac{\partial x^l}{\partial x'^j} A_{kl} + \beta \frac{\partial x^k}{\partial x'^i} \frac{\partial x^l}{\partial x'^j} B_{kl}$$

$$= \frac{\partial x^k}{\partial x'^i} \frac{\partial x^l}{\partial x'^j} (\alpha A_{kl} + \beta B_{kl})$$

$$= \frac{\partial x^k}{\partial x'^i} \frac{\partial x^l}{\partial x'^j} C_{kl}$$

Similar situation can be verified for contravariant and mixed tensors of any rank. As an example, consider A^{ij}_{klm} and B^{ij}_{klm} as mixed tensors of same type (two contravariant and three covariant indices) and same rank (rank five), then they can be added or subtracted accordingly as

$$A^{ij}_{klm} + B^{ij}_{klm} = C^{ij}_{klm}$$

$$A^{ij}_{klm} - B^{ij}_{klm} = D^{ij}_{klm}$$

Structures of the forms $A^i + B^{ij}, A^i_j + B^{ij}, A^{ij}_k - B^i_{jk}, A^{ij}_k - B^{ij}$, etc., for example, are not allowed.

(b) Equality of tensors Two tensors X and Y are said to be *equal* if their components are equal, that is $X^i_{jk} = Y^i_{jk}$ or $X^{ij}_k = Y^{ij}_k$, for all values of the indices.

Remark

It is not necessary to specify that the components of the tensor have to be equal in all coordinate systems. It is sufficient to know that both X and Y are tensors and that their components are equal in one particular coordinate system. This is true from the definition of a tensor.

(c) Inner and outer products Let A^i be a contravariant vector and B_i a covariant vector; then from the transformation laws of contravariant and covariant vectors, we have

$$A'^i B'_i = \left(\frac{\partial x'^i}{\partial x^j} A^j\right)\left(\frac{\partial x^k}{\partial x'^i} B_k\right)$$

$$= \frac{\partial x'^i}{\partial x^j}\frac{\partial x^k}{\partial x'^i} A^j B_k$$

$$= \frac{\partial x^k}{\partial x^j} A^j B_k$$

Now, since the coordinates x^j and x^k are independent, we have

$$\frac{\partial x^k}{\partial x^j} = \delta^k_j = \begin{cases} 1, & \text{for } k = j \\ 0, & \text{for } k \neq j \end{cases}$$

Hence, we have

$$A'^i B'_i = A^j B_j$$

showing that the product $A'^i B'_i$ remains invariant under the coordinate transformation and hence a scalar. This scalar product is called the *inner product* (of a contravariant vector with a covariant vector).

It may be noted that the inner product of the covariant and contravariant components is equal to the squared amplitude of the physical vector:

$$A^i A_i = \pm |A^2|$$

(see also Example 1.15).

While, on the other hand, the quantity $A^i B_j$ is called *outer product* of two vectors. Using the transformation law for A^i and B_j, we have

$$A'^i B'_j = \frac{\partial x'^i}{\partial x^k}\frac{\partial x^l}{\partial x'^j} A^k B_l$$

showing that the quantities $A^i B_j$ transforms like the components of a second rank tensor.

The outer product is defined for any type of tensors, the total rank of the resulting tensor is the sum of the individual ranks of the tensors. For example, the product of A^{ij}_k and B^l_m produces a tensor of rank five.

It may be noted that the product of a tensor by a scalar is again a tensor. For example, if A^{ij}_k is a tensor of rank three and ϕ is a scalar, then

$$\phi' A'^{ij}_k = \phi \left[\frac{\partial x'^i}{\partial x^l}\frac{\partial x'^j}{\partial x^m}\frac{\partial x^n}{\partial x'^k} A^{lm}_n\right]$$

$$= \left[\frac{\partial x'^i}{\partial x^l}\frac{\partial x'^j}{\partial x^m}\frac{\partial x^n}{\partial x'^k}\right] \phi A^{lm}_n$$

which shows that the quantities ϕA^{ij}_k transform like a mixed tensor of rank three and thus ϕA^{ij}_k is a tensor.

(d) Contraction The process of summing over a covariant and a contravariant index of a tensor to get another tensor such that the rank of this new tensor is lowered by two is called *contraction*.

For example, consider a mixed tensor A^i_{jkl}. Put $l = i$ to get the tensor A^i_{jki} whose rank is lowered by two as i appears as a dummy suffix. This can be shown as follows:

The fourth rank tensor A^i_{jkl} transforms as

$$A'^i_{jkl} = \frac{\partial x'^i}{\partial x^p} \frac{\partial x^q}{\partial x'^j} \frac{\partial x^r}{\partial x'^k} \frac{\partial x^s}{\partial x'^l} A^p_{qrs}$$

Set $l = i$ to get

$$A'^i_{jki} = \frac{\partial x'^i}{\partial x^p} \frac{\partial x^q}{\partial x'^j} \frac{\partial x^r}{\partial x'^k} \frac{\partial x^s}{\partial x'^i} A^p_{qrs}$$

$$= \frac{\partial x^q}{\partial x'^j} \frac{\partial x^r}{\partial x'^k} \frac{\partial x'^i}{\partial x^p} \frac{\partial x^s}{\partial x'^i} A^p_{qrs}$$

$$= \frac{\partial x^q}{\partial x'^j} \frac{\partial x^r}{\partial x'^k} \frac{\partial x^s}{\partial x^p} A^p_{qrs}$$

$$= \frac{\partial x^q}{\partial x'^j} \frac{\partial x^r}{\partial x'^k} \delta^s_p A^p_{qrs}$$

$$= \frac{\partial x^q}{\partial x'^j} \frac{\partial x^r}{\partial x'^k} A^s_{qrs}$$

$$= \frac{\partial x^q}{\partial x'^j} \frac{\partial x^r}{\partial x'^k} A_{qr}$$

which shows that A^i_{jki} is a covariant tensor of rank two.

As another example, consider a mixed tensor A^i_{jk} of rank three, then

$$A'^i_{jk} = \frac{\partial x'^i}{\partial x^p} \frac{\partial x^q}{\partial x'^j} \frac{\partial x^r}{\partial x'^k} A^p_{qr}$$

Taking $k = i$, we get

$$A'^i_{ji} = \frac{\partial x'^i}{\partial x^p} \frac{\partial x^q}{\partial x'^j} \frac{\partial x^r}{\partial x'^i} A^p_{qr}$$

$$= \frac{\partial x^q}{\partial x'^j} \frac{\partial x^r}{\partial x^p} A^p_{qr}$$

$$= \frac{\partial x^q}{\partial x'^j} A^p_{qp}$$

$$= \frac{\partial x^q}{\partial x'^j} A_q$$

and thus by contracting a rank three mixed tensor we get a rank one tensor.

Moreover, consider a second rank mixed tensor A^i_j which transforms as

$$A'^i_j = \frac{\partial x'^i}{\partial x^p} \frac{\partial x^q}{\partial x'^j} A^p_q$$

so that on setting $j = i$, we have

$$A'^i_i = \frac{\partial x'^i}{\partial x^p} \frac{\partial x^q}{\partial x'^i} A^p_q = \delta^q_p A^p_q = A^p_p$$

which is the transformation law of a scalar, or a tensor of rank zero. This is an invariant, called the *trace* of A^i_j, and has the same value in all coordinate systems.

In a similar way it can easily be seen that $A^i B_i, A_{ij} B^{ij}, A^i_j B^j_i$, etc. are all invariants.

(e) The quotient law. In tensor analysis, we often come across quantities about which we are not certain whether they are tensors or not. The direct method requires to find the appropriate transformation law and in practice this is not an easy job. However, we do have a criterion which tells us about the tensorial nature of a set of quantities, it is known as *quotient law* and is stated as *"a set of quantities, whose inner product with an arbitrary covariant (or contravariant) tensor is a tensor, is itself a tensor"*. This law is illustrated as follows.

Consider a set of quantities $A(ij)$ whose nature is not known and let B^j be any contravariant vector. Now consider the inner product $A(ij)B^j$ which transforms as

$$A'(ij)B'^j = \frac{\partial x'^i}{\partial x^k} \{A(kl)B^l\} \tag{1.40}$$

while the reverse transformation for B^l gives

$$B^l = \frac{\partial x^l}{\partial x'^j} B'^j \tag{1.41}$$

Put it in Eq. (1.40), we get

$$A'(ij)B'^j = \frac{\partial x'^i}{\partial x^k} \{A(kl) \frac{\partial x^l}{\partial x'^j} B'^j\}$$

which may be expressed as

$$\{A'(ij) - \frac{\partial x'^i}{\partial x^k} \frac{\partial x^l}{\partial x'^j} A(kl)\} B'^j = 0 \tag{1.42}$$

Since B'^j is an arbitrary vector, we can thus choose it in such a manner that only one of its components is non-zero. We repeat this process for all components of B'^j, then Eq. (1.42) can be satisfied only if

$$A'(ij) = \frac{\partial x'^i}{\partial x^k} \frac{\partial x^l}{\partial x'^j} A(kl) \tag{1.43}$$

which is the transformation law for a mixed tensor of rank two. Hence, $A(ij)$ is a tensor which can now be written as $A(ij) = A^i_j$.

As an another example, consider a contravariant vector A^i and δ^j_k to be the Kronecker delta and form the inner product $\delta^j_i A^i$ so that $\delta^j_i A^i = A^j$ which is tensor of rank one. Thus, by quotient law, δ^j_i is a mixed tensor of rank two.

EXAMPLE 1.12 If A^i and B^j are contravariant vectors and C_{ij} is a covariant tensor, find the nature of $A^i B^j C_{ij}$.

Solution From the transformation laws of tensors, we have

$$A'^k B'^l C'_{kl} = \left(\frac{\partial x'^k}{\partial x^i} A^i\right)\left(\frac{\partial x'^l}{\partial x^j} B^j\right)\left(\frac{\partial x^i}{\partial x'^k}\frac{\partial x^j}{\partial x'^l}\right) C_{ij} = A^i B^j C_{ij}$$

which shows that $A^i B^j C_{ij}$ is an invariant [that is, the double inner product $A^i B^j C_{ij}$ is an invariant (scalar)].

EXAMPLE 1.13 If A^i and B_{ij} are the components of the contravariant and covariant tensors of rank one and two, respectively. Show that $A^k B_{ik}$ is a tensor.

Solution Let $C_j = A^i B_{ij}$, then from the transformation laws for tensors, we have

$$C'_j = \left(\frac{\partial x'^i}{\partial x^k} A^{\cdot}\right)\left(\frac{\partial x^l}{\partial x'^i}\frac{\partial x^m}{\partial x'^j} B_{lm}\right)$$

$$= \frac{\partial x^l}{\partial x^k}\frac{\partial x^m}{\partial x'^j} A^k B_{lm}$$

$$= \delta^l_k \frac{\partial x^m}{\partial x'^j} A^k B_{lm}$$

$$= \frac{\partial x^m}{\partial x'^j} A^l B_{lm}$$

which shows that $A^i B_{ij}$ is a tensor.

EXAMPLE 1.14 Show that the contraction of the outer product of the tensors A^i and B_j is an invariant.

Solution Since A^i and B_j are tensors, therefore

$$A'^k = \frac{\partial x'^k}{\partial x^i} A^i, \quad B'_l = \frac{\partial x^j}{\partial x'^l} B_j$$

and

$$A'^k B'_l = \frac{\partial x'^k}{\partial x^i}\frac{\partial x^j}{\partial x'^l} A^i B_j$$

Contracting over k and l, we have

$$A'^k B'_k = \frac{\partial x'^k}{\partial x^i} \frac{\partial x^j}{\partial x'^k} A^i B_j = \delta^j_i A^i B_j = A^i B_i$$

which is an invariant.

It may be noted, in general, that the contraction of the outer product does not yield the inner product (invariant). For example, consider the outer product $A^{ij} B_{kl}$ and contract for i and k, it will lead to $A^j B_l$ which clearly is not the inner product.

EXAMPLE 1.15 Find a vector describing the static shear displacement A of a medium in rectangular coordinates. The displacement is assumed to occur only in x-direction and depend on y so that $A^x = ay$, where a is a constant. Also, find the inner product.

Solution Since given that $A^x = ay$, we can define a four component contravariant vector

$$A^i = (A^t, A^x, A^y, A^z) = (0, ay, 0, 0) \tag{1.44}$$

and transform to the cylindrical coordinate system. The transformation along with its inverse is

$$t = t', \; t' = t$$

$$x = r' \cos \theta', \; r' = (x^2 + y^2)^{1/2} \tag{1.45}$$

$$y = r' \sin \theta', \; \theta' = \tan^{-1}(y/x)$$

$$z = z', z' = z$$

From Eqs. (1.13), (1.14) and (1.45), we have

$$A'^t = 0, \; A'^r = \frac{axy}{r}, \; A'^\theta = -\frac{ay^2}{r}, \; A'^z = 0 \tag{1.46}$$

$$A'_t = 0, \; A'_r = -\frac{axy}{r}, \; A'_\theta = \frac{ay^2}{r}, \; A'_z = 0 \tag{1.46a}$$

From Eq. (1.46) and (1.46a), the inner product is

$$A'^i A'_i = A'^t A'_t + A'^r A'_r + A'^\theta A'_\theta + A'^z A'_z = -a^2 y^2$$

which shows that the inner product of the contravariant and covariant components of a vector yields the squared amplitude of the physical vector [see also, Section 1.8(c)].

This example provides the relationship between the contravariant and covariant components of a vector.

EXAMPLE 1.16 If the quantity B_{ijk} is such that $A^i B_{ijk}$ is a tensor for any vector A^i, then show that B_{ijk} is a tensor.

Solution Let $A^i B_{ijk} = C_{jk}$. Since it is given to be a tensor, therefore, from Eqs. (1.20) and (1.20a) we have

$$C'_{jk} = \frac{\partial x^p}{\partial x'^j} \frac{\partial x^q}{\partial x'^k} C_{pq}$$

and

$$C_{pq} = \frac{\partial x'^j}{\partial x^p} \frac{\partial x'^k}{\partial x^q} C'_{jk}$$

which leads to

$$A^o B_{opq} = \frac{\partial x'^j}{\partial x^p} \frac{\partial x'^k}{\partial x^q} A'^i B'_{ijk}$$

But from Eq. (1.13), we have

$$A'^i = \frac{\partial x'^i}{\partial x^o} A^o$$

Thus

$$A^o B_{opq} = \frac{\partial x'^j}{\partial x^p} \frac{\partial x'^k}{\partial x^q} \frac{\partial x'^i}{\partial x^o} A^o B'_{ijk}$$

which must hold for all values of A^o. Therefore

$$B_{opq} = \frac{\partial x'^i}{\partial x^o} \frac{\partial x'^j}{\partial x^p} \frac{\partial x'^k}{\partial x^q} B'_{ijk}$$

showing that B_{opq} is a tensor.

This example also holds if B_{ijk} is replaced by a quantity with any number of indices (either covariant, contravariant or mixed).

1.9   Irreducible Tensor

A tensor quantity is said to be *reducible* if it can be decomposed into parts which transform among themselves. If such a decomposition is not possible then the quantity is called *irreducible*. The irreducible tensors find their applications in the decomposition of the Riemann curvature tensor (cf., Chapter 5).

Consider a second rank mixed tensor T^i_j, then from Eq. (1.21), we have

$$T'^i_j = \frac{\partial x'^i}{\partial x^l} \frac{\partial x^k}{\partial x'^j} T^l_k$$

and thus $T = T^i_i = $ trace of T^i_j transforms as

$$T' = T'^i_i = \frac{\partial x'^i}{\partial x^l} \frac{\partial x^k}{\partial x'^i} T^l_k = \delta^k_l T^l_k = T^l_l = T$$

which shows that the trace of T^i_j transforms into itself and therefore the tensor T^i_j is reducible.

Now consider

$$S^j_i = T^j_i - \frac{1}{4}\delta^j_i T$$

Then from the transformation law (1.21), we have

$$S'^k_l = T'^k_l - \frac{1}{4}\delta'^k_l T$$

$$= \frac{\partial x'^k}{\partial x^j}\frac{\partial x^i}{\partial x'^l}(T^j_i - \frac{1}{4}\delta^j_i T)$$

$$= \frac{\partial x'^k}{\partial x^j}\frac{\partial x^i}{\partial x'^l}S^j_i$$

which cannot be further decomposed as it has no trace and accordingly S^j_i is irreducible. Moreover, the trace $T = T^i_i$ is also irreducible.

Thus, we have shown that the irreducible parts of T^j_i are its trace $T = T^i_i$ and the trace-free tensor S^j_i which is obtained from T^j_i by

$$S^j_i = T^j_i - \frac{1}{4}\delta^j_i T$$

EXERCISES

1.1 Prove that $JJ' = 1$, where J and J' are the Jacobians of the transformation.

1.2 In four dimensions, prove that

$$\delta^i_i = 4, \delta^{ij}_{kj} = 3\delta^i_k, \delta^{ijkl}_{mnol} = \delta^{ijk}_{mno}$$

1.3 If X^i and Y_j are the components of contravariant and covariant vectors, respectively, show that $Z^i_j = X^i Y_j$ are the components of a mixed tensor of rank two.

1.4 A covariant vector has components $2x - z, x^2 y, yz$ in rectangular coordinates. Find its components in: (i) spherical coordinates r, θ, ϕ and (ii) cylindrical coordinates ρ, ϕ, z.

1.5 If $xy, 2y - z^2$ and zx are the components of a covariant vector in rectangular coordinate system, find its components in the spherical coordinate system.

1.6 If x, y and z are the components of a covariant vector in Cartesian coordinates, find its components in terms of r, θ, ϕ.

1.7 Show that the inner product of tensors A^i_j and B^{kl}_m is a tensor of rank three.

1.8 If A^i is a contravariant vector and $B_{ij}A^i A^j$ is an invariant, then show that $B_{ij} + B_{ji}$ is a covariant tensor of rank two.

1.9 If a quantity $X(ijk)$ is such that in the coordinate system x^i, $X(ijk)Y_k^{jl} = Z_i^l$, where Y_k^{jl} is an arbitrary tensor and Z_i^l is a tensor, prove that $X(ijk)$ is a tensor.

1.10 If A^i and B^j are the components of contravariant vectors and $A^i B^j C_{ij}$ is an invariant, show that C_{ij} is a covariant tensor of rank two.

1.11 If the relation $B_{ijk}u^i u^j u^k = 0$ holds for any arbitrary contravariant vector u^i, show that

$$B_{ijk} + B_{jki} + B_{kij} + B_{jik} + B_{ikj} + B_{kji} = 0$$

1.12 If the tensor B_{ijk} is symmetric in i and j and the relation $B_{ijk}A^i A^j A^k = 0$ holds for any arbitrary contravariant vector A^i, show that

$$B_{ijk} + B_{jki} + B_{kij} = 0$$

1.13 If the relation $B_{ijkl}u^i u^j v^k v^l = 0$ holds for any arbitrary contravariant vectors u^i and v^i, show that

$$B_{ijkl} + B_{ilkj} + B_{kjil} + B_{klij} = 0$$

1.14 If A_{ij} is a skew symmetric tensor, show that

$$(\delta_j^i \delta_l^k + \delta_l^i \delta_j^k)A_{ik} = 0$$

1.15 If $b_{ij} \neq 0$ are the components of a covariant tensor of rank two and if $\phi b_{ij} + \psi b_{ji} = 0$ holds, then prove that either $\phi = \psi$ and b_{ij} is skew symmetric or $\phi = -\psi$ and b_{ij} is symmetric.

1.16 If A_{ij} is a symmetric tensor and B_i is a covariant vector such that

$$A_{ij}B_k + A_{jk}B_i + A_{ki}B_j = 0$$

show that $A_{ij} = 0$ or $B_i = 0$.

1.17 If $\psi = P_{ij}A^i A^j$, then show that $\psi = Q_{ij}A^i A^j$. where Q_{ij} is symmetric.

1.18 If $A_{jk}^i B^{jk} = C^i$ is a contravariant vector and B^{jk} is a skew symmetric tensor, then show that $A_{jk}^i + A_{kj}^i$ is a tensor.

1.19 If A_{ij} is a symmetric tensor and $B_{ij} = A_{ji}$, show that B_{ij} is a symmetric tensor.

1.20 If a tensor A_{ijkl} is symmetric in i and j and skew symmetric in j and l, show that $A_{ijkl} = 0$.

1.21 If A_{ij} is a skew symmetric tensor, then prove that $(A_{23}/\sqrt{g}. A_{31}/\sqrt{g}, A_{12}/\sqrt{g})$ are the components of a contravariant vector. Also show that $(A^{23}\sqrt{g}. A^{31}\sqrt{g}, A^{12}\sqrt{g})$ are the components of a covariant vector if A^{ij} is a skew symmetric tensor.

1.22 Show that

    (i) if $T_{[ij]k} = 0$, then $T_{(ijk)} = \frac{1}{3}(T_{ijk} + T_{jki} + T_{kij})$

    (ii) if $T_{(ij)k} = 0$, then $T_{[ijk]} = \frac{1}{3}(T_{ijk} + T_{jki} + T_{kij})$

    (iii) if $T_{[ij]k} = 0$ and $T_{i(jk)} = 0$, then $T_{ijk} = 0$

1.23 Prove that

$$A_{[ij]} = \frac{1}{2!} A_{kl} \delta_{ij}^{kl}, \quad A_{[ijk]} = \frac{1}{3!} A_{lmn} \delta_{ijk}^{lmn}, \quad A_{[ijkl]} = \frac{1}{4!} A_{mnop} \delta_{ijkl}^{mnop}$$

CHAPTER 2

Riemannian Space and Metric Tensor

2.1 Introduction

Consider a Euclidean plane in which rectangular Cartesian coordinates exist: if (x, y) and $(x + dx, y + dy)$ are two neighbouring points in this plane, then by Pythagoras theorem the distance ds between two points is

$$ds^2 = dx^2 + dy^2 \tag{2.1}$$

This formula is called the *metric* of the Euclidean plane and it can be shown that it contains within itself all the basic elements of the geometry of the plane; in particular that the straight line is the shortest distance between two points, that parallel lines are of infinite length and do not intersect in any finite part of the plane, and so on. In Eq. (2.1) the coefficients of the squares of dx and dy are both equal to unity and that, since no term in $dxdy$ occurs, the metric is said to be *orthogonal*. These properties are, however, due to the use of Cartesian coordinate system and disappear if any other coordinate systems are used. For example, when the polar coordinates (r, θ) are used, the metric (2.1) takes the form

$$ds^2 = dr^2 + r^2 d\theta^2$$

and the coefficients of the squares of dr and $d\theta$ are 1 and r^2, respectively. The orthogonality is still preserved. But if we use the coordinate system (u, v), where $x = uv, y = \frac{1}{2}(u^2 + v^2)$, the metric is then

$$ds^2 = (u^2 + v^2)du^2 + (4uv)dudv + (u^2 + v^2)dv^2$$

Here the coefficients of the quadratic terms in du and dv are $(u^2 + v^2), 4uv$ and $(u^2 + v^2)$, respectively; the orthogonality property also being masked by the use of the coordinate system. Thus, the expression for the metric of a space with a particular geometry (in this case, the Euclidean plane) may take many forms, according to the coordinate systems used; and the reduction of one form to another, when coordinate transformation is not known previously, is a problem of considerable difficulty.

In three-dimensional Euclidean space, the Cartesian form of the metric is

$$ds^2 = dx^2 + dy^2 + dz^2 \tag{2.2}$$

which is again a statement of Pythagoras theorem and in polar coordinates (r, θ, ϕ) takes the form

$$ds^2 = dr^2 + r^2 d\theta^2 + r^2 \sin^2 \theta d\phi^2$$

Hence, the metric of the two-dimensional surface formed by the points lying on the surface of a sphere of radius a is

$$ds^2 = a^2(d\theta^2 + \sin^2 \theta d\phi^2) \tag{2.3}$$

The geometry of the surface of the sphere is intrinsically different from that of Euclidean plane: straight lines are replaced by great circles which are of finite length, and necessarily intersect, so that there are no parallels in the Euclidean sense, and so on. This difference in geometry is due to a coordinate transformation that transforms Eq. (2.3) into Eq. (2.1) and vice versa. Thus, by the use of different coordinate systems the metric of a two-dimensional space take many forms, and in the process we have intrinsically different geometries.

Using the transformation

$$\sin \theta = \frac{r}{1 + \frac{r^2}{4}} \tag{2.4}$$

where r is a dimensionless variable that is to be distinguished from the radius vector of polar coordinates in Euclidean plane, the metric given by Eq. (2.3) takes the form

$$ds^2 = \frac{a^2 dr^2 + r^2 d\phi^2}{(1 + \frac{r^2}{4})^2} \tag{2.5}$$

As θ increases from 0 to π, r increases from 0 to 2 at $\frac{\pi}{2}$ and then to infinity at $\theta = \pi$.

The above expressions for the metric of two- and three-dimensional spaces have one feature in common: when expressed in orthogonal form, all the terms are positive. But this need not be so, and the introduction of negative terms is one way of obtaining spaces that do not have Euclidean geometries. As an example, consider a three-dimensional space which differs from three-dimensional Euclidean space in that its metric has the form

$$ds^2 = dx^2 + dy^2 - dz^2 \tag{2.6}$$

If the coordinates are changed to (r_1, θ, ϕ), where

$$x = r_1 \sinh \theta \cos \phi, \quad y = r_1 \sinh \theta \sin \phi, \quad z = r_1 \cosh \theta$$

then the metric becomes

$$ds^2 = -dr_1^2 + r_1^2 d\theta^2 + r_1^2 \sinh^2 \theta d\phi^2$$

and the metric of the surface $r_1 = a$ is

$$ds^2 = a^2(d\theta^2 + \sinh^2 \theta d\phi^2)$$

where a is a constant.

If we make the substitution

$$\sinh \theta = \frac{r}{1 - \frac{r^2}{4}}$$

then the above formula takes the form

$$ds^2 = \frac{a^2 dr^2 + r^2 d\phi^2}{(1 - \frac{r^2}{4})^2} \qquad (2.7)$$

a form analogous to Eq. (2.5). Clearly $r = 0$ when $\theta = 0$ and increases to $r = 2$ when θ is infinite.

2.2   The Metric Tensor

With the foregoing discussion on two-/three-dimensional space, we may move on to the general case of n-dimensional space. One way is to extend the dimensionality of this space from two/three to n, and a point (called the *world point*) in such a space will have coordinates $(x^1, x^2, \ldots, x^n)$. For the other way, we assume that the distance between two neighbouring points is given by

$$ds^2 = g_{ij} dx^i dx^j \qquad (2.8)$$

where $i, j = 1, 2, \ldots, n$ and the summation convention is used. Here g_{ij}'s are the functions of the coordinates and may vary from point to point. Equation (2.8) is called the *metric equation* and ds is the *interval* or *line element*. The space which satisfies Eq. (2.8) is called the *Riemannian space*. Our three-dimensional Euclidean space is a special case of Riemannian space. The functions g_{ij}'s are n^2 in number, real and need not be positive but are such that their determinant

$$g = \det g_{ij} = \mid g_{ij} \mid = \begin{vmatrix} g_{11} & g_{12} & \cdots & g_{1n} \\ g_{21} & g_{22} & \cdots & g_{2n} \\ \vdots & \vdots & \vdots & \vdots \\ g_{n1} & g_{n2} & \cdots & g_{nn} \end{vmatrix} \qquad (2.9)$$

is non-zero.

Since dx^i and dx^j in Eq. (2.8) are contravariant vectors and ds^2 is an invariant for any arbitrary choice of dx^i and dx^j, from quotient law, it follows that g_{ij} is a covariant tensor of rank two. This tensor is known as *metric tensor* or *fundamental tensor*.

Another way of showing that g_{ij} is a covariant tensor of rank two is as follows:

Since ds^2 is an invariant, from Eq. (2.8) it follows that

$$ds^2 = g_{ij}dx^i dx^j = g'_{kl}dx'^k dx'^l \qquad (2.10)$$

Applying the inverse transformation

$$dx^p = \frac{\partial x^p}{\partial x'^q}dx'^q$$

to Eq. (2.10), we get

$$g'_{kl}dx'^k dx'^l = g_{ij}\frac{\partial x^i}{\partial x'^k}\frac{\partial x^j}{\partial x'^l}dx'^k dx'^l$$

Since dx'^k and dx'^l are arbitrary contravariant vectors, we have

$$g'_{kl} = \frac{\partial x^i}{\partial x'^k}\frac{\partial x^j}{\partial x'^l}g_{ij}$$

which shows that g_{ij} is a second rank covariant tensor.

The metric tensor g_{ij} is also symmetric which can be seen as follows:

From Eq. (1.31), we have

$$g_{ij} = \frac{1}{2}(g_{ij} + g_{ji}) + \frac{1}{2}(g_{ij} - g_{ji}) = S_{ij} + A_{ij}$$

so that

$$g_{ij}dx^i dx^j = (S_{ij} + A_{ij})dx^i dx^j \qquad (2.11)$$

A change in dummy indices on the right-hand side of Eq. (2.11) leads to

$$g_{ij}dx^i dx^j = (S_{ji} + A_{ji})dx^j dx^i = (S_{ij} - A_{ij})dx^i dx^j \qquad (2.12)$$

Adding Eqs. (2.11) and (2.12), we have

$$2g_{ij}dx^i dx^j = 2S_{ij}dx^i dx^j$$

Thus

$$g_{ij} = S_{ij} = \frac{1}{2}(g_{ij} + g_{ji})$$

is a symmetric tensor.

Remarks

1. It may be noted that the determinant $g = |g_{ij}|$ does not transform like a scalar. For we have

$$g' = |g'_{ik}|$$

$$= \left| \frac{\partial x^l}{\partial x'^i} \frac{\partial x^m}{\partial x'^k} g_{lm} \right|$$

$$= \left| \frac{\partial x^l}{\partial x'^i} \right| \left| \frac{\partial x^m}{\partial x'^k} \right| |g_{lm}|$$

$$= [J\{x \longrightarrow x'\}]^2 g \qquad (2.13)$$

where J is the Jacobian of the transformation $x \longrightarrow x'$.

2. Since $dx^1 dx^2 dx^3 dx^4$ transforms as

$$dx^1 dx^2 dx^3 dx^4 = J\{x \longrightarrow x'\} dx'^1 dx'^2 dx'^3 dx'^4$$

It follows that $\sqrt{-g}\, dx^1 dx^2 dx^3 dx^4$ is an invariant.

In addition to the metric tensor there are two more fundamental tensors g^{ij} and δ^i_j which can be obtained in the following way:

Consider the determinant of g_{ij} [cf., Eq. (2.9)], find the cofactor of each of the elements g_{ij} in det g_{ij}, divide each cofactor by g and denote it by g^{ij}, i.e., we have

$$g^{ij} = \frac{\text{cofactor of } g_{ij} \text{ in det } g_{ij}}{\det g_{ij}} \qquad (2.14)$$

This g^{ij} is called the *conjugate* or *reciprocal tensor* of g_{ij}. Also, we have

$$g_{ij} g^{ik} = g_{ij} \left(\frac{\text{cofactor of } g_{ik} \text{ in det } g_{ik}}{\det g_{ik}} \right) = \delta^k_j \qquad (2.15)$$

The function g^{ij} in Eq. (2.14) is a contravariant tensor of rank two and this can be proved as follows:

Let A^j be any contravariant vector, then its inner product with g_{ik} gives an arbitrary covariant vector

$$B_k = g_{kj} A^j \qquad (2.16)$$

Also, since

$$g^{ki} B_k = g^{ki} g_{kj} A^j = \delta^i_j A^j = A^i \qquad (2.17)$$

i.e., the inner product of g^{ki} with an arbitrary covariant vector B_k gives a contravariant vector A^i and hence by quotient law, g^{ki} is a contravariant tensor of rank two. It is also symmetric.

Moreover, since g_{ij} and g^{ik} are covariant and contravariant rank two tensors, respectively, using quotient law in Eq. (2.15) it is seen that δ_j^k is a mixed tensor of rank two.

The three tensors defined through Eqs. (2.8), (2.14) and (2.15) are called *fundamental tensors* and are of basic importance in general theory of relativity. While in mechanics, the metric

$$ds^2 = g_{ij}dx^i dx^j$$

is related to the square of the speed through the relation

$$\left(\frac{ds}{dt}\right)^2 = v^2 = g_{ij}\frac{dx^i}{dt}\frac{dx^j}{dt}$$

A remarkable property of the mixed fundamental tensor δ_j^i is that its components have the same value in all coordinate systems, since by making a transformation to a new coordinate system we have

$$\delta_j^{\prime i} = \frac{\partial x^{\prime i}}{\partial x^k}\frac{\partial x^l}{\partial x^{\prime j}}\delta_l^k = \frac{\partial x^{\prime i}}{\partial x^k}\frac{\partial x^k}{\partial x^{\prime j}}\delta_k^k = \frac{\partial x^{\prime i}}{\partial x^{\prime j}} = \begin{cases} 1, & \text{for } i = j \\ 0. & \text{for } i \neq j \end{cases} = \delta_j^i$$

Hence, $\delta_j^{\prime i} = \delta_j^i$, i.e., it has constant components independent of the coordinate system.

Remark. It may be noted that g_{ij} and g^{ij} are *reciprocal* or *conjugate* if

$$g_{ij}g^{ik} = \delta_j^k \quad \text{and} \quad |g_{ij}||g^{ij}| \neq 0$$

We can thus say that two symmetric tensors of rank two, one covariant and other contravariant are reciprocal or conjugate if their outer product equals to Kronecker delta and the products of their determinants one non-zero, that is, if A_{ij} and B^{ij} are two symmetric covariant and symmetric contravariant tensors of rank two, then they are conjugate only when

$$A_{ij}B^{ik} = \delta_j^k \quad \text{and} \quad |A_{ij}||B^{ij}| \neq 0 \tag{2.18}$$

The line element for a four-dimensional Euclidean space is

$$ds^2 = (dx^1)^2 + (dx^2)^2 + (dx^3)^2 + (dx^4)^2$$

The metric tensor for the Euclidean space is, therefore

$$(g_{ij})_{\text{Euclidean}} = \begin{bmatrix} 1 & 0 & 0 & 0 \\ 0 & 1 & 0 & 0 \\ 0 & 0 & 1 & 0 \\ 0 & 0 & 0 & 1 \end{bmatrix} \tag{2.19}$$

while the metric of special relativity is

$$ds^2 = -dx^2 - dy^2 - dz^2 + c^2 dt^2$$

Using the coordinates $x^1 = x, x^2 = y, x^3 = z, x^4 = ct$, the above equation becomes

$$ds^2 = -(dx^1)^2 - (dx^2)^2 - (dx^3)^2 + (dx^4)^2$$

with the metric tensor

$$(g_{ij})_{\text{special relativity}} = \begin{bmatrix} -1 & 0 & 0 & 0 \\ 0 & -1 & 0 & 0 \\ 0 & 0 & -1 & 0 \\ 0 & 0 & 0 & 1 \end{bmatrix} \tag{2.20}$$

Also, using the Minkowski coordinates defined as $x = x^1, y = x^2, z = x^3$, $ict = x^4$, the metric (Minkowski metric) is

$$ds^2 = -dx^2 - dy^2 - dz^2 + (icdt)^2 = -[(dx^1)^2 + (dx^2)^2 + (dx^3)^2 + (dx^4)^2]$$

and

$$(g_{ij})_{\text{Minkowski}} = \begin{bmatrix} -1 & 0 & 0 & 0 \\ 0 & -1 & 0 & 0 \\ 0 & 0 & -1 & 0 \\ 0 & 0 & 0 & -1 \end{bmatrix} \tag{2.21}$$

For general theory of relativity, the metric is of more general form

$$ds^2 = g_{ij} dx^i dx^j, \quad (i, j = 1, 2, 3, 4)$$

Here, all elements of the metric tensor are functions of the coordinates:

$$g_{ij} = \begin{bmatrix} g_{11} & g_{12} & g_{13} & g_{14} \\ g_{21} & g_{22} & g_{23} & g_{24} \\ g_{31} & g_{32} & g_{33} & g_{34} \\ g_{41} & g_{42} & g_{43} & g_{44} \end{bmatrix} \tag{2.22}$$

Since g_{ij} is symmetric, it has only ten independent components.

The sequence of algebraic signs on the diagonal of a metric tensor is called the *signature* of the metric. In some literature, the sum of these, or the difference between the number of positive and the number of negative g_{ij}'s, or the trace of the matrix is the signature. Using the later definition, the signature of the metrics given by Eqs. (2.19), (2.20)–(2.21) is $+4, -2$ and -4, respectively. The overall sign of the signature, as we have noted, is arbitrary and depend upon the sign employed in the definition of ds^2.

EXAMPLE 2.1 Show that

(i) $dg_{kl} = -g_{ik}g_{jl}dg^{ij}$

(ii) $A^{kl}dg_{kl} = -A_{kl}dg^{kl}$

(iii) $\dfrac{dg}{g} = -g_{ij}dg^{ij}$

Solution

(i) We know that $g_{ik}g^{ij} = \delta_k^j$. Take the differential and multiply it by g_{jl} to get the result.

(ii) Multiply the above result (i) by A^{kl} and solve to get the required result.

(iii) Since $g_{ij}g^{ij} = 4$ (in 4-dimensions) and the definition of g^{ij} yields

$$\frac{\partial g}{\partial x^k}dx^k = gg^{ij}\frac{\partial g_{ij}}{\partial x^k}dx^k$$

After simplification, we get the required result.

EXAMPLE 2.2 Transform $ds^2 = dx^2 + dy^2 + dz^2$ into: (i) spherical polar and
(ii) cylindrical coordinates.

Solution Here $ds^2 = dx^2 + dy^2 + dz^2$ and $g_{11} = g_{22} = g_{33} = 1, g_{ij} = 0$ for $i \neq j$. The transformation law for g_{ij} is

$$\begin{aligned}
g'_{ij} &= \frac{\partial x^a}{\partial x'^i}\frac{\partial x^b}{\partial x'^j}g_{ab} \\
&= \frac{\partial x^a}{\partial x'^i}\frac{\partial x^a}{\partial x'^j}g_{aa} \\
&= \frac{\partial x^a}{\partial x'^i}\frac{\partial x^a}{\partial x'^j} \text{ as } g_{aa} = 1, (a = 1, 2, 3)
\end{aligned} \qquad (2.23)$$

(i) For spherical polar coordinates, we have

$$x = r\sin\theta\cos\phi, \quad y = r\sin\theta\sin\phi, \quad z = r\cos\theta$$

Put $x^1 = x, x^2 = y, x^3 = z; x'^1 = r, x'^2 = \theta, x'^3 = \phi$ then Eq. (2.23) leads to

$$\begin{aligned}
g'_{11} &= \frac{\partial x^a}{\partial x'^1}\frac{\partial x^a}{\partial x'^1} \\
&= \left(\frac{\partial x^1}{\partial x'^1}\right)^2 + \left(\frac{\partial x^2}{\partial x'^1}\right)^2 + \left(\frac{\partial x^3}{\partial x'^1}\right)^2 \\
&= \left(\frac{\partial x}{\partial y}\right)^2 + \left(\frac{\partial y}{\partial r}\right)^2 + \left(\frac{\partial z}{\partial r}\right)^2 \\
&= 1
\end{aligned}$$

In a similar manner, we have

$$g'_{22} = r^2, \quad g'_{33} = r^2 \sin^2 \theta, \quad g'_{12} = g'_{23} = g'_{31} = 0$$

Therefore, in polar coordinates, we have

$$ds^2 = g'_{ab} dx'^a dx'^b$$
$$= g'_{aa}(dx'^a)^2, \quad (a = 1, 2, 3)$$
$$= dr^2 + r^2 d\theta^2 + r^2 \sin^2 \theta d\phi^2$$

(ii) For cylindrical coordinates, we have

$$x = r \cos \theta, \quad y = r \sin \theta, \quad z = z$$

Put $x^1 = x$, $x^2 = y$, $x^3 = z$; $x'^1 = r$, $x'^2 = \theta$, $x'^3 = z$ then Eq. (2.23) leads to

$$g'^{11} = 1, \quad g'_{22} = r^2, \quad g'_{33} = 1, \quad g'_{12} = g'_{23} = g'_{31} = 0$$

and thus

$$ds^2 = dr^2 + r^2 d\theta^2 + dz^2$$

EXAMPLE 2.3 Show that the two-dimensional metric space given by

$$ds^2 = dv^2 - v^2 du^2$$

is a flat two-dimensional Minkowski space described by

$$ds^2 = dx^2 - dt^2$$

Solution From the analogy with polar coordinates, we have

$$x = v \cosh u, \quad x^2 - t^2 = v^2$$
$$t = v \sinh u, \quad \frac{x}{t} = \coth u$$

and

$$dx^2 = (dv \cosh u + duv \sinh u)^2$$
$$dt^2 = (dv \sinh u + duv \cosh u)^2$$

which yields

$$dx^2 - dt^2 = dv^2 - v^2 du^2$$

EXAMPLE 2.4 Show that the line-element

$$ds^2 = R^2[d\alpha^2 + \sin^2 \alpha(d\theta^2 + \sin^2 \theta d\phi^2)]$$

represents a hypersurface of radius R in Euclidean space of four-dimensions.

Solution The line element for a four dimensional Euclidean space is

$$ds^2 = dx_1^2 + dx_2^2 + dx_3^2 + dx_4^2 \tag{2.24}$$

and also the equation of a hypersurface of radius R is

$$x_1^2 + x_2^2 + x_3^2 + x_4^2 = R^2$$

On this hypersurface introduce the coordinates

$$x_4 = R\cos\alpha, \quad x_3 = R\sin\alpha\cos\theta$$
$$x_2 = R\sin\alpha\sin\theta\cos\phi, \quad x_1 = R\sin\alpha\sin\theta\sin\phi$$

Taking the differential of these equations (keeping R as constant) and substituting in Eq. (2.24), we get the required result.

2.3   Raising and Lowering of Indices— Associated Tensor

The metric tensor and its conjugate can be used for raising and lowering the indices of a tensor (vector). Thus, for a contravariant vector A^k, the corresponding covariant vector is

$$A_i = g_{ik}A^k \tag{2.25}$$

and for covariant vector B_k the corresponding contravariant vector is

$$B^i = g^{ik}B_k \tag{2.26}$$

From a second rank tensor A^{ij}, we have

$$A_k^i = g_{kj}A^{ij}$$

$$A_{ik} = g_{ip}A_k^p = g_{ip}g_{kj}A^{pj}$$

Moreover,

$$A^{jkl} = g^{jp}g^{kq}g^{lr}A_{pqr}$$

$$A_{pqr} = g_{jp}g_{kq}g_{lr}A^{jkl} \tag{2.27}$$

$$A_{jl}^k = g_{jp}g_{lr}A^{kpr}$$

$$A^{kpr} = g^{jp}g^{lr}A_{jl}^k$$

and

$$A_{tq}^{prs} = g^{pj}g^{rk}g_{tl}A_{jqk}^{sl}$$

$$A_{jqk}^{sl} = g_{pj}g_{rk}g^{tl}A_{qt}^{prs} \tag{2.27a}$$

etc. The process of raising and lowering an index can be applied for any tensor. Thus

$$T^{...i_r...}_{...k_s...}g_{i_r m}g^{k_s n} = T^{...n...}_{...m...} \tag{2.28}$$

It can be easily shown that the quantities obtained as a result of raising and lowering operations with the metric tensor are themselves tensors. Such tensors are called *associated tensors*.

2.4 Vector Magnitude

The fundamental quantities required for any geometrical measurement are length and angle. These can be defined and calculated with the help of the metric tensor and that is why the metric tensor often refers to as describing the geometry of the space. The distance between two neighbouring points is given by

$$ds^2 = g_{ij}dx^i dx^j$$

The square of length or *norm* of a vector A^i is defined by

$$A^2 = A^i A_i = g_{ij}A^i A^j \tag{2.29}$$

The magnitude of the contravariant vector A^i is A and is an invariant. For example, if A_j and A^k are the components of a covariant and contravariant vector, respectively, then from the law of transformation for these vectors, we have

$$A'_i A'^i = \frac{\partial x^j}{\partial x'^i}\frac{\partial x'^i}{\partial x^k}A_j A^k$$

$$= \delta^j_k A_j A^k$$

$$= A_k A^k$$

Also, $A^2 = A^i A_i = g^{ij}A_i A_j$ is an invariant. Thus, the norms (lengths) of any contravariant vector A^i and its associated covariant vector A_i are equal.

The metric in Eq. (2.29) is said to be *positive definite* or *negative definite* if for every vector A^i, $A^2 > 0$, or $A^2 < 0$, respectively; otherwise it is *indefinite*.

A vector whose magnitude is unity is called a *unit vector*. For example, from Eq. (2.8)

$$1 = g_{ij}\frac{dx^i}{ds}\frac{dx^j}{ds}$$

which means that $\dfrac{dx^i}{ds}$ is a unit contravariant vector. In fact, $\dfrac{dx^i}{ds}$ is a unit tangent vector to a curve (see also Example 1.2).

Since $A_i A^i$ and $B_j B^j$ are invariant, $\sqrt{(A_i A^i)(B_j B^j)}$ is an invariant and $\dfrac{g_{ij}A^i B^j}{\sqrt{(A_i A^i)(B_j B^j)}}$ is also an invariant. The angle between two vectors A^i and

B^j is defined by

$$\cos\theta = \frac{g_{ij}A^iB^j}{\sqrt{(A_iA^i)(B_jB^j)}} \tag{2.30}$$

Substitution of $\cos\theta$ from Eq. (2.30) into $\sin^2\theta = 1 - \cos^2\theta$ and using Eq. (2.29), we get

$$\sin^2\theta = 1 - \left[\frac{g_{ij}A^iB^j}{\sqrt{(g_{hi}A^hA^i)(g_{jk}B^jB^k)}}\right]^2$$

$$= \frac{(g_{hi}g_{jk} - g_{ij}g_{hk})A^hA^iB^jB^k}{g_{hi}g_{jk}A^hA^iB^jB^k} \tag{2.31}$$

Two vectors are said to be *orthogonal* if the angle between them is $\pi/2$, that is, $\cos\theta = 0$; and in such case Eq. (2.30) leads to

$$g_{ij}A^iB^j = A_i(g_{ij}B^j) = A^iB_i = 0$$

A vector is said to be *time-like* if its magnitude is real, it is *space like* if its magnitude is imaginary and *null vector* if the magnitude is zero; and for a null vector dx^i, from Eq. (2.29), we have

$$g_{ij}dx^idx^j = 0$$

which means that the null vectors are self-orthogonal. In other words, if the metric is indefinite (as in relativity theory) then there exists vectors which are orthogonal to themselves, that is, $g_{ij}A^iA^j = 0$. Such vectors are null vectors.

It may also be noted that: (i) the magnitude is a scalar and hence independent of the coordinate transformation and (ii) because we assumed the signature of the quadratic form [cf., Eq. (2.8)] to be -2, a null vector does not necessarily imply a zero vector (i.e., a null vector is itself not zero although its inner product with itself is zero).

EXAMPLE 2.5 If X^i and Y^i are unit orthogonal vectors, show that

$$(g_{hj}g_{ik} - g_{hk}g_{ij})X^hX^jY^iY^k = 1$$

Solution Since X^i and Y^i are unit orthogonal vectors, from the definition we have

$$\sin\theta = 1, \quad g_{ij}X^iX^j = 1, \quad g_{ij}Y^iY^j = 1$$

Equation (2.31), after proper simplifications, now leads to

$$(g_{hj}g_{ik} - g_{hk}g_{ij})X^hX^jY^iY^k = 1$$

EXAMPLE 2.6 For the metric (Minkowski spacetime of special relativity)

$$ds^2 = -dx^2 - dy^2 - dz^2 + c^2dt^2$$

show that the vectors having the components $(1, 0, 0, 0)$ and $(\sqrt{2}, 0, 0, \frac{\sqrt{3}}{c})$ are unit vectors. Also, show that the angle between them is not real.

Solution For the given metric, we have

$$g_{11} = g_{22} = g_{33} = -1, \quad g_{44} = c^2, \quad g_{ij} = 0, \quad i \neq j$$

If $A^i = (1, 0, 0, 0)$ and $B^i = (\sqrt{2}, 0, 0, \frac{\sqrt{3}}{c})$ then from the definition, we have

$$A^2 = g_{ij} A^i A^j = g_{11} A^1 A^1 = 1$$

and

$$B^2 = g_{ij} B^i B^j = g_{11} B^1 B^1 + g_{44} B^4 B^4 = 1$$

Thus, A^i and B^i are unit vectors. Also, from Eq. (2.30), we have

$$\cos \theta = \frac{g_{ij} A^i B^j}{\sqrt{(A_i A^i)(B_j B^j)}} = -\sqrt{2}$$

This leads to $|\cos \theta| = \sqrt{2}$ which is greater than 1 and thus the angle between A^i and B^i is not real.

EXAMPLE 2.7 Show, for a three-dimensional coordinate system, that the angles between the coordinate curves are

$$\cos \theta_{12} = \frac{g_{12}}{\sqrt{g_{11} g_{22}}}, \quad \cos \theta_{23} = \frac{g_{23}}{\sqrt{g_{22} g_{33}}}, \quad \cos \theta_{31} = \frac{g_{31}}{\sqrt{g_{33} g_{11}}}$$

Moreover, if the coordinate system is orthogonal then show that $g_{12} = g_{23} = g_{31} = 0$ and $g^{ij} = 1/g_{ij}$ for $i = j$.

Solution Let θ_{12}, θ_{23} and θ_{31} denote the angles between the coordinate curves in a three-dimensional coordinate system. Along the x^1-coordinate, curve $x^2 = $ constant and $x^3 = $ constant, then from $ds^2 = g_{11}(dx^1)^2$ we have $\frac{dx^1}{ds} = \frac{1}{\sqrt{g_{11}}}$ which shows that the unit tangent vector along the curve x^1 is $X_1^r = \frac{1}{\sqrt{g_{11}}} \delta_1^r$. Similarly, the unit tangent vectors along the curves x^2 and x^3 are $X_2^r = \frac{1}{\sqrt{g_{22}}} \delta_2^r$ and $X_3^r = \frac{1}{\sqrt{g_{33}}} \delta_3^r$, respectively. Now, the cosine of the angle θ_{12} between X_1^r and X_2^r is given by

$$\cos \theta_{12} = g_{ij} X_1^i X_2^j$$

$$= g_{ij} \frac{1}{\sqrt{g_{11}}} \frac{1}{\sqrt{g_{22}}} \delta_1^i \delta_2^j$$

$$= \frac{g_{12}}{\sqrt{g_{11}} \sqrt{g_{22}}}$$

Similarly

$$\cos \theta_{23} = \frac{g_{23}}{\sqrt{g_{22}}\sqrt{g_{33}}}$$

$$\cos \theta_{31} = \frac{g_{31}}{\sqrt{g_{33}}\sqrt{g_{11}}}$$

Now, for an orthogonal coordinate system, we have $\theta_{12} = \theta_{23} = \theta_{31} = 90°$ and the above equations lead to $g_{12} = g_{23} = g_{31} = 0$. Now, since g_{ij} is symmetric, hence $g_{ij} = 0$ when $i \neq j$ for an orthogonal coordinate system. Moreover, using the mixed fundamental tensor it can be shown that for an orthogonal system $g^{ij} = 1/g_{ij}$ when $i = j$.

EXAMPLE 2.8 Show that a conformal transformation of a metric, i.e., $g_{ij} \longrightarrow \phi(x^k)g_{ij}$ preserves all angles for an arbitrary function ϕ. Also show that all null curves remain null curves.

Solution Consider the coordinate transformation $g_{ij} \longrightarrow \phi(x^k)g_{ij}$, then the angle θ between two vectors A^i and B^j is given by

$$\cos \theta = \frac{g_{ij}A^iB^j}{\sqrt{(g_{kl}A^kA^l)(g_{mn}B^mB^n)}}$$

$$\longrightarrow \frac{\phi(x^p)g_{ij}A^iB^j}{\sqrt{[\phi(x^p)g_{kl}A^kA^l][\phi(x^p)g_{mn}B^mB^n]}}$$

$$= \frac{g_{ij}A^iB^j}{\sqrt{(g_{kl}A^kA^l)(g_{mn}B^mB^n)}}$$

which shows that the angle θ remains same, i.e., preserved (see also Section 5.3).

Moreover, for null curves

$$g_{ij}\frac{dx^i}{ds}\frac{dx^j}{ds} = 0$$

which for $g_{ij} \longrightarrow \phi(x^k)g_{ij}$ leads to

$$\phi(x^k)g_{ij}\frac{dx^i}{ds}\frac{dx^j}{ds} = 0$$

This shows that square of the tangent vector $\dfrac{dx^i}{ds}$ is zero and the null curves remain null curves.

2.5 Relative and Absolute Tensors

If the components of a quantity $\mathcal{A}_{j_1 j_2 \ldots j_s}^{i_1 i_2 \ldots i_r}$ transform according to the law

$$\mathcal{A}_{m_1 m_2 \ldots m_s}^{\prime l_1 l_2 \ldots l_r} = \left| \frac{\partial x}{\partial x'} \right|^W \left(\frac{\partial x'^{l_1}}{\partial x^{i_1}} \frac{\partial x'^{l_2}}{\partial x^{i_2}} \cdots \frac{\partial x'^{l_r}}{\partial x^{i_r}} \right)$$

$$\times \left(\frac{\partial x^{j_1}}{\partial x'^{m_1}} \frac{\partial x^{j_2}}{\partial x'^{m_2}} \cdots \frac{\partial x^{j_s}}{\partial x'^{m_s}} \right) \mathcal{A}_{j_1 j_2 \ldots j_s}^{i_1 i_2 \ldots i_r} \tag{2.32}$$

then the quantity $\mathcal{A}_{j_1 j_2 \ldots j_s}^{i_1 i_2 \ldots i_r}$ is called a *relative tensor of density W*, where $J = \left| \dfrac{\partial x}{\partial x'} \right|$ is the Jacobian of the transformation. The constant W is known as the *weight* of the tensor density and it may be a positive or negative integer.

If $W = 0$ then a relative tensor is known as an *absolute tensor* and this is the tensor with which we have dealt so far. Unless or otherwise stated we are dealing with absolute tensors in this text. If $W = 1$, the relative tensor is called the *tensor density*. A tensor density of order one is called a *vector density* and a tensor density of order zero is a *scalar density*.

As an example of scalar density, consider the determinant of an ordinary covariant tensor A_{ij} of rank two. The transformation law for such tensor A_{ij} can be regarded as the matrix equation

$$A'_{ij} = \frac{\partial x^k}{\partial x'^i} \frac{\partial x^l}{\partial x'^j} A_{kl}$$

From the properties of the determinant of a product of matrices, we have

$$\det A'_{ij} = \left| \frac{\partial x}{\partial x'} \right|^2 \det A_{kl}$$

Therefore, the determinant of a covariant tensor of rank two is a scalar density of weight two.

EXAMPLE 2.9 Prove that $\sqrt{g}$ is a tensor density.

Solution The elements of the determinant g given by g_{ij} transform according to the equation

$$g'_{kl} = \frac{\partial x^i}{\partial x'^k} \frac{\partial x^j}{\partial x'^l} g_{ij}$$

Taking the determinant of both sides, we get

$$g' = \left| \frac{\partial x^i}{\partial x'^k} \right| \left| \frac{\partial x^j}{\partial x'^l} \right| g = J^2 g \tag{2.33}$$

which leads to

$$\sqrt{g'} = J \sqrt{g}$$

showing that $\sqrt{g}$ is a tensor density (relative tensor of weight one).

The algebraic operations (e.g., addition, subtraction, multiplication, contraction, etc.) of relative tensors are same as that of absolute tensors (ordinary tensors) and we have

1. A linear combination of tensor densities of the same type and same weight is a new tensor density of the same type and same weight.

2. The inner product of two tensor densities of order p and q and weights W_1 and W_2, respectively, lead to a tensor density of order $p + q$ and weight $W_1 + W_2$.

3. The contraction of indices on a mixed tensor density of order p and weight W is a tensor density of order $p - 2$ and weight W.

From these rules it follows that [see also Eq. (2.32)] a tensor density of weight W can be expressed as the product of an ordinary tensor and a scalar density of weight W. Thus, the weight of the tensor density remains unchanged by raising and lowering of indices, through metric tensor, of tensor densities. Further, the symmetry properties of tensor densities follow the same procedure as that of ordinary tensors (absolute tensors).

2.6　Levi-Civita Tensor

Introduce the totally skew symmetric symbol (in four dimensions)

$$e^{ijkl} = \begin{cases} +1, & \text{if } ijkl \text{ is an even permutation of 1234} \\ -1, & \text{if } ijkl \text{ is an odd permutation of 1234} \\ 0, & \text{otherwise} \end{cases} \tag{2.34}$$

The quantity e^{ijkl} defined by Eq. (2.34) can be taken as a contravariant tensor density of weight $W = +1$. This tensor density is known as the *Levi-Civita contravariant tensor density*.

In a similar way, the covariant tensor density e_{ijkl} of weight $W = -1$ can be defined. The components of e_{ijkl} are obtained from e^{ijkl} by lowering the indices (using metric tensor) and multiplying by $(-g)^{-1}$ as follows:

$$e_{ijkl} = g_{im}g_{jn}g_{ko}g_{lp}(-g)^{-1}e^{mnop} \tag{2.35}$$

The components of e_{ijkl} can be found easily, for example

$$e_{1234} = g_{1m}g_{2n}g_{3o}g_{4p}(-g)^{-1}e^{mnop}$$

$$= (-g)^{-1}|g_{mn}| \tag{2.36}$$

$$= -1$$

Thus, for the *covariant Levi-Civita tensor density* of weight $W = -1$, we have

$$e_{ijkl} = \begin{cases} -1, & \text{if } ijkl \text{ is an even permutation of 1234} \\ +1, & \text{if } ijkl \text{ is an odd permutation of 1234} \\ 0, & \text{otherwise} \end{cases} \tag{2.37}$$

The Levi-Civita contravariant and covariant tensor densities have an important property illustrated by the following example:

EXAMPLE 2.10 Show that the components of Levi-Civita contravariant and covariant densities e^{ijkl} and e_{ijkl} are invariant under coordinate transformation.

Solution From the transformation law (2.32) for the tensor density, the component e'^{1234} transforms as

$$e'^{1234} = \left| \frac{\partial x}{\partial x'} \right| \frac{\partial x'^1}{\partial x^i} \frac{\partial x'^2}{\partial x^j} \frac{\partial x'^3}{\partial x^k} \frac{\partial x'^4}{\partial x^l} e^{ijkl}$$

$$= \left| \frac{\partial x}{\partial x'} \right| \left| \frac{\partial x'}{\partial x} \right| e^{1234}$$

$$= J J^{-1} e^{1234}$$

$$= e^{1234} \text{ since } J = \left| \frac{\partial x}{\partial x'} \right| \text{ and } J J^{-1} = 1$$

Similarly

$$e'_{1234} = \left| \frac{\partial x}{\partial x'} \right|^{-1} \frac{\partial x^i}{\partial x'^1} \frac{\partial x^j}{\partial x'^2} \frac{\partial x^k}{\partial x'^3} \frac{\partial x^l}{\partial x'^4} e_{ijkl}$$

$$= \left| \frac{\partial x}{\partial x'} \right|^{-1} \left| \frac{\partial x}{\partial x'} \right| e_{1234}$$

$$= J^{-1} J e_{1234}$$

$$= e_{1234}$$

In a similar manner we can show that all the other components of e^{ijkl} and e_{ijkl} remain invariant under coordinate transformation.

The Levi-Civita contravariant and covariant tensor densities defined by Eqs. (2.34) and (2.37), respectively, are used to define ordinary contravariant and covariant tensors and we have

$$\epsilon^{ijkl} = \frac{1}{\sqrt{-g}} e^{ijkl} \tag{2.38}$$

and

$$\epsilon_{ijkl} = \sqrt{-g} \, e_{ijkl} \tag{2.39}$$

The quantities ϵ^{ijkl} and ϵ_{ijkl} defined by Eqs. (2.38) and (2.39), respectively, are tensors. This can be seen as follows:

Consider the coordinate transformation $x \longrightarrow x'$, then from the definition of tensor density and Eq. (2.33), we have

$$\epsilon'^{ijkl} = \frac{1}{\sqrt{-g'}} e'^{ijkl}$$

$$= \left|\frac{\partial x}{\partial x'}\right|^{-1} \frac{1}{\sqrt{-g}} \left|\frac{\partial x}{\partial x'}\right| \frac{\partial x'^i}{\partial x^m} \frac{\partial x'^j}{\partial x^n} \frac{\partial x'^k}{\partial x^o} \frac{\partial x'^l}{\partial x^p} e^{mnop}$$

$$= J^{-1} J \left(\frac{\partial x'^i}{\partial x^m} \frac{\partial x'^j}{\partial x^n} \frac{\partial x'^k}{\partial x^o} \frac{\partial x'^l}{\partial x^p} \right) \frac{1}{\sqrt{-g}} e^{mnop}$$

$$= \left(\frac{\partial x'^i}{\partial x^m} \frac{\partial x'^j}{\partial x^n} \frac{\partial x'^k}{\partial x^o} \frac{\partial x'^l}{\partial x^p} \right) \epsilon^{mnop} \quad (\text{since} J^{-1}J = 1)$$

which is the transformation law for the ordinary contravariant tensor of rank four.

In a similar way, we have

$$\epsilon'_{ijkl} = \sqrt{-g'} e'_{ijkl}$$

$$= \left|\frac{\partial x}{\partial x'}\right| (\sqrt{-g}) \left|\frac{\partial x}{\partial x'}\right|^{-1} \frac{\partial x^m}{\partial x'^i} \frac{\partial x^n}{\partial x'^j} \frac{\partial x^o}{\partial x'^k} \frac{\partial x^p}{\partial x'^l} e_{mnop}$$

$$\epsilon'_{ijkl} = J J^{-1} \left(\frac{\partial x^m}{\partial x'^i} \frac{\partial x^n}{\partial x'^j} \frac{\partial x^o}{\partial x'^k} \frac{\partial x^p}{\partial x'^l} \right) \sqrt{-g} e_{mnop}$$

$$= \left(\frac{\partial x^m}{\partial x'^i} \frac{\partial x^n}{\partial x'^j} \frac{\partial x^o}{\partial x'^k} \frac{\partial x^p}{\partial x'^l} \right) \epsilon_{mnop}$$

which shows that ϵ_{ijkl} is a rank four covariant tensor.

The tensors defined through Eqs. (2.38) and (2.39) are known as the *Levi-Civita alternating tensors*. They satisfy the relations

$$\epsilon^{ijkl} = g^{im} g^{jn} g^{ko} g^{lp} \epsilon_{mnop} \tag{2.40}$$

and

$$\epsilon_{ijkl} = g_{im} g_{jn} g_{ko} g_{lp} \epsilon^{mnop} \tag{2.41}$$

Moreover, the product of two Levi-Civita tensors can be expressed in terms of the Kronecker delta $\delta_b^a = g_b^a$ as follows:

$$\epsilon_{abcd} \epsilon^{pqmn} = -24 g_a^{[p} g_b^q g_c^m g_d^{n]} \tag{2.42}$$

When all the four indices have different values then the components of this symbol differ from zero. Therefore, the product is not zero only when the values of the indices coincide pairwise. Contraction of Eq. (2.42), using

$\delta_a^a = g_a^a = 4$, yields

$$\epsilon_{abcd}\epsilon^{aqmn} = -g_b^q g_c^m g_d^n - g_b^m g_c^n g_d^q - g_b^n g_c^q g_d^m$$
$$+ g_b^q g_c^n g_d^m + g_b^n g_c^m g_d^q + g_b^m g_c^q g_d^n \tag{2.43}$$

$$\epsilon_{abcd}\epsilon^{abmn} = -2(g_c^m g_d^n - g_c^n g_d^m) \tag{2.44}$$

$$\epsilon_{abcd}\epsilon^{abcn} = -6g_d^n \tag{2.45}$$

$$\epsilon_{abcd}\epsilon^{abcd} = -24 \tag{2.46}$$

Further, if F_{ij} is a skew symmetric tensor of rank two, then

$$^*\mathcal{F}^{ij} = \frac{1}{2}e^{ijkl}F_{kl} \tag{2.47}$$

is called the *dual* of F_{kl}. This dual is a *pseudo-tensor*, while the product $^*\mathcal{F}^{ij}F_{ij}$ is a *pseudo-scalar,* and we have

$$^*\mathcal{F}_{ij} = \frac{1}{2}e_{ijkl}F^{kl} \tag{2.48}$$

The duals of the ordinary tensors are defined with the help of the Levi-Civita alternating tensors, and we have

$$^*F^{ij} = \frac{1}{2}\epsilon^{ijkl}F_{kl} \tag{2.49}$$

$$^*F_{ij} = \frac{1}{2}\epsilon_{ijkl}F^{kl} \tag{2.50}$$

Remarks

1. A completely skew symmetric tensor T_{ijk} of rank three has exactly four different components (in four dimensions), for example, $T_{123}, T_{124}, T_{134}$ and T_{234} which are same as the number of components of a vector (in four dimensions). For example

$$\epsilon^{ijkl}T_{ijk} = T^l, T_{ijk} = \frac{1}{3!}\epsilon_{lijk}T^l$$

Such a vector T^l is a *pseudo vector*.

2. A completely skew symmetric tensor of rank four has essentially only one component as
$$\epsilon^{ijkl}T_{ijkl} = T$$

Such a scalar is a *pseudo scalar*.

3. In a four-dimensional space there do not exist completely skew symmetric tensors of rank higher than four.

4. It is known that a physical field is always produced by a source, which is termed as its charge. Manifestation of fields when charges are at rest

is called *electric*, and *magnetic* when they are in motion. This general feature is exemplified by the Maxwell's theory of electromagnetism from which the terms of electric and magnetic are derived. If F_{ij} is the skew symmetric Maxwell tensor (electromagnetic field tensor) and v^a is the four velocity of the observer such that $v_a v^a = -1$, then the *electric* and *magnetic parts* of the electromagnetic field are, respectively, defined by

$$E_i = F_{ij} v^j \tag{2.51}$$

and

$$H_i = \, ^*F_{ij} v^j \tag{2.52}$$

where $^*F_{ij}$ is given by Eq. (2.50).

The skew symmetry of F_{ij} leads to $E_i v^i = 0$ and $H_i v^i = 0$. Moreover, if $^*E_i$ and $^*H_i$ are the electric and magnetic parts of $^*F_{ij}$, then $^*E_i = -H_i$ and $^*H_i = -E_i$ and thus

$$^*(^*F_{ij}) = -F_{ij} \tag{2.53}$$

(see also Example 2.11).

It may be noted that the electromagnetic field can be constructed from its electric and magnetic parts. This can be done as follows:

Let

$$H_{ij} = H_i v_j - H_j v_i \quad \text{and} \quad E_{ij} = E_i v_j - E_j v_i$$

then

$$^*H_{ij} = \epsilon_{ijkl} H^k v^l \quad \text{and} \quad ^*E_{ij} = \epsilon_{ijkl} E^k v^l$$

From the skew symmetry property, we have

$$H_{ij} v^j = H_i, \quad E_{ij} v^j = E_i$$

and

$$^*H_{ij} v^j = 0, \quad ^*E_{ij} v^j = 0$$

This leads to the following decomposition of electromagnetic field into its electric and magnetic parts

$$F_{ij} = E_{ij} - \, ^*H_{ij} \tag{2.54}$$

as

$$E_i = (E_{ij} - \, ^*H_{ij}) v^j, \quad H_i = (^*E_{ij} - \, ^{**}H_{ij}) v^j = (^*E_{ij} + H_{ij}) v^j$$

Moreover

$$^*F_{ij} = \, ^*E_{ij} + H_{ij} \tag{2.55}$$

EXAMPLE 2.11 If F^{ij} is a skew symmetric tensor of rank two and the dual of F^{ij} is defined by $^*F^{ij} = \frac{1}{2}\epsilon^{ijkl}F_{kl}$, show that

$$^{**}F^{ij} = -F^{ij}$$

Solution Given that $^*F^{ij} = \frac{1}{2}\epsilon^{ijkl}F_{kl}$, then

$$^*F^{ij} = \frac{1}{2}g_{ia}g_{jb}\epsilon^{abkl}F_{kl}$$

$$= \frac{1}{2}\epsilon_{ij}^{kl}F_{kl}$$

$$= \frac{1}{2}(\epsilon_{ijmn}g^{km}g^{ln})F_{kl}$$

$$= \frac{1}{2}\epsilon_{ijmn}(g^{km}g^{ln}F_{kl})$$

$$= \frac{1}{2}\epsilon_{ijmn}F^{mn}$$

$$= \frac{1}{2}\epsilon_{ijkl}F^{kl}$$

and

$$^*(^*F^{ij}) = \frac{1}{2}\epsilon^{ijkl}(^*F_{kl})$$

$$= \frac{1}{4}\epsilon^{ijkl}\epsilon_{klmn}F^{mn}$$

But, from Eq. (2.44), we have

$$\epsilon^{ijkl}\epsilon_{klmn} = -2\delta_{mn}^{ij}$$

$$\epsilon^{ijkl}\epsilon_{klmn} = 1, \text{if } m = i, n = j$$

$$= -1, \text{if } m = j, n = i$$

$$= 0, \text{otherwise}$$

Thus

$$\delta_{mn}^{ij} = \delta_m^i\delta_n^j - \delta_n^i\delta_m^j$$

and therefore

$$^*(^*F^{ij}) = -\frac{1}{2}\delta_{mn}^{ij}F^{mn}$$

$$= -\frac{1}{2}(F^{ij} - F^{ji})$$

$$= -F^{ij}$$

EXAMPLE 2.12   Show that $A_i A^i = -\dfrac{1}{3!}*A_{abc}*A^{abc}$.

Solution   From the definition, we have

$$*A^{abc} = A_d \epsilon^{dabc}$$

and

$$*A_{abc}*A^{abc} = A^e A_d \epsilon_{eabc} \epsilon^{dabc}$$

Since e must be different index than that of a, b or c, and d must also be different, we therefore have

$$\epsilon_{eabc} \epsilon^{dabc} = k\delta_e^d$$

for some constant k. Now summing over e and d and using $\delta_e^d = 4$ and $\epsilon_{ijkl}\epsilon^{ijkl} = -24$, we get $k = -6$ and thus

$$*A_{abc}*A^{abc} = -6\delta_e^d A^e A_d$$

which gives

$$A_i A^i = -\frac{1}{6}*A_{abc}*A^{abc}$$

EXERCISES

2.1   Show that $g = \det g_{ij}$ is not a scalar.

2.2   Find g_{ij}, g^{ij} and g for the metric

$$ds^2 = 5(dx^1)^2 + 3(dx^2)^2 + 4(dx^3)^2 - 6dx^1 dx^2 + 4dx^2 dx^3$$

and show that the product of the matrices (g_{ij}) and (g^{ij}) is the unit matrix.

2.3   Find g_{ij} and g^{ij} for the metric

$$ds^2 = adx^2 + bdy^2 + cdz^2 + 2fdydz + 2gdzdx + 2hdxdy$$

2.4   Find the metric and conjugate metric tensors in (i) parabolic cylindrical and (ii) elliptic cylindrical coordinates.

2.5   Show that under the coordinate transformation

$$x^1 = x'^1 x'^2 \cos x'^3, \quad x^2 = x'^1 x'^2 \sin x'^3, \quad x^3 = \frac{1}{2}[(x'^1)^2 + (x'^2)^2]$$

the metric is

$$ds^2 = [(x'^1)^2 + (x'^2)^2][(dx'^1)^2 + (dx'^2)^2] + (x'^1 x'^2)^2(dx'^3)^2$$

2.6   A space seems to be a three-dimensional space with metric

$$ds^2 = dx^2 + dy^2 + dz^2 - \left(\frac{3}{13}dx + \frac{4}{13}dy + \frac{12}{13}dz\right)^2$$

Show that it is in fact a two-dimensional space.

2.7 If g_{ij} are the components of a metric tensor, then for a V_n prove that

$$(g_{hj}g_{ik} - g_{hi}g_{jk})g^{hj} = (n-1)g_{ik}$$

2.8 If g_{ij} and a_{ij} are the components of two symmetric tensors and

$$g_{ij}a_{kl} - g_{il}a_{jk} + g_{jk}a_{il} - g_{kl}a_{ij} = 0$$

$(i, j, k = 1, 2, \ldots, n)$, show that $a_{ij} = \alpha g_{ij}$, where α is a scalar.

2.9 Show that the vectors $\left(-1, -1, 1, \dfrac{\sqrt{3}}{c}\right)$ and $\left(-1, 0, 0, \dfrac{1}{c}\right)$ are null vectors for the space whose metric is

$$ds^2 = -dx^2 - dy^2 - dz^2 + c^2 dt^2$$

2.10 Show that the inner and outer products of two relative tensors are themselves realtive tensors of rank and weight equal to the sum of the ranks and sum of weights of the given relative tensors, respectively.

2.11 Prove that the sum and difference of two relative tensors of the same weight and type is also a relative tensor of the same weight and type.

2.12 If A_k^{ij} is a relative tensor of weight W, show that $g^{-W/2}A_k^{ij}$ is an absolute tensor.

2.13 If $A(i, j)B_l^{jk} = C_{il}^k$, where B_l^{jk} is an arbitrary relative tensor of weight W_1 and C_{il}^k is a known relative tensor of weight W_2, then prove that $A(i, j)$ is a relative tensor of weight $W_2 - W_1$ (This is known as *quotient law for relative tensors.*)

2.14 In an orthonormal frame (where $g_{ij} = \eta_{ij}$) show that $\epsilon_{ijkl} = -\epsilon^{ijkl}$ and also with the metric g_{ij} show that $\epsilon_{ijkl} = (\det g_{ab})\epsilon^{ijkl}$.

2.15 Show that $\epsilon^{ijkl}\epsilon_{ijmn} = 2(\delta_m^k\delta_n^l - \delta_n^k\delta_m^l)$ and $\epsilon^{ijkl}\epsilon_{ijkm} = 6\delta_m^l$.

CHAPTER 3

Christoffel Symbols and Covariant Differentiation

3.1 Introduction

Physical laws are often described by differential equations and differential equations are concerned with the rate of change of physical quantities with respect to space and time. These physical quantities are vectors, tensors etc. In earlier chapters we have defined and discussed vectors and tensors and their transformation laws. This chapter includes the rate of change of vectors and tensors and related results.

3.2 Christoffel Symbols

From the metric tensor g_{ij} and its conjugate g^{ij}, defined in the previous chapter, we can construct two functions. These functions are not tensors but are used to define the differentiation of tensors. They are known as Christoffel symbols and are defined as

$$\Gamma_{kij} = \frac{1}{2}\left(\frac{\partial g_{ki}}{\partial x^j} + \frac{\partial g_{jk}}{\partial x^i} - \frac{\partial g_{ij}}{\partial x^k}\right) \tag{3.1}$$

and

$$\Gamma^i_{jk} = \frac{1}{2}g^{im}\left(\frac{\partial g_{jm}}{\partial x^k} + \frac{\partial g_{km}}{\partial x^j} - \frac{\partial g_{jk}}{\partial x^m}\right) \tag{3.2}$$

The symbols given by Eqs. (3.1) and (3.2) are, respectively, called *Christoffel symbols of first* and *second kind*.

Since g_{ij} is symmetric, so are the Christoffel symbols, i.e.,

$$\Gamma_{kij} = \Gamma_{kji}, \quad \Gamma^i_{jk} = \Gamma^i_{kj} \tag{3.3}$$

Now, replacing k by m in Eq. (3.1), we get

$$\Gamma_{mij} = \frac{1}{2}\left(\frac{\partial g_{mi}}{\partial x^j} + \frac{\partial g_{jm}}{\partial x^i} - \frac{\partial g_{ij}}{\partial x^m}\right)$$

54

Multiply this equation by g^{km} to get

$$g^{km}\Gamma_{mij} = \frac{1}{2}g^{km}\left(\frac{\partial g_{mi}}{\partial x^j} + \frac{\partial g_{jm}}{\partial x^i} - \frac{\partial g_{ij}}{\partial x^m}\right) = \Gamma_{ij}^k \qquad (3.4)$$

Consider now Eq. (3.2), interchange i and m and multiply the resulting equation by g_{im}, to get

$$g_{im}\Gamma_{jk}^m = \frac{1}{2}g_{im}g^{mp}\left(\frac{\partial g_{pj}}{\partial x^k} + \frac{\partial g_{kp}}{\partial x^j} - \frac{\partial g_{jk}}{\partial x^p}\right)$$

$$= \frac{1}{2}\left(\frac{\partial g_{ij}}{\partial x^k} + \frac{\partial g_{ki}}{\partial x^j} - \frac{\partial g_{jk}}{\partial x^i}\right)$$

$$= \Gamma_{kij} \qquad (3.5)$$

Equations (3.4) and (3.5) are the relationships between the Christoffel symbols of first and second kind.

Remarks

1. A comparison of Eqs. (3.4) and (3.5) with Eqs. (2.25) and (2.26) suggest that the process of going from Christoffel symbol of first kind to second kind and vice versa is same as the process of raising and lowering of indices.

2. The Christoffel symbols of first and second kind are also denoted as $[k, ij]$ and $\{_{jk}^i\}$, respectively.

3. It seems worthwhile to mention that when the generalizations of the Riemannian geometry are considered there appears a quantity, known as *affine connection;* the Christoffel symbol of second kind is a particular case of such quantity. The affine connection Γ_{jk}^i given by Eq. (3.2) is exclusively valid in Riemannian geometry. Usually, in non-Riemannian geometry affine connections are non-symmetric in their lower indices.

   A symmetric connection defined in n-dimensional space has $\frac{1}{2}n^2(n+1)$ independent components. Thus, for a four-dimensional Riemannian space, which is a space of interest in general theory of relativity, each of the Christoffel symbol has 40 independent components. If the affine connection is not symmetric, we define the tensor

$$\Gamma_{[jk]}^i = \frac{1}{2}(\Gamma_{jk}^i - \Gamma_{kj}^i)$$

   which is skew symmetric in j and k. This tensor is called the *torsion* of the spacetime.

The Christoffel symbols of first and second kind have the following properties:

(i)
$$\Gamma_{ljk} + \Gamma_{jlk} = \frac{\partial g_{jl}}{\partial x^k} \qquad (3.6)$$

Proof   Use definition (3.1) and the symmetry of g_{ij}.

(ii)
$$\Gamma^j_{jk} = \frac{\partial}{\partial x^k} \log \sqrt{g} = \frac{1}{\sqrt{g}} \frac{\partial \sqrt{g}}{\partial x^k} \tag{3.7}$$

Proof   Differentiate the det $g = |g_{ij}|$ and use

$$g^{jl} = \frac{\text{cofactor of } g_{jl} \text{ in } (\det g_{jl})}{\det g_{jl}}$$

to get

$$\frac{\partial g}{\partial x^k} = g^{jl} g \frac{\partial g_{jl}}{\partial x^k}$$

$$= g g^{jl} (\Gamma_{ljk} + \Gamma_{jlk}) \qquad \text{[from Eq. (3.6)]}$$

$$= g(\Gamma^j_{jk} + \Gamma^j_{jk})$$

$$= 2g\Gamma^j_{jk}$$

which leads to

$$\Gamma^j_{jk} = \frac{1}{2g} \frac{\partial g}{\partial x^k}$$

$$= \frac{\partial}{\partial x^k} \log \sqrt{g}$$

$$= \frac{1}{\sqrt{g}} \frac{\partial \sqrt{g}}{\partial x^k}$$

Note: For g to be negative, Eq. (3.7) reduces to

$$\Gamma^j_{jk} = \frac{\partial}{\partial x^k} \log \sqrt{-g} = \frac{1}{\sqrt{-g}} \frac{\partial \sqrt{-g}}{\partial x^k} \tag{3.8}$$

(iii)
$$\frac{\partial g^{pq}}{\partial x^m} = -g^{pj}\Gamma^q_{jm} - g^{qj}\Gamma^p_{jm} \tag{3.9}$$

Proof   We know that

$$g_{jk} g^{kl} = \delta^l_j$$

Differentiate it with respect to x^m, we get

$$g_{jk} \frac{\partial g^{kl}}{\partial x^m} + g^{kl} \frac{\partial g_{jk}}{\partial x^m} = 0 \text{ as } \delta^l_j = \begin{cases} 1, & \text{for } l = j \\ 0, & \text{for } l \neq j \end{cases}$$

Multiply this equation by g^{jp} and use property (i), to get

$$\delta^p_k \frac{\partial g^{kl}}{\partial x^m} + g^{kl} g^{jp} (\Gamma_{kjm} + \Gamma_{jkm}) = 0$$

Since g_{ij} is symmetric, therefore

$$\frac{\partial g^{pl}}{\partial x^m} + g^{pj}g^{lk}\Gamma_{kjm} + g^{lk}g^{pj}\Gamma_{jkm} = 0$$

or

$$\frac{\partial g^{pl}}{\partial x^m} = -g^{pj}\Gamma^l_{jm} - g^{lk}\Gamma^p_{km}$$

Now replace k by j and l by q to get required result.

3.3 Transformation Laws for Christoffel Symbols

We shall now find the transformation laws for the Christoffel symbols and show that they are not tensors.

Since g_{ij} is a second rank covariant tensor, thus under coordinate transformation, it transforms as

$$g'_{lk} = \frac{\partial x^i}{\partial x'^l}\frac{\partial x^j}{\partial x'^k}g_{ij}$$

Differentiate it with respect to x'^p and use

$$\frac{\partial g_{ij}}{\partial x'^p} = \frac{\partial g_{ij}}{\partial x^m}\frac{\partial x^m}{\partial x'p}$$

to get

$$\frac{\partial g'_{lk}}{\partial x'^p} = \frac{\partial}{\partial x'^p}\left(\frac{\partial x^i}{\partial x'^l}\frac{\partial x^j}{\partial x'^k}\right)g_{ij}$$

$$= \left[\frac{\partial^2 x^i}{\partial x'^p \partial x'^l}\frac{\partial x^j}{\partial x'^k} + \frac{\partial x^i}{\partial x'^l}\frac{\partial^2 x^j}{\partial x'^p \partial x'^k}\right]g_{ij} + \frac{\partial x^i}{\partial x'^l}\frac{\partial x^j}{\partial x'^k}\frac{\partial g_{ij}}{\partial x^m}\frac{\partial x^m}{\partial x'^p}$$

Interchanging the dummy suffix i and j in the first term of the square bracket and using the symmetry property of g_{ij}, we get

$$\frac{\partial g'_{lk}}{\partial x'^p} = \left[\frac{\partial^2 x^j}{\partial x'^p \partial x'^l}\frac{\partial x^i}{\partial x'^k} + \frac{\partial^2 x^j}{\partial x'^p \partial x'^k}\frac{\partial x^i}{\partial x'^l}\right]g_{ij} + \frac{\partial x^i}{\partial x'^l}\frac{\partial x^j}{\partial x'^k}\frac{\partial x^m}{\partial x'^p}\frac{\partial g_{ij}}{\partial x^m} \quad (3.10)$$

By cyclic permutation of indices i, j, m and l, k, p we get two more similar equations which on suitable change of dummy indices can be written as

$$\frac{\partial g'_{kp}}{\partial x'^l} = \left[\frac{\partial^2 x^i}{\partial x'^l \partial x'^k}\frac{\partial x^j}{\partial x'^p} + \frac{\partial^2 x^i}{\partial x'^l \partial x'^p}\frac{\partial x^j}{\partial x'^k}\right]g_{ij} + \frac{\partial x^i}{\partial x'^l}\frac{\partial x^j}{\partial x'^k}\frac{\partial x^m}{\partial x'^p}\frac{\partial g_{jm}}{\partial x^i} \quad (3.11)$$

and

$$\frac{\partial g'_{pl}}{\partial x'^k} = \left[\frac{\partial^2 x^i}{\partial x'^k \partial x'^p}\frac{\partial x^j}{\partial x'^l} + \frac{\partial^2 x^i}{\partial x'^k \partial x'^l}\frac{\partial x^j}{\partial x'^p}\right]g_{ij} + \frac{\partial x^i}{\partial x'^l}\frac{\partial x^j}{\partial x'^k}\frac{\partial x^m}{\partial x'^p}\frac{\partial g_{mi}}{\partial x^j} \quad (3.12)$$

Now subtract Eq. (3.10) from the sum of Eqs. (3.11) and (3.12) and divide the resulting equation throughout by 2 and use Eq. (3.1) to get

$$\Gamma'_{plk} = \frac{\partial x^i}{\partial x'^l} \frac{\partial x^j}{\partial x'^k} \frac{\partial x^m}{\partial x'^p} \Gamma_{mij} + \frac{\partial^2 x^i}{\partial x'^l \partial x'^k} \frac{\partial x^j}{\partial x'^p} g_{ij} \tag{3.13}$$

Equation (3.13) is the transformation law for the Christoffel symbol of first kind.

To get the transformation law for the Christoffel symbol of second kind, we use the transformation law of the contravariant tensor of rank two as

$$g'^{pq} = \frac{\partial x'^p}{\partial x^r} \frac{\partial x'^q}{\partial x^s} g^{rs} \tag{3.14}$$

Now multiply both sides of Eq. (3.13) by the corresponding side of Eq. (3.14), and after simplification, we get

$$\Gamma'^q_{lk} = \frac{\partial x^i}{\partial x'^l} \frac{\partial x^j}{\partial x'^k} \frac{\partial x'^q}{\partial x^s} \Gamma^s_{ij} + \frac{\partial^2 x^i}{\partial x'^l \partial x'^k} \frac{\partial x'^q}{\partial x^i} \tag{3.15}$$

which is the transformation law for the Christoffel symbol of second kind.

From Eqs. (3.13) and (3.15) it may be noted that Γ'_{plk} and Γ'^q_{lk}, respectively, behave like rank three tensors as far as the first terms in right-hand sides of these equations are concerned, but the second terms of Eqs. (3.13) and (3.15) introduce the inhomogeneous terms in the transformation laws. Hence Γ'_{plk} and Γ'^q_{lk} do not transform like tensors. However, in the particular case when the coordinate transformations are linear, the term $\dfrac{\partial^2 x^i}{\partial x'^l \partial x'^k} = 0$ and thus the quantities Γ'_{plk} and Γ'^q_{lk} in this particular case behave like the components of a tensor. Such tensors are called *pseudo tensors*.

3.4   Equation of a Geodesic

What do we mean by a straight line in Euclidean space? One meaning implied by the adjective *"straight"* is that its direction remains unchanged as we move along it. The other property associated with the straight line is that it represents the path of the shortest distance between any two given points. Here we shall find out what curves are implied by the later definition in a more general space, i.e., the Riemannian space. The implication of the former definition shall be considered in Section 3.11.

The path (world line) of a particle between two points P and Q is a geodesic and is determined by the condition that the interval between two points P and Q given by $\int_P^Q ds$ be stationary. In other words, a geodesic is defined by the condition that

$$\delta \int_P^Q ds = 0 \tag{3.16}$$

where δ denotes the variation from the actual path (world line) between the two points P and Q on it, to any other path in the neighbourhood of this line (actual path). Equation (3.16) is the analogue of the condition of shortest distance between two points in Euclidean space.

To obtain the equation of geodesic, consider the metric of the Riemannian space, i.e.,

$$ds^2 = g_{ij}dx^i dx^j \tag{3.17}$$

and take the δ-variation of both sides of Eq. (3.17) so that $\delta(ds^2) = \delta(g_{ij}dx^i dx^j)$ leads to

$$2ds\delta(ds) = dx^i dx^j \delta g_{ij} + g_{ij}dx^j \delta(dx^i) + g_{ij}dx^i \delta(dx^j)$$

$$= dx^i dx^j \frac{\partial g_{ij}}{\partial x^k}\delta x^k + g_{ij}dx^j \delta(dx^i) + g_{ij}dx^i \delta(dx^j) \tag{3.18}$$

where δx^k denotes an arbitrary infinitesimal displacement from the actual path. Divide now both sides of Eq. (3.18) by ds and use

$$\delta\left(\frac{dx^i}{ds}\right) = \frac{d}{ds}(\delta x^i) \tag{3.19}$$

to get

$$\delta(ds) = \frac{1}{2}\left[\frac{dx^i}{ds}\frac{dx^j}{ds}\frac{\partial g_{ij}}{\partial x^k}\delta x^k + g_{ij}\frac{dx^j}{ds}\frac{d}{ds}(\delta x^i) + g_{ij}\frac{dx^i}{ds}\frac{d}{ds}(\delta x^j)\right]ds \tag{3.20}$$

from which condition (3.16) becomes

$$\frac{1}{2}\int_P^Q\left[\frac{dx^i}{ds}\frac{dx^j}{ds}\frac{\partial g_{ij}}{\partial x^k}\delta x^k + g_{ij}\frac{dx^j}{ds}\frac{d}{ds}(\delta x^i) + g_{ij}\frac{dx^i}{ds}\frac{d}{ds}(\delta x^j)\right]ds = 0$$

Changing the dummy suffices in the last two terms, we get

$$\frac{1}{2}\int_P^Q\left[\frac{dx^i}{ds}\frac{dx^j}{ds}\frac{\partial g_{ij}}{\partial x^k}\delta x^k + \left(g_{kj}\frac{dx^j}{ds} + g_{ik}\frac{dx^i}{ds}\right)\frac{d}{ds}(\delta x^k)\right]ds = 0$$

Consider the second term of the above equation and integrate it by parts, remembering that the δ-variation at the end (fixed) points P and Q is zero, we have

$$\frac{1}{2}\int_P^Q\left[\frac{dx^i}{ds}\frac{dx^j}{ds}\frac{\partial g_{ij}}{\partial x^k} - \frac{d}{ds}\left(g_{kj}\frac{dx^j}{ds} + g_{ik}\frac{dx^i}{ds}\right)\right]\delta x^k ds = 0$$

Since the variation δx^k is arbitrary, therefore, for the integral to be stationary the coefficient of δx^k in the square bracket in the above equation must vanish at all points of the path, i.e.,

$$\frac{1}{2}\left[\frac{dx^i}{ds}\frac{dx^j}{ds}\frac{\partial g_{ij}}{\partial x^k} - \frac{d}{ds}\left(g_{kj}\frac{dx^j}{ds} + g_{ik}\frac{dx^i}{ds}\right)\right] = 0 \qquad (3.21)$$

which may be written as

$$\frac{1}{2}\frac{dx^i}{ds}\frac{dx^j}{ds}\frac{\partial g_{ij}}{\partial x^k} - \frac{1}{2}\frac{dg_{ik}}{ds}\frac{dx^i}{ds} - \frac{1}{2}g_{ik}\frac{d^2x^i}{ds^2} - \frac{1}{2}\frac{dg_{kj}}{ds}\frac{dx^j}{ds} - \frac{1}{2}g_{kj}\frac{d^2x^j}{ds^2} = 0$$
$$(3.22)$$

But

$$\frac{dg_{ik}}{ds} = \frac{\partial g_{ik}}{\partial x^j}\frac{dx^j}{ds}, \qquad \frac{dg_{kj}}{ds} = \frac{\partial g_{kj}}{\partial x^i}\frac{dx^i}{ds} \qquad (3.23)$$

Equation (3.22) thus takes the form

$$\frac{1}{2}\frac{dx^i}{ds}\frac{dx^j}{ds}\left[\frac{\partial g_{ij}}{\partial x^k} - \frac{\partial g_{ik}}{\partial x^j} - \frac{\partial g_{kj}}{\partial x^i}\right] - g_{pk}\frac{d^2x^p}{ds^2} = 0$$

Multiply this equation by g^{kt}, to get

$$\frac{1}{2}\frac{dx^i}{ds}\frac{dx^j}{ds}g^{kt}\left[\frac{\partial g_{ij}}{\partial x^k} - \frac{\partial g_{ik}}{\partial x^j} - \frac{\partial g_{kj}}{\partial x^i}\right] - \delta_p^t\frac{d^2x^p}{ds^2} = 0$$

or

$$\frac{d^2x^t}{ds^2} + \frac{1}{2}g^{kt}\left[-\frac{\partial g_{ij}}{\partial x^k} + \frac{\partial g_{ik}}{\partial x^j} + \frac{\partial g_{kj}}{\partial x^i}\right]\frac{dx^i}{ds}\frac{dx^j}{ds} = 0$$

which, from the definition of Christoffel symbol of second kind, takes the form

$$\frac{d^2x^t}{ds^2} + \Gamma_{ij}^t\frac{dx^i}{ds}\frac{dx^j}{ds} = 0 \qquad (3.24)$$

This is the required condition for the given integral $\int_P^Q ds$ to be stationary. The *"straight line"* given by Eq. (3.24) is the *equation of geodesic* [see also Eq. (3.24a)].

Remarks

1. For $t = 1, 2, 3, 4$ Eq. (3.24) gives four equations which determine the geodesic. Now, since ds is an element of the world line, we can interpret these equations as the equations of motion of a particle which moves along a world line. When the components of the metric tensor are constant, then Γ_{ij}^t is zero and Eq. (3.24) in this case reduces to

$$\frac{d^2x^t}{ds^2} = 0 \qquad (3.25)$$

which shows that the particle moves with a uniform velocity in a straight line.

2. The occurrance of the Christoffel symbols in mechanics and its relationship with the equation of geodesic is illustrated as follows:

Consider evolution of time of a mechanical system for which, in generalized coordinates $x^i(t)$, the velocity is $\dot{x}^i = \dfrac{dx^i}{dt}$, the kinetic energy is $T = \dfrac{1}{2}g_{ik}\dot{x}^i\dot{x}^k$ and $F_i = -\dfrac{\partial V}{\partial x^i}$ is the generalized force obtainable from a generalized potential V. In analytical dynamics, the metric is $T dt^2 = ds^2$. The Lagrange's equations of motion are

$$\frac{d}{dt}\left(\frac{\partial L}{\partial \dot{x}^i}\right) - \frac{\partial L}{\partial x^i} = 0$$

where $L = T - V$ is the Lagrangian. These Lagrange's equations lead to

$$g_{ik}\ddot{x}^k + \frac{1}{2}\left[\frac{\partial g_{ik}}{\partial x^l} + \frac{\partial g_{il}}{\partial x^k} - \frac{\partial g_{lk}}{\partial x^i}\right]\dot{x}^l\dot{x}^k = F_i$$

Multiply this equation by g^{ik}, to get

$$\ddot{x}^i + \Gamma^i_{lk}\dot{x}^l\dot{x}^k = F^i \tag{3.26}$$

which clearly indicates the appearance of the Christoffel symbol in the Lagrange equations of motion of a particle. If there are no forces, $F_i = 0$, Eq. (3.26) is just Eq. (3.24) and defines *geodesic lines*. But in Eq. (3.26), the differentiation is performed with respect to a time parameter t along the trajectory while in Eq. (3.24) the differentiation is carried with respect to the arc length parameter s along the geodesics. Since both s and t are normal parameters, we have $ds \propto dt$. It may be noted that this proportionality holds only on the geodesic lines: along other curves the notion of time of transit and arc length are different (see also Remark 2 of Section 3.11).

3.5   Affine Parameter

The equation of a geodesic given by Eq. (3.24) has been derived in terms of the infinitesimal distance ds along the geodesic lines. This equation can also be obtained in terms of the other parameters. If we choose the parameter α, then

$$\frac{dx^i}{ds} = \frac{dx^i}{d\alpha}\frac{d\alpha}{ds} \tag{3.27}$$

and

$$\frac{d}{ds}\left(\frac{dx^i}{ds}\right) = \frac{d}{ds}\left(\frac{dx^i}{d\alpha}\frac{d\alpha}{ds}\right) = \frac{d}{d\alpha}\left(\frac{dx^i}{d\alpha}\frac{d\alpha}{ds}\right)\frac{d\alpha}{ds}$$

or

$$\frac{d^2x^i}{ds^2} = \frac{d^2x^i}{d\alpha^2}\left(\frac{d\alpha}{ds}\right)^2 + \frac{dx^i}{d\alpha}\frac{d^2\alpha}{ds^2} \tag{3.28}$$

From Eqs. (3.27) and (3.28), Eq. (3.24) takes the form

$$\frac{d^2x^i}{d\alpha^2} + \Gamma^i_{jk}\frac{dx^j}{d\alpha}\frac{dx^k}{d\alpha} = -\frac{d^2\alpha/ds^2}{(d\alpha/ds)^2}\frac{dx^i}{d\alpha} \qquad (3.29)$$

which is true for an arbitrary parameter α. If we choose the right-hand side of Eq. (3.29) to zero, then

$$\frac{d^2x^i}{d\alpha^2} + \Gamma^i_{jk}\frac{dx^j}{d\alpha}\frac{dx^k}{d\alpha} = 0 \qquad (3.30)$$

This geodesic equation is same as that of Eq. (3.24) except the parameter α replacing the distance parameter s. It may be noted that the right-hand side of Eq. (3.29) is zero only when

$$\frac{d^2\alpha}{ds^2} = 0$$

which has the solution

$$\alpha = as + b \qquad (3.31)$$

where a and b are two arbitrary real constants. Equation (3.31) shows that the two parameters α and s are related to each other through a linear transformation.

A parameter of the geodesic line (here it is α) due to which the geodesic equation retains the standard form of Eq. (3.30) is called an *affine parameter*. Equation (3.31) shows that any other parameter, say β, will also be related to s through Eq. (3.31) and consequently all affine parameters are related to each other by a linear transformation (see also Section 3.11).

3.6   Geodesic Coordinate System

We have seen earlier that in Euclidean space, when Cartesian coordinates are considered, the components of the metric tensor are constant and consequently the Christoffel symbols vanish at every point of the Euclidean space. But no such coordinates exist in case of Riemannian space. If this is so, then such a coordinate system is called *geodesic coordinate system* and we have

Theorem 3.1   It is always possible to choose a coordinate system in which all the components of the Christoffel symbols vanish at a given point.

Proof   Consider a point P in the coordinate system x^i and suppose that the Christoffel symbols do not vanish at P. Now introduce a coordinate system x'^i by means of the transformation

$$x'^i = x^i - (x^i)_P + \frac{1}{2}(\Gamma^i_{jk})_P[x^j - (x^j)_P][x^k - (x^k)_P] \qquad (3.32)$$

where the subscript P denotes the value at the given point P and $(x'^i)_P = 0$.

We now calculate, using Eq. (3.15), the Christoffel symbol in the new coordinate system. Differentiating Eq. (3.32) with respect to x^l, we get

$$\frac{\partial x'^i}{\partial x^l} = \frac{\partial x^i}{\partial x^l} + \frac{1}{2}(\Gamma^i_{jk})_P \frac{\partial x^j}{\partial x^l}[x^k - (x^k)_P] + \frac{1}{2}(\Gamma^i_{jk})_P \frac{\partial x^k}{\partial x^l}[x^j - (x^j)_P]$$

$$= \frac{\partial x^i}{\partial x^l} + \frac{1}{2}(\Gamma^i_{jk})_P \delta^j_l[x^k - (x^k)_P] + \frac{1}{2}(\Gamma^i_{jk})_P \delta^k_l[x^j - (x^j)_P]$$

$$= \frac{\partial x^i}{\partial x^l} + \frac{1}{2}(\Gamma^i_{lk})_P[x^k - (x^k)_P] + \frac{1}{2}(\Gamma^i_{jl})_P[x^j - (x^j)_P]$$

$$= \frac{\partial x^i}{\partial x^l} + \frac{1}{2}(\Gamma^i_{lj})_P[x^j - (x^j)_P] + \frac{1}{2}(\Gamma^i_{lj})_P[x^j - (x^j)_P]$$

$$= \frac{\partial x^i}{\partial x^l} + (\Gamma^i_{lj})_P[x^j - (x^j)_P] \tag{3.33}$$

Thus

$$\left(\frac{\partial x'^i}{\partial x^l}\right)_P = \delta^i_l \tag{3.34}$$

which means that the Jacobian $J = \left| \left(\frac{\partial x'^i}{\partial x^l}\right)_P \right| \neq 0$ and the transformation (3.32) is allowed in the neighbourhood of P. Taking the inner product of Eq. (3.33) with $\frac{\partial x^l}{\partial x'^k}$, we get

$$\left(\frac{\partial x'^i}{\partial x^l}\right)\left(\frac{\partial x^l}{\partial x'^k}\right) = \left(\frac{\partial x^i}{\partial x^l}\right)\left(\frac{\partial x^l}{\partial x'^k}\right) + (\Gamma^i_{lj})_P[x^j - (x^j)_P]\frac{\partial x^l}{\partial x'^k}$$

or,

$$\delta^i_k = \frac{\partial x^i}{\partial x'^k} + (\Gamma^i_{lj})_P[x^j - (x^j)_P]\frac{\partial x^l}{\partial x'^k} \tag{3.35}$$

which leads to

$$\left(\frac{\partial x^i}{\partial x'^k}\right)_P = \delta^i_k \tag{3.36}$$

Now differentiating Eq. (3.35) with respect to x'^m and using Eq. (3.36), we get

$$\left(\frac{\partial^2 x^i}{\partial x'^l \partial x'^m}\right)_P = -(\Gamma^i_{lm})_P \tag{3.37}$$

From Eqs. (3.34), (3.36) and (3.37), Eq. (3.15) thus leads to

$$(\Gamma'^q_{lk})_P = \left(\frac{\partial x^i}{\partial x'^l}\right)_P \left(\frac{\partial x^j}{\partial x'^k}\right)_P \left(\frac{\partial x'^q}{\partial x^s}\right)_P (\Gamma^s_{ij})_P + \left(\frac{\partial^2 x^i}{\partial x'^l \partial x'^k}\right)_P \left(\frac{\partial x'^q}{\partial x^i}\right)_P$$

$$= \delta^i_k \delta^j_k \delta^q_s (\Gamma^s_{ij})_P - \delta^q_i (\Gamma^i_{lk})_P$$

$$= (\Gamma^q_{lk})_P - (\Gamma^q_{lk})_P$$

$$= 0$$

which completes the proof.

Remarks

1. If the point P in Theorem 3.1 is taken as origin, then in a similar way it can be shown that the coordinate system defined by

$$x'^i = x^i + \frac{1}{2}(\Gamma^i_{jk})_P x^j x^k \tag{3.38}$$

   is a geodesic coordinate system [here $(x^i)_P = 0$].

2. The choice of the vanishing of the Christoffel symbols at a point of the spacetime (four-dimensional Riemannian space) has a fascinating and deep physical meaning explained as follows:

   If $F^i = 0$ in Eq. (3.26), then

$$\ddot{x}^i + \Gamma^i_{lk} \dot{x}^l \dot{x}^k = 0$$

   which means that the acceleration of the particle, moving in the gravitational field, is proportional to the Christoffel symbol. The vanishing of the Christoffel symbol at a point means that we can choose a coordinate system in which the acceleration of the particle at a given point of the spacetime is zero, that is, the gravitational force acting on the particle vanishes at this point, or, in other words, by means of a coordinate transformation, the gravitational effects can be eliminated. But this happens only at a point and not in a finite region of the spacetime. These considerations are related to the *principle of equivalence* − a postulate of general theory of relativity.

3. For other coordinate systems, the reader is referred to Section 6.3.

EXAMPLE 3.1   Show that

$$\Gamma_{jki} + \Gamma_{kij} + \Gamma_{ijk} = \frac{1}{2}\left(\frac{\partial g_{ij}}{\partial x^k} + \frac{\partial g_{jk}}{\partial x^i} - \frac{\partial g_{ki}}{\partial x^j}\right)$$

Solution   Use the definition of Christoffell symbol of first kind to write the left-hand side and simplify to get the result.

EXAMPLE 3.2   Find the components of the Christoffel symbols for the metric

$$ds^2 = r^2 d\theta^2 + r^2 \sin^2\theta d\phi^2$$

(This metric represents the surface of a sphere in a two-dimensional Riemannain space.)

Solution Here $x^1 = \theta, x^2 = \phi$,

$$g_{ij} = \begin{bmatrix} r^2 & 0 \\ 0 & r^2 \sin^2\theta \end{bmatrix}, \quad g^{ij} = \begin{bmatrix} 1/r^2 & 0 \\ 0 & 1/r^2 \sin^2\theta \end{bmatrix}$$

$$\det g_{ij} = g = r^4 \sin^2\theta$$

From Eq. (3.1), we have

$$\Gamma_{ijk} = \frac{1}{2}\left(\frac{\partial g_{ij}}{\partial x^k} + \frac{\partial g_{ki}}{\partial x^j} - \frac{\partial g_{jk}}{\partial x^i} \right), i, j, k = 1, 2$$

which leads to

$$\Gamma_{111} = \frac{1}{2}\left(\frac{\partial g_{11}}{\partial x^1} + \frac{\partial g_{11}}{\partial x^1} - \frac{\partial g_{11}}{\partial x^1} \right)$$

$$= \frac{1}{2}\frac{\partial g_{11}}{\partial x^1}$$

$$= \frac{1}{2}\frac{\partial r^2}{\partial\theta}$$

$$= 0$$

$$\Gamma_{212} = \frac{1}{2}\left(\frac{\partial g_{21}}{\partial x^2} + \frac{\partial g_{22}}{\partial x^1} - \frac{\partial g_{12}}{\partial x^2} \right)$$

$$= \frac{1}{2}\frac{\partial g_{22}}{\partial x^1}$$

$$= \frac{1}{2}\frac{\partial r^2 \sin^2\theta}{\partial\theta}$$

$$= r^2 \sin\theta\cos\theta$$

In a similar way, we have

$$\Gamma_{121} = \Gamma_{211} = \Gamma_{222} = 0, \quad \Gamma_{122} = -r^2 \sin\theta\cos\theta$$

Also from the definition of Christoffel symbol of second kind, we have

$$\Gamma^k_{ij} = g^{km}\Gamma_{mij}$$

which leads to

$$\Gamma^1_{22} = g^{1m}\Gamma_{m22}$$

$$= g^{11}\Gamma_{122} + g^{12}\Gamma_{222}$$

$$= -\sin\theta\cos\theta$$

Similarly, $\Gamma^2_{12} = \cot\theta$; while the remaining $\Gamma^i_{jk} = 0$.

EXAMPLE 3.3   Obtain all the Christoffel symbols for the metric

$$ds^2 = -A(dx^1)^2 - B(dx^2)^2 - C(dx^3)^2 + D(dx^4)^2$$

where A, B, C and D are real positive quantities and functions of all the four coordinates x^1, x^2, x^3 and x^4.

Solution   Here

$$g_{11} = -A, \quad g_{22} = -B, \quad g_{33} = -C, \quad g_{44} = D, \quad g_{ij} = 0 \quad \text{for } i \neq j$$

$$g^{11} = -1/A, \quad g^{22} = -1/B, \quad g^{33} = -1/C, \quad g^{44} = 1/D, \quad g^{ij} = 0 \quad \text{for } i \neq j$$

$$\det g_{ij} = -ABCD$$

From Eqs. (3.1) and (3.4), we have

$$\Gamma_{ijk} = \frac{1}{2}\left(\frac{\partial g_{ij}}{\partial x^k} + \frac{\partial g_{ki}}{\partial x^j} - \frac{\partial g_{jk}}{\partial x^i}\right)$$

$$\Gamma^i_{jk} = g^{im}\Gamma_{mjk}$$

These equations lead to

$$\Gamma^1_{11} = g^{1m}\Gamma_{m11}$$

$$= g^{11}\Gamma_{111} + g^{12}\Gamma_{211} + g^{13}\Gamma_{311} + g^{14}\Gamma_{411}$$

$$= g^{11}\Gamma_{111}$$

$$= \frac{1}{2}g^{11}\left(\frac{\partial g_{11}}{\partial x^1}\right)$$

$$= \frac{1}{2A}\frac{\partial A}{\partial x^1}$$

$$\Gamma^1_{21} = g^{1m}\Gamma_{m21}$$

$$= g^{11}\Gamma_{121}$$

$$= \frac{1}{2}g^{11}\left(\frac{\partial g_{11}}{\partial x^2}\right)$$

$$= \frac{1}{2A}\frac{\partial A}{\partial x^2}$$

In a similar manner, the remaining components of the Christoffel symbols can be calculated and all the components are given as follows:

$$\Gamma^1_{11} = \frac{1}{2A}\frac{\partial A}{\partial x^1}, \quad \Gamma^1_{12} = \frac{1}{2A}\frac{\partial A}{\partial x^2}, \quad \Gamma^1_{13} = \frac{1}{2A}\frac{\partial A}{\partial x^3}, \quad \Gamma^1_{14} = \frac{1}{2A}\frac{\partial A}{\partial x^4}$$

$$\Gamma^2_{21} = \frac{1}{2B}\frac{\partial B}{\partial x^1}, \quad \Gamma^2_{22} = \frac{1}{2B}\frac{\partial B}{\partial x^2}, \quad \Gamma^2_{23} = \frac{1}{2B}\frac{\partial B}{\partial x^3}, \quad \Gamma^2_{24} = \frac{1}{2B}\frac{\partial B}{\partial x^4}$$

$$\Gamma^3_{31} = \frac{1}{2C}\frac{\partial C}{\partial x^1}, \quad \Gamma^3_{32} = \frac{1}{2C}\frac{\partial C}{\partial x^2}, \quad \Gamma^3_{33} = \frac{1}{2C}\frac{\partial C}{\partial x^3}, \quad \Gamma^3_{34} = \frac{1}{2C}\frac{\partial C}{\partial x^4}$$

$$\Gamma^4_{41} = \frac{1}{2D}\frac{\partial D}{\partial x^1}, \quad \Gamma^4_{42} = \frac{1}{2D}\frac{\partial D}{\partial x^2}, \quad \Gamma^4_{43} = \frac{1}{2D}\frac{\partial D}{\partial x^3}, \quad \Gamma^4_{44} = \frac{1}{2D}\frac{\partial D}{\partial x^4}$$

$$\Gamma^1_{21} = \frac{1}{2A}\frac{\partial A}{\partial x^2}, \quad \Gamma^1_{22} = -\frac{1}{2A}\frac{\partial B}{\partial x^2}, \quad \Gamma^1_{23} = 0, \quad \Gamma^1_{24} = 0$$

$$\Gamma^1_{31} = \frac{1}{2A}\frac{\partial A}{\partial x^3}, \quad \Gamma^1_{32} = 0, \quad \Gamma^1_{33} = -\frac{1}{2A}\frac{\partial C}{\partial x^1}, \quad \Gamma^1_{34} = 0$$

$$\Gamma^1_{41} = \frac{1}{2A}\frac{\partial A}{\partial x^4}, \quad \Gamma^1_{42} = 0, \quad \Gamma^1_{43} = 0, \quad \Gamma^1_{44} = \frac{1}{2A}\frac{\partial D}{\partial x^1}$$

$$\Gamma^2_{11} = -\frac{1}{2B}\frac{\partial A}{\partial x^2}, \quad \Gamma^2_{12} = \frac{1}{2B}\frac{\partial A}{\partial x^1}, \quad \Gamma^2_{13} = 0, \quad \Gamma^2_{14} = 0$$

$$\Gamma^2_{31} = 0, \quad \Gamma^2_{32} = \frac{1}{2B}\frac{\partial B}{\partial x^3}, \quad \Gamma^2_{33} = -\frac{1}{2B}\frac{\partial C}{\partial x^2}, \quad \Gamma^2_{34} = 0$$

$$\Gamma^2_{41} = 0, \quad \Gamma^2_{42} = \frac{1}{2B}\frac{\partial B}{\partial x^4}, \quad \Gamma^2_{43} = 0, \quad \Gamma^2_{44} = \frac{1}{2B}\frac{\partial D}{\partial x^2}$$

$$\Gamma^3_{11} = -\frac{1}{2C}\frac{\partial A}{\partial x^3}, \quad \Gamma^3_{12} = 0, \quad \Gamma^3_{13} = \frac{1}{2C}\frac{\partial C}{\partial x^1}, \quad \Gamma^3_{14} = 0$$

$$\Gamma^3_{21} = 0, \quad \Gamma^3_{22} = -\frac{1}{2C}\frac{\partial B}{\partial x^3}, \quad \Gamma^3_{23} = \frac{1}{2C}\frac{\partial C}{\partial x^2}, \quad \Gamma^3_{24} = 0$$

$$\Gamma^3_{41} = 0, \Gamma^3_{42} = 0, \quad \Gamma^3_{43} = \frac{1}{2C}\frac{\partial C}{\partial x^4}, \quad \Gamma^3_{44} = \frac{1}{2C}\frac{\partial D}{\partial x^3}$$

$$\Gamma^4_{11} = \frac{1}{2D}\frac{\partial A}{\partial x^4}, \quad \Gamma^4_{12} = 0, \quad \Gamma^4_{13} = 0, \quad \Gamma^4_{14} = \frac{1}{2D}\frac{\partial D}{\partial x^1}$$

$$\Gamma^4_{21} = 0, \quad \Gamma^4_{22} = \frac{1}{2D}\frac{\partial B}{\partial x^4}, \quad \Gamma^4_{23} = 0, \quad \Gamma^4_{24} = \frac{1}{2D}\frac{\partial D}{\partial x^2 4}$$

$$\Gamma^4_{31} = 0, \quad \Gamma^4_{32} = 0, \quad \Gamma^4_{33} = \frac{1}{2D}\frac{\partial C}{\partial x^4}, \quad \Gamma^4_{34} = \frac{1}{2D}\frac{\partial D}{\partial x^3}$$

EXAMPLE 3.4 If $g_{ij} = 0$ for $i \neq j$ and if i, j, k are unequal suffixes, then show that

(i) $\Gamma_{ijk} = 0$

(ii) $\Gamma_{iij} = -\Gamma_{jii} = \dfrac{1}{2}\dfrac{\partial g_{ii}}{\partial x^j}$

(iii) $\Gamma^i_{jk} = 0$

(iv) $\Gamma^j_{ii} = -\dfrac{1}{2}\dfrac{1}{g_{ii}}\dfrac{\partial g_{ii}}{\partial x^j}$

(v) $\Gamma^i_{ij} = \dfrac{1}{2}\dfrac{\partial}{\partial x^j}\log g_{ii}$

(vi) $\Gamma^i_{ii} = \dfrac{1}{2}\dfrac{\partial}{\partial x^i}\log g_{ii}$

(vii) $\Gamma_{iii} = \dfrac{1}{2}\dfrac{\partial g_{ii}}{\partial x^i}$

Solution From the given condition, we have

$$g_{ij} = g_{jk} = g_{ki} = 0, \quad g^{ij} = g^{jk} = g^{ki} = 0 \quad \text{and} \quad g^{pp} = \frac{1}{g_{pp}} \qquad (3.39)$$

(i) Use definition of Γ_{ijk} with Eq. (3.39).

(ii) From the definition and symmetry of g_{ij}, we have

$$\Gamma_{iij} = \frac{1}{2}\frac{\partial g_{ii}}{\partial x^j} \quad \text{and} \quad \Gamma_{jii} = -\frac{1}{2}\frac{\partial g_{ii}}{\partial x^j}$$

(iii) We have

$$\Gamma^i_{jk} = g^{ih}\Gamma_{hjk} = 0 \quad \text{as} \quad g^{ih} = 0 \quad \text{for} \quad i \neq j$$

(iv) Here

$$\Gamma^j_{ii} = g^{jh}\Gamma_{hii} = g^{jj}\Gamma_{jii} = \frac{1}{g_{jj}}\Gamma_{jii} = -\frac{1}{2g_{jj}}\frac{\partial g_{ii}}{\partial x^j}$$

(v) We have

$$\Gamma^i_{ij} = g^{ih}\Gamma_{hij} = g^{ii}\Gamma_{iij} = \frac{1}{g_{ii}}\Gamma_{iij} = \frac{1}{2g_{ii}}\frac{\partial g_{ii}}{\partial x^j} = \frac{1}{2}\frac{\partial}{\partial x^j}\log g_{ii}$$

(vi) From definition, we have

$$\Gamma^i_{ii} = g^{ih}\Gamma_{hii} = g^{ii}\Gamma_{iii} = \frac{1}{2}\frac{\partial g_{ii}}{\partial x^i}$$

(vii) Follows from the definition.

EXAMPLE 3.5 For the metric $ds^2 = -dx^2 - dy^2 - dz^2 + c^2 dt^2$ obtain the equations of motion.

Solution For the given metric, we have

$$g_{11} = g_{22} = g_{33} = -1, \quad g_{44} = c^2, \quad g_{ij} = 0 \quad \text{for } i \neq j$$

and

$$g^{11} = g^{22} = g^{33} = -1, \quad g^{44} = 1/c^2, \quad g^{ij} = 0 \quad \text{for } i \neq j$$

so that $\Gamma^i_{jk} = 0$ for all i, j, k.

The equation of motion (3.24), in this case, reduces to

$$\frac{d^2 x^i}{ds^2} = 0$$

that is

$$\frac{d^2x}{ds^2} = \frac{d^2y}{ds^2} = \frac{d^2z}{ds^2} = \frac{d^2t}{ds^2} = 0$$

which are the required equations of motion.

EXAMPLE 3.6 If $v^2 = \left(\frac{dx}{dt}\right)^2 + \left(\frac{dy}{dt}\right)^2 + \left(\frac{dz}{dt}\right)^2$ and

$$ds^2 = \frac{dt^2}{1-kx} - \frac{1}{c^2}\left[\frac{dx^2 + dy^2 + dz^2}{(1-kx)^2}\right]$$

then show that $V^2 - v^2 = kc^2x$ along a geodesic, where V and k are constants.

Solution Here $x^1 = x, x^2 = y, x^3 = z$ and $x^4 = t$. For the given metric, we have

$$g_{11} = g_{22} = g_{33} = -\frac{1}{c^2(1-kx)^2}, \quad g_{44} = \frac{1}{1-kx}$$

$$g_{ij} = 0 \quad \text{for } i \neq j, \quad g^{ij} = 0 \quad \text{for } i \neq j \quad \text{and} \quad g^{ii} = \frac{1}{g_{ii}}$$

The non-vanishing components of Γ^i_{jk} are

$$\Gamma^1_{11} = \Gamma^1_{22} = \Gamma^1_{33} = \Gamma^2_{12} = \Gamma^2_{21} = \Gamma^3_{13} = \Gamma^3_{31} = \frac{k}{1-kx}$$

$$\Gamma^1_{44} = \frac{kc^2}{2}, \quad \Gamma^4_{14} = \Gamma^4_{41} = \frac{k}{2(1-kx)}$$

For $i = 4$, Eq. (3.24) yields

$$\frac{d^2t}{ds^2} + \Gamma^4_{jk}\frac{dx^j}{ds}\frac{dx^k}{ds} = 0$$

or

$$\frac{d^2t}{ds^2} + \Gamma^4_{14}\frac{dx^1}{ds}\frac{dx^4}{ds} + \Gamma^4_{41}\frac{dx^4}{ds}\frac{dx^1}{ds} = 0$$

or

$$\frac{d^2t}{ds^2} + \frac{2k}{2(1-kx)}\frac{dt}{ds}\frac{dx}{ds} = 0$$

or

$$\left(\frac{d^2t}{ds^2}\right)/\left(\frac{dt}{ds}\right) = -\frac{k}{1-kx}\frac{dx}{ds}$$

Integrating this equation, we get

$$\log\frac{dt}{ds} = \log(1-kx) + \log a$$

which gives

$$\frac{ds}{dt} = \frac{1}{a(1-kx)} \tag{3.40}$$

Now from the given form of the metric and the given value of v^2, Eq. (3.40) can be expressed as

$$\left(\frac{ds}{dt}\right)^2 = \frac{1}{a^2(1 - kx)^2} = \frac{1}{1 - kx} - \frac{v^2}{c^2(1 - kx)^2}$$

which gives $V^2 - v^2 = kc^2 x$, where $V^2 = c^2 - \dfrac{c^2}{a^2} = \text{constant}$.

EXAMPLE 3.7   For a two-dimensional Riemannian space

$$ds^2 = \frac{dr^2 + r^2 d\theta^2}{r^2 - a^2} - \frac{r^2 dr^2}{(r^2 - a^2)^2}, \quad (r > a)$$

show that the differential equation of the geodesic is

$$a^2 \left(\frac{dr}{d\theta}\right)^2 + a^2 r^2 = k^2 r^4$$

where k^2 is a constant.

Solution   The given metric can be written as

$$ds^2 = \frac{-a^2 dr^2}{(r^2 - a^2)^2} + \frac{r^2 d\theta^2}{r^2 - a^2} \tag{3.41}$$

so that

$$g_{11} = -\frac{a^2}{(r^2 - a^2)^2}, \quad g_{22} = \frac{r^2}{r^2 - a^2}, \quad g_{12} = 0$$

$$g^{11} = \frac{1}{g_{11}}, \quad g^{22} = \frac{1}{g_{22}}, \quad g^{12} = 0$$

Setting $x^1 = r, x^2 = \theta$, the non-vanishing components of Γ^i_{jk} are

$$\Gamma^1_{11} = -\frac{2r}{r^2 - a^2}, \quad \Gamma^1_{22} = -r, \quad \Gamma^2_{121} = \Gamma^2_{21} = -\frac{a^2}{r(r^2 - a^2)}$$

For $i = 1$, Eq. (3.24) yields

$$\frac{d^2 r}{ds^2} + \Gamma^1_{jk} \frac{dx^j}{ds} \frac{dx^k}{ds} = 0$$

or

$$\frac{d^2 r}{ds^2} + \Gamma^1_{11} \left(\frac{dr}{ds}\right)^2 + \Gamma^1_{22} \left(\frac{d\theta}{ds}\right)^2 = 0$$

or

$$\frac{d^2 r}{ds^2} - \frac{2r}{r^2 - a^2} \left(\frac{dr}{ds}\right)^2 - r^2 \left(\frac{d\theta}{ds}\right)^2 = 0$$

while for $i = 2$, Eq. (3.24) leads to

$$\frac{d^2\theta}{ds^2} + 2\Gamma_{12}^2 \frac{dr}{ds}\frac{d\theta}{ds} = 0$$

or

$$\frac{d^2\theta}{ds^2} = 2\left(\frac{r}{r^2 - a^2} - \frac{1}{r}\right)\frac{dr}{ds}\frac{d\theta}{ds}$$

Now separating the variables and integrating, we get

$$\frac{d\theta}{ds} = \frac{B(r^2 - a^2)}{r^2}$$

where B is a constant. Thus, after simplification, from Eq. (3.41), we have

$$a^2\left(\frac{dr}{d\theta}\right)^2 + a^2 r^2 = k^2 r^4$$

where $k^2 = (B^2 - 1)/B^2$ is a constant.

EXAMPLE 3.8   For the metric

$$ds^2 = -e^{2kt}(dx^2 + dy^2 + dz^2) + dt^2$$

find the equations of geodesics.

Solution   For the given metric, the non-vanishing components of Γ_{jk}^i are

$$\Gamma_{14}^1 = \Gamma_{41}^1 = \Gamma_{24}^2 = \Gamma_{42}^2 = \Gamma_{34}^3 = \Gamma_{43}^3 = k$$
$$\Gamma_{11}^4 = \Gamma_{22}^4 = \Gamma_{33}^4 = ke^{2kt}$$

For $i = 1$, Eq. (3.24) leads to

$$\frac{d^2x}{ds^2} + 2k\frac{dx}{ds}\frac{dt}{ds} = 0$$

which on integration yields

$$\frac{dx}{ds} = ae^{-2kt}$$

Similarly, from Eq. (3.24), for $i = 2, 3, 4$, respectively, we have

$$\frac{dy}{ds} = be^{-2kt}$$

$$\frac{dz}{ds} = ce^{-2kt}$$

$$\frac{d^2t}{ds^2} = -kp^2 e^{-2kt}$$

where $p^2 = a^2 + b^2 + c^2$ and a, b, c are constants of integration.

3.7　Covariant Differentiation

In Chapter 1, we have seen that if ϕ is a scalar then its derivative $\dfrac{\partial \phi}{\partial x^i}$ is a covariant vector (a tensor of rank one). Now, if A^i is a vector, then what is the nature of its derivative $\dfrac{\partial A^i}{\partial x^j}$? Will it be a tensor or not? This and similar types of questions shall be addressed in this section.

Consider a contravariant vector A^i which transforms as

$$A'^i = \frac{\partial x'^i}{\partial x^j} A^j$$

Differentiating this equation partially with respect to x'^k, we get

$$\frac{\partial A'^i}{\partial x'^k} = \frac{\partial}{\partial x'^k}\left(\frac{\partial x'^i}{\partial x^j} A^j\right)$$

$$= \frac{\partial}{\partial x^p}\left(\frac{\partial x'^i}{\partial x^j} A^j\right)\frac{\partial x^p}{\partial x'^k}$$

$$= \frac{\partial x'^i}{\partial x^j}\frac{\partial x^p}{\partial x'^k}\frac{\partial A^j}{\partial x^p} + \frac{\partial^2 x'^i}{\partial x^p \partial x^j}\frac{\partial x^p}{\partial x'^k} A^j \tag{3.42}$$

If $\dfrac{\partial A'^i}{\partial x'^k}$ is a tensor then Eq. (3.42) should contain only the first term on the right-hand side. But due to presence of the second term on the right-hand side of Eq. (3.42), the quantity $\dfrac{\partial A'^i}{\partial x'^k}$ does not behave like a tensor, i.e., the outcome of the differentiation of a tensor is not a tensor; and in tensor analysis only those operations are allowed which when performed on a tensor lead to a tensor. Thus, the quantity $\dfrac{\partial A'^i}{\partial x'^k}$ will be a tensor only when the quantity $\dfrac{\partial^2 x'^i}{\partial x^p \partial x^j}$ vanishes, i.e., if the coordinates x'^i are linear function of the coordinates x^j then Eq. (3.42) is the transformation law of a tensor.

The process of obtaining tensors through the process of partial differentiation is known as *covariant differentiation* and is being developed as follows:

(a) Covariant derivatives of contravariant and covariant vectors

We know that [cf. Eq. (3.15)]

$$\Gamma'^q_{lk} = \frac{\partial x^i}{\partial x'^l}\frac{\partial x^j}{\partial x'^k}\frac{\partial x'^q}{\partial x^s}\Gamma^s_{ij} + \frac{\partial^2 x^i}{\partial x'^l \partial x'^k}\frac{\partial x'^q}{\partial x^i}$$

Take its inner product with $\dfrac{\partial x^r}{\partial x'^q}$, to get

$$\frac{\partial x^r}{\partial x'^q}\Gamma'^q_{lk} = \frac{\partial x^i}{\partial x'^l}\frac{\partial x^j}{\partial x'^k}\frac{\partial x'^q}{\partial x^s}\frac{\partial x^r}{\partial x'^q}\Gamma^s_{ij} + \frac{\partial^2 x^i}{\partial x'^l \partial x'^k}\frac{\partial x'^q}{\partial x^i}\frac{\partial x^r}{\partial x'^q}$$

which gives

$$\frac{\partial^2 x^r}{\partial x'^l \partial x'^k} = \frac{\partial x^r}{\partial x'^q} \Gamma'^q_{lk} - \frac{\partial x^i}{\partial x'^l} \frac{\partial x^j}{\partial x'^k} \Gamma^r_{ij} \tag{3.43}$$

Interchanging the x and x' coordinates in Eq. (3.43), we get

$$\frac{\partial^2 x'^r}{\partial x^l \partial x^k} = \frac{\partial x'^r}{\partial x^q} \Gamma^q_{lk} - \frac{\partial x'^i}{\partial x^l} \frac{\partial x'^j}{\partial x^k} \Gamma'^r_{ij} \tag{3.44}$$

Substituting this value in Eq. (3.42), we have

$$\frac{\partial A'^i}{\partial x'^k} = \frac{\partial x'^i}{\partial x^j} \frac{\partial x^p}{\partial x'^k} \frac{\partial A^j}{\partial x^p} + \left[\frac{\partial x'^i}{\partial x^q} \Gamma^q_{pj} - \frac{\partial x'^a}{\partial x^p} \frac{\partial x'^b}{\partial x^j} \Gamma'^i_{ab} \right] \frac{\partial x^p}{\partial x'^k} A^j$$

$$= \frac{\partial x'^i}{\partial x^j} \frac{\partial x^p}{\partial x'^k} \frac{\partial A^j}{\partial x^p} + \Gamma^q_{pj} \frac{\partial x'^i}{\partial x^q} \frac{\partial x^p}{\partial x'^k} A^j - \frac{\partial x'^a}{\partial x'^k} \frac{\partial x'^b}{\partial x^j} \Gamma'^i_{ab} A^j$$

$$= \frac{\partial x'^i}{\partial x^j} \frac{\partial x^p}{\partial x'^k} \frac{\partial A^j}{\partial x^p} + \Gamma^q_{pj} \frac{\partial x'^i}{\partial x^q} \frac{\partial x^p}{\partial x'^k} A^j - \frac{\partial x'^a}{\partial x'^k} \Gamma'^i_{ab} A'^b$$

Since x'^a and x'^k are independent, therefore, $\dfrac{\partial x'^a}{\partial x'^k} = \delta^a_k$ and the above equation reduces to

$$\frac{\partial A'^i}{\partial x'^k} = \frac{\partial x'^i}{\partial x^j} \frac{\partial x^p}{\partial x'^k} \frac{\partial A^j}{\partial x^p} + \Gamma^q_{pj} \frac{\partial x'^i}{\partial x^q} \frac{\partial x^p}{\partial x'^k} A^j - \Gamma'^i_{ak} A'^a$$

which leads to

$$\frac{\partial A'^i}{\partial x'^k} + \Gamma'^i_{ak} A'^a = \frac{\partial x'^i}{\partial x^j} \frac{\partial x^p}{\partial x'^k} \frac{\partial A^j}{\partial x^p} + \Gamma^q_{pj} \frac{\partial x'^i}{\partial x^q} \frac{\partial x^p}{\partial x'^k} A^j$$

$$= \left(\frac{\partial x'^i}{\partial x^j} \frac{\partial x^p}{\partial x'^k} \right) \frac{\partial A^j}{\partial x^p} + \Gamma^j_{pq} \left(\frac{\partial x'^i}{\partial x^j} \frac{\partial x^p}{\partial x'^k} \right) A^q$$

$$= \frac{\partial x'^i}{\partial x^j} \frac{\partial x^p}{\partial x'^k} \left[\frac{\partial A^j}{\partial x^p} + \Gamma^j_{qp} A^q \right] \tag{3.45}$$

Now introduce the notation

$$A^j_{;p} = \frac{\partial A^j}{\partial x^p} + \Gamma^j_{qp} A^q \tag{3.46}$$

so that Eq. (3.45) can be written as

$$A'^i_{;k} = \frac{\partial x'^i}{\partial x^j} \frac{\partial x^p}{\partial x'^k} A^j_{;p} \tag{3.47}$$

which shows that the quantity $A^j_{;p}$ defined through Eq. (3.46) transforms like the components of a mixed tensor of rank two. This quantity $A^j_{;p}$ is called the *covariant derivative of a contravariant vector.*

We also know that the transformation law for a covariant vector A_p is given by

$$A'_j = \frac{\partial x^p}{\partial x'^j} A_p$$

Differentiate this equation partially with respect to x'^k and proceed in the same manner as above, to obtain

$$A_{j;k} = \frac{\partial A_j}{\partial x^k} - \Gamma^p_{jk} A_p \tag{3.48}$$

which is known as the *covariant derivative of a covariant vector.*

(b) Covariant derivatives of rank two tensors

Consider a covariant tensor A_{ij} of rank two and let $t^i = \dfrac{dx^i}{ds}$ be a unit tangent vector along the geodesic, then

$$\frac{d}{ds}(A_{ij}t^it^j) = \frac{dA_{ij}}{ds}t^it^j + A_{ij}\frac{dt^i}{ds}t^j + A_{ij}t^i\frac{dt^j}{ds}$$

$$= \frac{\partial A_{ij}}{\partial x^p}\frac{dx^p}{ds}t^it^j + A_{ij}\frac{d}{ds}\left(\frac{dx^i}{ds}\right)t^j + A_{ij}t^i\frac{d}{ds}\left(\frac{dx^j}{ds}\right)$$

$$= \frac{\partial A_{ij}}{\partial x^p}t^pt^it^j + A_{ij}\frac{d^2x^i}{ds^2}t^j + A_{ij}t^i\frac{d^2x^j}{ds^2}$$

$$= \frac{\partial A_{ij}}{\partial x^p}t^it^jt^p + A_{kj}\frac{d^2x^k}{ds^2}t^j + A_{ik}t^i\frac{d^2x^k}{ds^2}$$

But from Eq. (3.24), we have

$$\frac{d^2x^k}{ds^2} = -\Gamma^k_{ij}\frac{dx^i}{ds}\frac{dx^j}{ds}$$

Using this value and the definition of t^i in the above equation, we get

$$\frac{d}{ds}(A_{ij}t^it^j) = \left[\frac{\partial A_{ij}}{\partial x^p} - \Gamma^k_{ip}A_{kj} - \Gamma^k_{pj}A_{ik}\right]t^it^jt^p \tag{3.49}$$

In Eq. (3.49), the left-hand side is a scalar (a tensor of rank zero) and $(t^it^jt^p)$ is a rank three contravariant tensor. It, therefore, follows from the quotient rule that the quantity in the square bracket on the right-hand side of Eq. (3.49) is a tensor of rank three. We denote this quantity as

$$A_{ij;p} = \frac{\partial A_{ij}}{\partial x^p} - \Gamma^k_{ip}A_{kj} - \Gamma^k_{pj}A_{ik} \tag{3.50}$$

The covariant rank three tensor $A_{ij;p}$ is known as the *covariant derivative of a covariant tensor of rank two*.

In a similar way, the *covariant derivatives of contravariant* and *mixed tensors of rank two* are defined through the following equations:

$$A^{ij}_{;p} = \frac{\partial A^{ij}}{\partial x^p} + \Gamma^i_{pk} A^{kj} + \Gamma^j_{pk} A^{ik} \tag{3.51}$$

and

$$A^i_{j;p} = \frac{\partial A^i_j}{\partial x^p} + \Gamma^i_{pk} A^k_j - \Gamma^k_{pj} A^i_k \tag{3.51a}$$

(c) Covariant derivative of tensors of higher rank

The process of covariant differentiation can be applied to tensors of higher ranks and in general, for a mixed tensor of rank $(p+q)$, the covariant derivative is defined as

$$A^{i_1 i_2 \ldots i_p}_{j_1 j_2 \ldots j_q; k} = \frac{\partial A^{i_1 i_2 \ldots i_p}_{j_1 j_2 \ldots j_q}}{\partial x^k} + \Gamma^{i_1}_{mk} A^{m i_2 \ldots i_p}_{j_1 j_2 \ldots j_q} + \Gamma^{i_2}_{mk} A^{i_1 m i_3 \ldots i_p}_{j_1 j_2 \ldots j_q} + \cdots$$

$$+ \Gamma^{i_p}_{mk} A^{i_1 i_2 \ldots i_{p-1} m}_{j_1 j_2 \ldots j_q} - \Gamma^m_{j_1 k} A^{i_1 i_2 \ldots i_p}_{m j_2 \ldots j_q} - \Gamma^m_{j_2 k} A^{i_1 i_2 \ldots i_p}_{j_1 m \ldots j_q} - \cdots - \Gamma^m_{j_q k} A^{i_1 i_2 \ldots i_p}_{j_1 j_2 \ldots j_{q-1} m} \tag{3.52}$$

Remarks

1. The covariant differentiation is denoted by a semi-colon (;) while the partial differentiation is denoted by a comma (,).

2. It may be noted that the covariant derivative is an operator which reduces to partial derivative in flat space (where g_{ij} are constants) with Cartesian coordinates but transforms as a tensor on an arbitrary manifold.

3. For a vector A^i, the covariant derivative $A^i_{;j}$, for each direction j, will be given by the partial derivative opeartor $\frac{\partial}{\partial x^j}$ plus a correction specified by Γ^i_{jk}.

4. From Eqs. (3.46), (3.48), (3.50) and (3.51), it may be noted that through the process of covariant differentiation, we get tensors of higher rank. Thus, the rank of a tensor can be raised by differentiating it covariantly, while the rank of the tensor is lowered by the process of contraction.

5. From Eq. (2.8), we have

$$1 = g_{ij} \frac{dx^i}{ds} \frac{dx^j}{ds} = g_{ij} u^i u^j$$

Here $u^i = \frac{dx^i}{ds}$ is a unit tangent vector. The equation of geodesic given by Eq. (3.24) can be expressed as

$$\frac{d}{ds}\left(\frac{dx^k}{ds}\right) + \Gamma^k_{lm} \frac{dx^l}{ds} \frac{dx^m}{ds} = 0$$

or

$$\frac{d}{ds}u^k + \Gamma^k_{lm}u^l u^m = 0$$

But $\dfrac{du^k}{ds} = \dfrac{\partial u^k}{\partial x^l}\dfrac{dx^l}{ds} = \dfrac{\partial u^k}{\partial x^l}u^l$, hence, the above equation can now be written as

$$\left(\frac{\partial u^k}{\partial x^l} + \Gamma^k_{lm}u^m\right)u^l = 0$$

which, using the definition of covariant derivative of a contravariant vector [cf., Eq. (3.46)], takes the form

$$u^k_{;l}u^l = 0 \tag{3.24a}$$

This equation is another form of the *equation of geodesic* when u^l is regarded as the unit tangent vector to the curve [see also Eq. (3.24)].

6. In a Riemannian space V_n, the geodesic is also defined as a curve whose first curvature relative to V_n is zero at all points. The first curvature is defined as

$$p^i = u^i_{;j}u^j$$

where u^i is the unit tangent vector. From this definition of geodesic, we again get Eq. (3.24a).

3.8   Rules for Covariant Differentiation

The rules for covariant differentiation are as follows:

1. *The covariant derivative of a linear combination of tensors, with constant coefficients, equals to the linear combination of these tensors after the covariant differentiation was performed.*

   Thus, for example, if A^i_j and B^i_j are two mixed tensors of rank two and a and b are scalars then

$$(aA^i_j \pm bB^i_j)_{;k} = \frac{\partial}{\partial x^k}(aA^i_j \pm bB^i_j) + \Gamma^i_{lk}(aA^l_k \pm bB^l_k) - \Gamma^l_{jk}(aA^i_l \pm bB^i_l)$$

$$= a\left[\frac{\partial A^i_j}{\partial x^k} + \Gamma^i_{lk}A^l_k - \Gamma^l_{jk}A^i_l\right] \pm b\left[\frac{\partial B^i_j}{\partial x^k} + \Gamma^i_{lk}B^l_k - \Gamma^l_{jk}B^i_l\right]$$

$$= aA^i_{j;k} \pm bB^i_{j;k} \tag{3.53}$$

2. *The covariant derivatives of outer and inner products of tensors obey the same rules as that of the usual derivatives.*

Thus, for example, using Eq. (3.52), we have

$$(A^i B_{jk})_{;p} = \frac{\partial}{\partial x^p}(A^i B_{jk}) + \Gamma^i_{mp} A^m B_{jk} - \Gamma^m_{jp} A^i B_{mk} - \Gamma^m_{kp} A^i B_{jm}$$

$$= \frac{\partial A^i}{\partial x^p} B_{jk} + A^i \frac{\partial B_{jk}}{\partial x^p} + \Gamma^i_{mp} A^m B_{jk} -$$

$$A^i \Gamma^m_{jp} B_{mk} - A^i \Gamma^m_{kp} A^i B_{jm}$$

$$= \left(\frac{\partial A^i}{\partial x^p} + \Gamma^i_{mp} A^m \right) B_{jk} - A^i \left(\frac{\partial B_{jk}}{\partial x^p} - \Gamma^m_{jp} B_{mk} - \Gamma^m_{kp} B_{jm} \right)$$

$$= A^i_{;p} B_{jk} + A^i B_{jk;m} \tag{3.54}$$

and

$$(A^i B_i)_{;j} = \frac{\partial}{\partial x^j}(A^i B_i) + \Gamma^i_{mj} A^m B_i - \Gamma^m_{ij} A^i B_m$$

$$= \frac{\partial A^i}{\partial x^j} B_i + A^i \frac{\partial B^i}{\partial x^j} + \Gamma^i_{mj} A^m B_i - \Gamma^m_{ij} A^i B_m$$

$$= A^i_{;j} B_i + A^i B_{i;j} \tag{3.55}$$

Since $A^i B_i$ is an invariant, therefore

$$(A^i B_i)_{;j} = \frac{\partial}{\partial x^i}(A^i B_j)$$

3. *The covariant derivative of an invariant is same as its ordinary derivative.*

   Thus, for example, if ϕ is an invariant and A_j is a covariant vector, then from the definition we have

$$(\phi A_j)_{;i} = \frac{\partial}{\partial x^i}(\phi A_j) - \Gamma^m_{ji} \phi A^m$$

$$= \frac{\partial \phi}{\partial x^i} A_j + \phi \frac{\partial A_j}{\partial x^i} - \phi \Gamma^m_{ji} A^m$$

$$= \frac{\partial \phi}{\partial x^i} A_j + \phi A_{j;i} \tag{3.56}$$

Also, from the product rule of covariant differentiation, we have

$$(\phi A_j)_{;i} = \phi_{;i} A_j + \phi A_{j;i} \tag{3.57}$$

Since A_j is arbitrary, from Eqs. (3.56) and (3.57), we have

$$\phi_{;i} = \frac{\partial \phi}{\partial x^i} \tag{3.58}$$

4. *The fundamental tensors are covariantly constant.*

That is, the covariant derivative of fundamental tensors is zero. For example, first consider g_{ij} and its covariant derivative

$$g_{ij;k} = \frac{\partial g_{ij}}{\partial x^k} - \Gamma^p_{ik} g_{pj} - \Gamma^p_{jk} g_{ip}$$

$$= \frac{\partial g_{ij}}{\partial x^k} - \Gamma_{jik} - \Gamma_{ijk}$$

$$= \frac{\partial g_{ij}}{\partial x^k} - \frac{\partial g_{ij}}{\partial x^k}$$

$$= 0 \qquad\qquad (3.59)$$

Similarly, for δ^i_j, we have

$$\delta^i_{j;k} = \frac{\partial \delta^i_j}{\partial x^k} + \Gamma^i_{pk} \delta^p_j - \Gamma^p_{jk} \delta^i_p$$

$$= \Gamma^i_{jk} - \Gamma^i_{jk}$$

$$= 0 \qquad\qquad (3.60)$$

and moreover, since $g_{ij} g^{kj} = \delta^k_i$, therefore the covariant derivative of g^{kj} is also zero. Thus, the covariant derivative of all the three fundamental tensors is zero. Further

$$(g_{ij} A^{kl}_m)_{;n} = g_{ij;n} A^{kl}_m + g_{ij} A^{kl}_{m;n} = g_{ij} A^{kl}_{m;n} \qquad\qquad (3.61)$$

Hence, in a covariant differentiation g_{ij} can be regarded as a constant.

Since the covariant derivative of the metric tensor vanishes, it may be noted that raising and lowering of indices of tensors is not affected by the operation of covariant differentiation. Thus, for example

$$A^i_{;j} = (g^{ik} A_k)_{;j} = g^{ik} A_{k;j} \qquad\qquad (3.62)$$

Remarks

1. The covariant derivative of a non-tensor has no meaning.

2. The laws of physics must be valid in all coordinate systems and thus they must be expressible through tensor equations. This is known as the *principle of covariance*—one of the basic postulate of general theory of relativity. So, whenever a tensor equation involves the derivative of a tensor quantity, it must be a covariant derivative; and the field equations of physics must be written in such a way that the ordinary derivatives be replaced by covariant derivatives.

EXAMPLE 3.9 From the rules of the covariant derivatives of contravariant, covariant and mixed vectors, prove that

$$A_{ij;k} = \frac{\partial A_{ij}}{\partial x^k} - \Gamma_{ki}^l A_{lj} - \Gamma_{kj}^l A_{il}$$

$$A_{;k}^{ij} = \frac{\partial A^{ij}}{\partial x^k} + \Gamma_{kl}^i A^{lj} + \Gamma_{kl}^j A^{il}$$

$$A_{j;k}^i = \frac{\partial A_j^i}{\partial x^k} + \Gamma_{kl}^i A_j^l - \Gamma_{kj}^l A_l^i$$

Solution Let P^i and Q_j be contravariant and covariant vectors, and if we express A_j^i as the product of P^i and Q_j then from the rules of the covariant differentiation of contravariant and covariant vectors, we have

$$A_{j;k}^i = (P^i Q_j)_{;k}$$

$$= P_{;k}^i Q_j + P^i Q_{j;k}$$

$$= \left(\frac{\partial P^i}{\partial x^k} + \Gamma_{kl}^i P^l \right) Q_j + P^i \left(\frac{\partial Q_j}{\partial x^k} - \Gamma_{kj}^l Q_l \right)$$

$$= \frac{\partial P^i}{\partial x^k} Q_j + P^i \frac{\partial Q_j}{\partial x^k} + \Gamma_{kl}^i P^l Q_j - \Gamma_{kj}^l P^i Q_l$$

$$= \frac{\partial}{\partial x^k} (P^i Q_j) + \Gamma_{kl}^i P^l Q_j - \Gamma_{kj}^l P^i Q_l$$

$$= \frac{\partial A_j^i}{\partial x^k} + \Gamma_{kl}^i A_j^l - \Gamma_{kj}^l A_l^i$$

In a similar way, other two formulas can be proved.

3.9 Some Useful Formulas

Here we shall derive some useful formulas which are related to the concept of covariant differentiation.

(a) Divergence of a vector field

Let A^i be a contravariant vector and $A_{;i}^k$ be its covariant derivative, then $A_{;i}^i$, a unique scalar (invariant), is called the *divergence of a vector field* A^i.

From the definition of covariant differentiation, we have

$$\text{div } A^i = A_{;i}^i$$

$$= \frac{\partial A^i}{\partial x^i} + \Gamma_{ij}^i A^j$$

$$= \frac{\partial A^i}{\partial x^i} + \frac{1}{\sqrt{g}} \frac{\partial \sqrt{g}}{\partial x^j} A^j$$

$$= \frac{1}{\sqrt{g}} \frac{\partial}{\partial x^k} (A^k \sqrt{g}) \qquad (3.63)$$

Consider the metric of a three-dimensional Euclidean space

$$ds^2 = dx^2 + dy^2 + dz^2$$

Here $g_{11} = g_{22} = g_{33} = 1$ and $\det g_{ij} = 1$. Equation (3.63) in this case reduces to

$$\mathrm{div} A^i = \frac{\partial A^1}{\partial x} + \frac{\partial A^2}{\partial y} + \frac{\partial A^3}{\partial z}$$

which is the well known expression for divergence in ordinary vector calculus. Moreover, equation

$$A^i_{;i} = \frac{1}{\sqrt{g}} \frac{\partial}{\partial x^k} (A^k \sqrt{g}) = 0$$

is called the *equation of continuity* satisfied by the contravariant vector A^i.

(b) Gradient of a scalar and the Laplacian

The *gradient* of a scalar ϕ is a covariant vector defined as

$$\mathrm{grad} \phi = \nabla \phi = \frac{\partial \phi}{\partial x^l} = \phi_{,l} \qquad (3.64)$$

Therefore, the covariant and contravariant vectors A_l and A^l associated with $\phi_{,l}$ are given by

$$A_l = \phi_{,l} = \frac{\partial \phi}{\partial x^l} \qquad (3.65)$$

and

$$A^l = g^{lk} A_k = g^{lk} \frac{\partial \phi}{\partial x^k} \qquad (3.66)$$

From Eq. (3.63), we have

$$\mathrm{div} A_i = \mathrm{div} A^i = \frac{1}{\sqrt{g}} \frac{\partial}{\partial x^k} (A^k \sqrt{g}) = \frac{1}{\sqrt{g}} \frac{\partial}{\partial x^k} (g^{kj} A_j \sqrt{g})$$

Thus

$$\mathrm{div\ grad}\ \phi = \mathrm{div} \nabla \phi = \nabla^2 \phi = \frac{1}{\sqrt{g}} \frac{\partial}{\partial x^i} \left(\sqrt{g} g^{ij} \frac{\partial \phi}{\partial x^j} \right) \qquad (3.67)$$

which is the *Laplacian* of a scalar field.

If g is negative, then in the above equation $\sqrt{g}$ must be replaced by $\sqrt{-g}$.

(c) Curl of a vector

Consider the covariant vector and use Eq. (3.48) so that

$$A_{i;j} - A_{j;i} = \left(\frac{\partial A_i}{\partial x^j} - \Gamma_{ij}^m A_m\right) - \left(\frac{\partial A_j}{\partial x^i} - \Gamma_{ji}^m A_m\right) = \frac{\partial A_i}{\partial x^j} - \frac{\partial A_j}{\partial x^i} \quad (3.68)$$

This difference is, of course, a tensor and does not involve Christoffel symbols. This tensor is skew symmetric and is known as the *curl* or *rotation* of the vector A_i. The curl operation is not applicable to contravariant vectors and tensors of higher rank, for example

$$A_{;j}^i - A_{;i}^j = \left(\frac{\partial A^i}{\partial x^j} + \Gamma_{pj}^i A_p\right) - \left(\frac{\partial A_j}{\partial x^i} + \Gamma_{pi}^j A_p\right) \neq \frac{\partial A^i}{\partial x^j} - \frac{\partial A^j}{\partial x^i}$$

From Eq. (3.68) it may be noted that we can construct a skew symmetric tensor field from a vector field. Moreover, Eq. (3.68) leads to the following necessary and sufficient condition.

Theorem 3.2 The first covariant derivative of a covariant vector A_i is symmetric, if and only if the vector itself is gradient of a scalar ϕ.

Proof Let A_i be a covariant vector and given that $A_{i;j} = A_{j;i}$ which gives $\frac{\partial A_i}{\partial x^j} = \frac{\partial A_j}{\partial x^i}$ and $\frac{\partial A_i}{\partial x^j} dx^j = \frac{\partial A_j}{\partial x^i} dx^i$ so that after integration, we have

$$\int dA_i = \frac{\partial}{\partial x^i} \int A_j dx^j$$

or

$$A_i = \frac{\partial \phi}{\partial x^i} = \text{grad } \phi, \quad \text{where} \int A_j dx^j = \phi$$

Conversely, given that $A_i = \frac{\partial \phi}{\partial x^i}$ then

$$A_{i;j} - A_{j;i} = \left(\frac{\partial \phi}{\partial x^i}\right)_{;j} - \left(\frac{\partial \phi}{\partial x^j}\right)_{;i}$$

$$= \left[\frac{\partial}{\partial x^j}\left(\frac{\partial \phi}{\partial x^i}\right) - \Gamma_{ij}^a \frac{\partial \phi}{\partial x^a}\right] - \left[\frac{\partial}{\partial x^i}\left(\frac{\partial \phi}{\partial x^j}\right) - \Gamma_{ji}^a \frac{\partial \phi}{\partial x^a}\right]$$

$$= \frac{\partial^2 \phi}{\partial x^j \partial x^i} - \frac{\partial^2 \phi}{\partial x^i \partial x^j}$$

$$= 0$$

which completes the proof.

(d) Divergence of a tensor field

Let A^{ij} be a second rank contravariant tensor and $A_{;k}^{ij}$ be its covariant derivative then the vector $A^{ik}_{;k}$ associated with A^{ij} is called the *divergence of the tensor field* A^{ij} and we have

$$A^{ij}_{;k} = \frac{\partial A^{ij}}{\partial x^k} + \Gamma^i_{kp} A^{pj} + \Gamma^j_{kp} A^{ip}$$

A contraction of this equation with j and k leads to

$$A^{ik}_{;k} = \frac{\partial A^{ik}}{\partial x^k} + \Gamma^i_{kp} A^{pk} + \Gamma^k_{kp} A^{ip}$$

$$= \frac{\partial A^{ik}}{\partial x^k} + \Gamma^i_{kp} A^{pk} + \frac{1}{\sqrt{g}} \frac{\partial \sqrt{g}}{\partial x^p} A^{ip}$$

$$= \frac{1}{\sqrt{g}} \frac{\partial}{\partial x^k} (A^{ik} \sqrt{g}) + \Gamma^i_{kp} A^{pk} \tag{3.69}$$

In a similar way, we also have

$$A^{kj}_{;k} = \frac{1}{\sqrt{g}} \frac{\partial}{\partial x^k} (A^{kj} \sqrt{g}) + \Gamma^j_{kp} A^{kp} \tag{3.70}$$

If the tensor A^{ij} is symmetric then the two divergences given by Eqs. (3.69) and (3.70) are same, otherwise not. Moreover, for a symmetric tensor A_{ij}, we have

$$A^j_{i;j} = \frac{\partial A^j_i}{\partial x^j} + \Gamma^j_{jk} A^k_i - \Gamma^l_{ij} A^j_l$$

$$= \frac{\partial A^j_i}{\partial x^j} + \frac{1}{\sqrt{g}} \frac{\partial \sqrt{g}}{\partial x^k} A^k_i - \Gamma^l_{ij} A^j_l$$

$$= \frac{\partial A^j_i}{\partial x^j} + \frac{1}{\sqrt{g}} \frac{\partial \sqrt{g}}{\partial x^j} A^j_i - \Gamma^l_{ij} A^j_l$$

$$= \frac{1}{\sqrt{g}} \frac{\partial}{\partial x^j} (A^j_i \sqrt{g}) - \Gamma^l_{ij} A^j_l \tag{3.71}$$

Using the definition of Γ^l_{ij}, we have

$$\Gamma^l_{ij} A^j_l = \frac{1}{2} g^{lk} \Gamma_{kij} A^j_l$$

$$= \frac{1}{2} g^{lk} A^j_l \left(\frac{\partial g_{ki}}{\partial x^j} - \frac{\partial g_{ij}}{\partial x^k} + \frac{\partial g_{jk}}{\partial x^i} \right)$$

$$= \frac{1}{2} A^{kj} \frac{\partial g_{jk}}{\partial x^i} \quad (\text{as} A^{kj} \text{is symmetric})$$

Equation (3.71) now becomes

$$A^j_{i;j} = \frac{1}{\sqrt{g}} \frac{\partial}{\partial x^j} (A^j_i \sqrt{g}) - \frac{1}{2} A^{kj} \frac{\partial g_{jk}}{\partial x^i} \tag{3.72}$$

Now, differentiating both sides of $g_{kj}g^{km} = \delta_j^m$, we get

$$\frac{\partial g_{kj}}{\partial x^i}g^{km} + g_{kj}\frac{\partial g_{km}}{\partial x^i} = 0$$

or

$$g^{km}\frac{\partial g_{kj}}{\partial x^i} = -g_{kj}\frac{\partial g_{km}}{\partial x^i} \tag{3.73}$$

and we have

$$\frac{1}{2}A^{kj}\frac{\partial g_{jk}}{\partial x^i} = \frac{1}{2}g^{km}g^{jl}A_{ml}\frac{\partial g_{jk}}{\partial x^i}$$

$$= \frac{1}{2}A_{ml}g^{jl}\left(-g_{kj}\frac{\partial g^{km}}{\partial x^i}\right) \quad \text{[from Eq. (3.73)]}$$

$$= -\frac{1}{2}A_{ml}\delta_k^l\frac{\partial g^{km}}{\partial x^i}$$

$$= -\frac{1}{2}A_{ml}\frac{\partial g^{ml}}{\partial x^i}$$

Thus, Eq. (3.72) can be expressed as

$$A_{i;j}^j = \frac{1}{\sqrt{g}}\frac{\partial}{\partial x^j}(A_i^j\sqrt{g}) + \frac{1}{2}A_{lm}\frac{\partial g^{lm}}{\partial x^i} \tag{3.74}$$

The divergence and curl of tensors, as discussed above, can be used to express the thoerems of Green and Stokes in tensorial form as follows.

Tensorial form of divergence theorem

Let A^i be tensor field of rank one and U_k denote the outward drawn unit normal to any point of a closed surface S bounding a volume V. Then the statement of divergence theorem (*Green's theorem in space*) is

$$\int_V A_{;i}^i dV = \int_S A^i U_i dS$$

The invariant $A_{;i}^i$ is the divergence of A^i and the invariant $A^i U_i$ is the scalar product of A^i and U_i which is analogous to $\mathbf{A} \cdot \hat{n}$ in vector notation.

Tensorial form of Stokes' theorem

If $\dfrac{dx^i}{ds}$ is the unit tangent vector to the closed curve C and U^i the positive unit normal to the surface S which has C as boundary, then Stoke's theorem states that

$$\int_C A_i\frac{dx^i}{ds}ds = -\int_S \epsilon^{ijk}A_{j;k}U_i dS$$

which can also be written as

$$\int_C A_i dx^i = -\frac{1}{2} \int_S \left(\frac{\partial A_i}{\partial x_j} - \frac{\partial A_j}{\partial x_i} \right) dS^{ij}$$

EXAMPLE 3.10   For the metric $ds^2 = dx^2 + x^2 dy^2$, show that div $A_i = 0$ if the vector A_i has the components $(x \cos 2y, -x^2 \sin 2y)$.

Solution   Here

$$g_{ij} = \begin{bmatrix} 1 & 0 \\ 0 & x^2 \end{bmatrix}, \quad g^{ij} = \begin{bmatrix} 1 & 0 \\ 0 & 1/x^2 \end{bmatrix}, \quad \det g_{ij} = g = x^2$$

and

$$A^1 = g^{1i} A_i = g^{11} A_1 = x \cos 2y, \quad A^2 = g^{2i} A_i = g^{22} A_2 = -\sin 2y$$

Thus

$$\text{div} A^i = \frac{1}{\sqrt{g}} \frac{\partial}{\partial x^k} (\sqrt{g} A^k)$$

$$= \frac{1}{x} \left[\frac{\partial}{\partial x^1} (\sqrt{g} A^1) + \frac{\partial}{\partial x^2} (\sqrt{g} A^2) \right]$$

$$= \frac{1}{x} [2x \cos 2y - 2x \cos 2y]$$

$$= 0$$

EXAMPLE 3.11   If ψ and ϕ are scalars, then show that

$$\text{div}(\phi \psi_{,i}) = \phi \nabla^2 \psi + g^{ij} \psi_{,i} \phi_{,j}$$

Solution   We have

$$\text{div} (\phi \psi_{,i}) = g^{jk} (\phi \psi_{,j})_{,k}$$

$$= g^{jk} (\phi_{,k} \psi_{,j} + \phi \psi_{,j,k})$$

$$= g^{jk} \phi_{,k} \psi_{,j} + g^{jk} \phi \psi_{,j,k}$$

$$= \phi \nabla^2 \psi + g^{ij} \psi_{,i} \phi_{,j}$$

EXAMPLE 3.12   For a scalar ϕ, show that curl (grad ϕ) = 0.

Solution Since grad $\phi = \dfrac{\partial \phi}{\partial x^i}$, therefore

$$\text{curl (grad } \phi) = \text{curl} \left(\frac{\partial \phi}{\partial x^i} \right)$$

$$= \left(\frac{\partial \phi}{\partial x^i} \right)_{;j} - \left(\frac{\partial \phi}{\partial x^j} \right)_{;i}$$

$$= \frac{\partial}{\partial x^j} \left(\frac{\partial \phi}{\partial x^i} \right) - \Gamma^p_{ij} \frac{\partial \phi}{\partial x^p} - \frac{\partial}{\partial x^i} \left(\frac{\partial \phi}{\partial x^j} \right) + \Gamma^p_{ji} \frac{\partial \phi}{\partial x^p}$$

$$= 0$$

EXAMPLE 3.13 Evaluate $\nabla^2 \psi$ in spherical polar coordinates (r, θ, ϕ).

Solution Here the metric is

$$ds^2 = dr^2 + r^2 d\theta^2 + r^2 \sin^2 \theta d\phi^2$$

and

$$g_{ij} = \begin{bmatrix} 1 & 0 & 0 \\ 0 & r^2 & 0 \\ 0 & 0 & r^2 \sin^2 \theta \end{bmatrix}, \quad g^{ij} = \begin{bmatrix} 1 & 0 & 0 \\ 0 & 1/r^2 & 0 \\ 0 & 0 & 1/r^2 \sin^2 \theta \end{bmatrix}$$

$$\det g_{ij} = g = r^4 \sin^2 \theta$$

thus

$$\nabla^2 \phi = \frac{1}{\sqrt{g}} \frac{\partial}{\partial x^i} \left(\sqrt{g} g^{ij} \frac{\partial \psi}{\partial x^j} \right)$$

$$= \frac{1}{\sqrt{g}} \left[\frac{\partial}{\partial r} \left(\sqrt{g} g^{11} \frac{\partial \psi}{\partial r} \right) + \frac{\partial}{\partial \theta} \left(\sqrt{g} g^{22} \frac{\partial \psi}{\partial \theta} \right) + \frac{\partial}{\partial \phi} \left(\sqrt{g} g^{33} \frac{\partial \psi}{\partial \phi} \right) \right]$$

$$= \frac{1}{r^2 \sin \theta} \left[\frac{\partial}{\partial r} \left(r^2 \sin \theta \frac{\partial \psi}{\partial r} \right) + \frac{\partial}{\partial \theta} \left(\sin \theta \frac{\partial \psi}{\partial \theta} \right) + \frac{\partial}{\partial \phi} \left(\frac{1}{\sin \theta} \frac{\partial \psi}{\partial \phi} \right) \right]$$

$$= \frac{1}{r^2 \sin \theta} \left[2r \sin \theta \frac{\partial \psi}{\partial r} + r^2 \sin \theta \frac{\partial^2 \psi}{\partial r^2} \right.$$

$$\left. + \cos \theta \frac{\partial \psi}{\partial \theta} + \sin \theta \frac{\partial^2 \psi}{\partial \theta^2} + \frac{1}{\sin \theta} \left(\frac{\partial^2 \psi}{\partial \phi^2} \right) \right]$$

$$= \frac{1}{r^2} \frac{\partial}{\partial r} \left(r^2 \frac{\partial \psi}{\partial r} \right) + \frac{1}{r^2 \sin \theta} \frac{\partial}{\partial \theta} \left(\sin \theta \frac{\partial \psi}{\partial \theta} \right) + \frac{1}{r^2 \sin^2 \theta} \frac{\partial^2 \psi}{\partial \phi^2}$$

which is the expression for the Laplacian in spherical polar coordinates. Thus, by a method of tensor analysis the well-known formula of vector calculus has been obtained in a straightforward manner.

EXAMPLE 3.14 If F_{ij} is a rank two skew symmetric tensor representing the curl of the covariant vector A_i, then show that

$$F_{ij;k} + F_{jk;i} + F_{ki;j} = 0$$

Further, show that

$$\frac{\partial F_{ij}}{\partial x^k} + \frac{\partial F_{jk}}{\partial x^i} + \frac{\partial F_{ki}}{\partial x^j} = 0$$

(see also Chapter 6).

Solution From the definition of the covariant derivative of a second rank covariant tensor, we have

$$
\begin{aligned}
F_{ij;k} + F_{jk;i} + F_{ki;j} &= \frac{\partial F_{ij}}{\partial x^k} - \Gamma_{ik}^m F_{mj} - \Gamma_{jk}^m F_{im} \\
&\quad + \frac{\partial F_{jk}}{\partial x^i} - \Gamma_{ji}^m F_{mk} - \Gamma_{ki}^m F_{jm} \\
&\quad + \frac{\partial F_{ki}}{\partial x^j} - \Gamma_{kj}^m F_{mi} - \Gamma_{ij}^m F_{km} \\
&= \frac{\partial F_{ij}}{\partial x^k} + \frac{\partial F_{jk}}{\partial x^i} + \frac{\partial F_{ki}}{\partial x^j} \qquad (3.75)
\end{aligned}
$$

because the terms containing Christoffel symbols cancel each other due to skew symmetry of F_{ij}.

Also given that F_{ij} is the curl of A_i, that is

$$F_{ij} = \frac{\partial A_i}{\partial x^j} - \frac{\partial A_j}{\partial x^i}$$

which when used in Eq. (3.75) leads to

$$F_{ij;k} + F_{jk;i} + F_{ki;j} = 0 \qquad (3.76)$$

which of course is equivalent to

$$\frac{\partial F_{ij}}{\partial x^k} + \frac{\partial F_{jk}}{\partial x^i} + \frac{\partial F_{ki}}{\partial x^j} = 0$$

EXAMPLE 3.15 Find the covariant derivative of the Levi-Civita contravariant tensor density of weight $W = +1$ and show that it is zero.

Solution From the definition of covariant differentiation, we have

$$e_{;m}^{ijkl} = \frac{\partial e^{ijkl}}{\partial x^m} + \Gamma_{nm}^i e^{njkl} + \Gamma_{nm}^j e^{inkl} + \Gamma_{nm}^k e^{ijnl} + \Gamma_{nm}^l e^{ijkn} - \Gamma_{nm}^n e^{ijkl}$$

Since e^{ijkl} (from definition) is constant, the first term on the right-hand side of this equation is zero. To find the sum of the remaining five terms we calculate $e^{1234}_{;m}$ and we have

$$e^{1234}_{;m} = \Gamma^1_{nm}e^{n234} + \Gamma^2_{nm}e^{1n34} + \Gamma^3_{nm}e^{12n4} + \Gamma^4_{nm}e^{123n} - \Gamma^n_{nm}e^{1234}$$

$$= \Gamma^1_{1m}e^{1234} + \Gamma^2_{2m}e^{1234} + \Gamma^3_{3m}e^{1234} + \Gamma^4_{4m}e^{1234} - \Gamma^n_{nm}e^{1234}$$

$$= \Gamma^1_{1m} + \Gamma^2_{2m} + \Gamma^3_{3m} + \Gamma^4_{4m} - \Gamma^n_{nm}$$

$$= 0$$

Similarly, it can be shown that the other components of Levi-Civita tensor density e^{ijkl} gives the same result and thus $e^{ijkl}_{;m} = 0$.

3.10 Intrinsic Derivative: Parallel Transport

The *intrinsic* or *absolute derivative* of the vector A_i along a curve $x^j = x^j(t)$ is defined as the inner product of the covariant derivative of A_i and $\dfrac{dx^j}{dt}$. It is denoted by $\dfrac{\delta A_i}{\delta t}$ and is given by

$$\frac{\delta A_i}{\delta t} = A_{i;j}\frac{dx^j}{dt}$$

$$= \left(\frac{\partial A_i}{\partial x^j} - \Gamma^k_{ij}A_k\right)\frac{dx^j}{dt}$$

$$= \frac{\partial A_i}{\partial x^j}\frac{dx^j}{dt} - \Gamma^k_{ij}A_k\frac{dx^j}{dt}$$

$$= \frac{dA_i}{dt} - \Gamma^k_{ij}A_k\frac{dx^j}{dt} \tag{3.77}$$

Similarly, we have

$$\frac{\delta A^i}{\delta t} = \frac{dA^i}{dt} + \Gamma^i_{jk}A^k\frac{dx^j}{dt} \tag{3.78}$$

Moving a vector/tensor from one point to another while keeping it constant is called the parallel transport. In a Euclidean space we can move a vector from one point to another without changing it but we cannot carry out this operation in curved space. In curved space the result of parallel transport will depend on the path taken. The vectors A_i or A^i are said to *move parallely* or *parallely transported* along a curve if their intrinsic derivatives along the curve are zero, that is, from Eqs. (3.77) and (3.78) for the parallel displacement of vectors A_i and A^i, we have

$$\frac{dA_i}{dt} = \Gamma^k_{ij}A_k\frac{dx^j}{dt} \tag{3.79}$$

and

$$\frac{dA^i}{dt} = -\Gamma^i_{jk} A^k \frac{dx^j}{dt} \tag{3.79a}$$

Equation (3.79) is known as the equation of parallel transport. The intrinsic (absolute) derivative of an invariant is

$$\frac{\delta\phi}{\delta t} = \phi_{;j}\frac{dx^j}{dt} = \frac{\partial\phi}{\partial x^j}\frac{dx^j}{dt} = \frac{d\phi}{dt} \tag{3.80}$$

Also, the absolute derivatives of A^j_k and A^{jk}_{lmn} are, respectively, given by

$$\frac{\delta A^j_k}{\delta t} = A^j_{k;i}\frac{dx^i}{dt} = \frac{dA^j_k}{dt} - \Gamma^p_{ki} A^j_p \frac{dx^i}{dt} + \Gamma^j_{ip} A^p_k \frac{dx^i}{dt} \tag{3.81}$$

and

$$\frac{\delta A^{jk}_{lmn}}{\delta t} = A^{jk}_{lmn;i}\frac{dx^i}{dt}$$

$$= \frac{dA^{jk}_{lmn}}{dt} - \Gamma^p_{li} A^{jk}_{pmn} \frac{dx^i}{dt} - \Gamma^p_{mi} A^{jk}_{lpn} \frac{dx^i}{dt}$$

$$- \Gamma^p_{ni} A^{jk}_{lmp} \frac{dx^i}{dt} + \Gamma^j_{ip} A^{pk}_{lmn} \frac{dx^i}{dt} + \Gamma^k_{ip} A^{jp}_{lmn} \frac{dx^i}{dt} \tag{3.82}$$

Moreover,

$$\frac{\delta g_{ij}}{\delta t} = g_{ij;k}\frac{dx^k}{dt} = 0, \qquad \frac{\delta g^{ij}}{\delta t} = 0, \qquad \frac{\delta(\delta^i_j)}{\delta t} = 0 \tag{3.83}$$

We now prove

Theorem 3.3 For a Riemannian space there exists only one connection (Christoffel symbol of second kind) with respect to which the parallel displacement preserves scalar product.

Proof Let A^i and B^i be two unit vectors defined along a curve in a Riemannian space. These vectors are parallely displaced only when their intrinsic derivatives vanish, that is

$$A^i_{;j}\frac{dx^j}{dt} = 0, \qquad B^i_{;j}\frac{dx^j}{dt} = 0$$

The scalar product of A^i and B^i is defined as $g_{ij}A^iB^j$, where g_{ij} is the metric of the Riemannian space. The intrinsic derivative of this scalar product is

$$(g_{ij}A^iB^j)_{;k}\frac{dx^k}{dt} = g_{ij;k}A^iB^j\frac{dx^k}{dt} + g_{ij}A^i_{;k}B^j\frac{dx^k}{dt} + g_{ij}A^iB^j_{;k}\frac{dx^k}{dt} = 0$$

[from above equations and Eq. (3.83)] which shows that the scalar product is preserved under parallel displacement.

Note. This theorem is often referred to as the *fundamental theorem of Riemannian geometry.*

Remark

With the concept of absolute differentiation, we can formulate Newton's second law in tensorial form as follows:

If a particle moves along the curve $x^i = x^i(t)$, where t is the time parameter, then $v^i = \dfrac{dx^i}{dt}$ is the velocity of the particle and is a contravariant tensor of rank one. The quantity $\dfrac{dv^i}{dt} = \dfrac{d^2x^i}{dt^2}$ is, in general, not a tensor and thus cannot represent the physical quantity "acceleration" in all coordinate systems. We define acceleration as the intrinsic derivative of the velocity, i.e., $a^i = \dfrac{\delta v^i}{\delta t}$ which is a rank one contravariant tensor. Let m be the mass (an invariant and independent of time) of the particle, then $ma^i = F^i$ is a rank one contravariant tensor and is called the force acting on the particle. *Newton's second law* thus takes the form

$$F^i = ma^i = m\frac{\delta v^i}{\delta t} \tag{3.84}$$

We also have

$$a^i = \frac{\delta v^i}{\delta t}$$

$$= \frac{dv^i}{dt} + \Gamma^i_{jp} v^p \frac{dx^j}{dt}$$

$$= \frac{d^2x^i}{dt^2} + \Gamma^i_{jp} \frac{dx^j}{dt}\frac{dx^p}{dt} \tag{3.85}$$

Since for a Euclidean space $g_{ij} = 0$ and $\Gamma^i_{jk} = 0$, Eq. (3.85), therefore, leads to the usual acceleration $a^i = \dfrac{d^2x^i}{dt^2}$.

3.11   Null Geodesics

In Section 3.4, we have mentioned the answer to the question "what do we mean by a straight line in Euclidean space?" The first definition of a straight line is that its direction remain unchanged as we move along it. What is the implication of this definition in a more general space—the Riemannian space? We will answer this question in this section (using the second definition of the straight line we have already obtained the equation of a "straight line" in the Riemannian space [cf. Eq. (3.24)]); and thus find the condition for null geodesic.

Let the coordinate of a point P on the curve η be $x^i(\lambda)$, the curve η is given by real parameter λ. In terms of this parameter λ the tangent vector t^i at the point P has the components $t^i = \dfrac{dx^i}{d\lambda}$. Now, if the curve η does not change its direction as we move along it, then the rate of change of t^i along t^i is zero, i.e.,

$$t^i t^j_{;i} = 0 \tag{3.86}$$

which from the definition of t^i and covariant differentiation yield (see also Remark 5 of Section 3.7)

$$\frac{d^2 x^i}{d\lambda^2} + \Gamma^i_{kj} \frac{dx^k}{d\lambda} \frac{dx^j}{d\lambda} = 0 \tag{3.87}$$

To know the nature of the parametr λ, we multiply Eq. (3.87) by $2g_{ip} \dfrac{dx^p}{d\lambda}$ so that

$$2g_{ip} \frac{dx^p}{d\lambda} \frac{d^2 x^i}{d\lambda^2} + \Gamma^i_{kj} \frac{dx^k}{d\lambda} \frac{dx^j}{d\lambda} 2g_{ip} \frac{dx^p}{d\lambda} = 0$$

Using the definition of Γ^i_{jk} and symmetry and skew symmetry with respect to k and p in the second term of the above equation, we get

$$2g_{ip} \frac{d^2 x^i}{d\lambda^2} \frac{dx^p}{d\lambda} + \frac{\partial g_{pk}}{\partial x^j} \frac{dx^k}{d\lambda} \frac{dx^j}{d\lambda} \frac{dx^p}{d\lambda} = 0$$

Since $g_{ik} = g_{ki}$, the first integral of this equation is

$$g_{ip} \frac{dx^i}{d\lambda} \frac{dx^p}{d\lambda} = \text{constant} \tag{3.88}$$

Thus, λ can atmost be replaced by $a\lambda + b$, where $a(\neq 0)$ and b are arbitrary real constants.

The "straight line" given by Eq. (3.87) is called the *geodesic*. If the constant in Eq. (3.88) is zero, positive or, negative, the geodesic is known as *null, time like* or *space like*. In the latter two cases we can choose the constant to be $+1$ or -1 and replace λ by s, the distance measured along the geodesic. Thus, for a non-null geodesic, we have

$$\frac{d^2 x^i}{ds^2} + \Gamma^i_{kj} \frac{dx^k}{ds} \frac{dx^j}{ds} = 0 \tag{3.89}$$

and

$$g_{ik} \frac{dx^i}{ds} \frac{dx^k}{ds} = 1 \tag{3.89a}$$

while for null geodesic, we have

$$\frac{d^2 x^i}{d\lambda^2} + \Gamma^i_{kj} \frac{dx^k}{d\lambda} \frac{dx^j}{d\lambda} = 0 \tag{3.90}$$

along with

$$g_{ik} \frac{dx^i}{d\lambda} \frac{dx^k}{d\lambda} = 0 \tag{3.90a}$$

The parameter in terms of which the geodesic equation can take the form of Eq. (3.87) is the affine parameter (see also Section 3.5). It may be noted that Eq. (3.89) and (3.89a) is same as of Eq. (3.24) and thus *a geodesic may be looked upon both as a line of stationary distance* and *as a line of unchanging direction.*

The geodesic Eq. (3.87) expresses the parallel transport of a vector and states that the tangent vector $t^i = \dfrac{dx^i}{dt}$ of a geodesic remains parallel to itself.

Remarks

1. In the context of general theory of relativity, the equation of geodesic [cf., Eq. (3.24) and (3.87)] describes the motion of a test particle in the gravitational field, while the null geodesic Eq. [(3.90) and (3.90a)[describes the propagation of zero-rest mass particles (for example, the propagation of electromagnetic waves).

2. The fact that the vector x^i does not change its length when parallely transported can be expressed by the equation (see also Remark 2 of Section 3.4)

$$T = \frac{1}{2}g_{ik}\dot{x}^i\dot{x}^k = \text{constant}$$

which is simply the *principle of conservation of energy.*

Since $s = \displaystyle\int \sqrt{g_{ik}\dot{x}^i\dot{x}^k}\,dt$, we have $s = \sqrt{2T}t$ which determines the proportionality factor discussed in Remark 2 of Section 3.4.

EXAMPLE 3.16 If the intrinsic derivative of a vector A^i along a curve vanishes at every point of the curve, show that the magnitude of the vector is constant along the curve.

Solution From the definition of intrinsic derivative, we have

$$\frac{\delta}{\delta t}(A^2) = \frac{\delta}{\delta t}(A^i A_i)$$

$$= (A^i A_i)_{;j}\frac{dx^j}{dt}$$

$$= A^i_{;j}A_i\frac{dx^j}{dt} + A^i A_{i;j}\frac{dx^j}{dt} \qquad (3.91)$$

Given that the intrinsic derivative of A^i is zero, i.e., $A^i_{;j}\dfrac{dx^j}{dt} = 0$. Also $A_i = g_{ik}A^k$ and $g_{ik;j} = 0$ which leads to $g_{ik}A^k_{;j}\dfrac{dx^j}{dt} = 0$. Therefore, from Eq. (3.91)

$$\frac{\delta}{\delta t}(A^2) = \frac{d}{dt}(A^2) = 0$$

and A^2 being the magnitude of A^i is constant, as A^2 is an invariant [cf., Eq. (3.80)].

EXAMPLE 3.17 If A^i and B^i are two unit vectors defined along a curve such that their intrinsic derivatives along the curve are zero, show that the angle between the vectors A^i and B^i is constant.

Solution Given that

$$\frac{\delta A^i}{\delta t} = A^i_{;j}\frac{dx^j}{dt} = 0, \quad \frac{\delta B^i}{\delta t} = B^i_{;j}\frac{dx^j}{dt} = 0 \tag{3.92}$$

and since $A_i = g_{ij}A^j$ and $g_{ij;k} = 0$, we have

$$A_{i;j}\frac{dx^j}{dt} = 0, \quad B_{i;j}\frac{dx^j}{dt} = 0 \tag{3.93}$$

If θ is the angle between A^i and B^i then

$$\cos\theta = \frac{A_i B^i}{\sqrt{(A_i A^i)(B_j B^j)}} = A_i B^i$$

which on differentiation leads to [using Eq. (3.80)]

$$-\sin\theta\frac{d\theta}{dt} = (A_i B^i_{;j} + A_{i;j}B^i)\frac{dx^j}{dt}$$

From Eqs. (3.92) and (3.93), this equation yields

$$\frac{d\theta}{dt} = 0$$

Thus, θ is a constant.

EXAMPLE 3.18 Show that a geodesic that is time-like (space-like, null) at a given point remains time-like (space-like, null) along its path through the space.

Solution Here we shall consider the parallel transport of a vector A_i and show that $A_i A^i$ is constant. Now, if A_i is parallely transported then from Eq. (3.78), $\dfrac{\delta A^i}{\delta t} = 0$ and

$$\frac{\delta}{\delta t}(A^i A_i) = A^i\frac{\delta A_i}{\delta t} + A_i\frac{\delta A^i}{\delta t} = 0$$

The path element dx^i along a geodesic itself is being parallely transported and thus $\dfrac{\delta}{\delta t}(dx^i/dt) = 0$ and so $\left(\dfrac{dx^i}{dt}\right)\left(\dfrac{dx_i}{dt}\right)$ remains constant and hence $dx^i dx_i$ continues to be time-like (space-like, null) if it is started as time-like (space-like, null).

EXAMPLE 3.19 Show that the curve whose parametric representation is

$$x = c \int r \cos \theta \cos \phi \, ds$$

$$y = c \int r \cos \theta \sin \phi \, ds$$

$$z = c \int r \sin \theta \, ds$$

$$t = \int r \, ds$$

a null curve in a space whose metric is

$$ds^2 = -dx^2 - dy^2 - dz^2 + c^2 dt^2$$

Solution Here

$$ds^2 = -dx^2 - dy^2 - dz^2 + c^2 dt^2$$

$$= -(cr \cos \theta \cos \phi)^2 - (cr \cos \theta \sin \phi)^2 - (cr \sin \theta)^2 + c^2 r^2$$

$$= -c^2 r^2 \cos^2 \theta (\cos^2 \theta + \sin^2 \theta) - c^2 r^2 \sin^2 \theta + c^2 r^2$$

$$= 0$$

Thus, the curve given in the problem is a null curve. Obviously every curve satisfying $ds^2 = 0$ can be presented in the form given in the problem.

3.12 Alternative Derivation of Equation of Geodesic

In this section, we shall use the techniques of calculus of variations (Ahsan, 2013) to obtain the equation of geodesic and in such case we have to solve the variational problem

$$\delta I = \delta \int L \, ds = 0 \tag{3.94}$$

where L is the Lagrangian. The conditions under which the integral $\int L \, ds$ has an extremum are the Lagrange's equations

$$\frac{d}{ds} \frac{\partial L}{\partial (dx^i/ds)} - \frac{\partial L}{\partial x^i} = 0 \tag{3.95}$$

Consider the Lagrangian L as

$$L = \left(g_{ij} \frac{dx^i}{ds} \frac{dx^j}{ds} \right)^{1/2} \tag{3.96}$$

whose value is unity along the geodesic curve. Since along geodesic lines $ds^2 = g_{jk} dx^j dx^k$

$$\frac{\partial L}{\partial (dx^i/ds)} = \left(g_{jk} \frac{dx^j}{ds} \frac{dx^k}{ds} \right)^{-1/2} g_{il} \frac{dx^l}{ds} = g_{il} \frac{dx^l}{ds}$$

which on differentiation with respect to s leads to

$$\frac{d}{ds} \left[\frac{\partial L}{\partial (dx^i/ds)} \right] = \frac{d}{ds} \left(g_{il} \frac{dx^l}{ds} \right) = \frac{dg_{il}}{ds} \frac{dx^l}{ds} + g_{il} \frac{d^2 x^l}{ds^2}$$

$$= \frac{\partial g_{il}}{\partial x^m} \frac{dx^l}{ds} \frac{dx^m}{ds} + g_{il} \frac{d^2 x^l}{ds^2} \tag{3.97}$$

Again, since $ds^2 = g_{jk} dx^j dx^k$, we have

$$\frac{\partial L}{\partial x^i} = \frac{1}{2} \left(g_{jk} \frac{dx^j}{ds} \frac{dx^k}{ds} \right)^{-1/2} \frac{\partial g_{lm}}{\partial x^i} \frac{dx^l}{ds} \frac{dx^m}{ds}$$

$$= \frac{1}{2} \frac{\partial g_{lm}}{\partial x^i} \frac{dx^l}{ds} \frac{dx^m}{ds} \tag{3.98}$$

From Eqs. (3.97) and (3.98), Eq. (3.95) reduces to

$$\frac{\partial g_{il}}{\partial x^m} \frac{dx^l}{ds} \frac{dx^m}{ds} + g_{il} \frac{d^2 x^l}{ds^2} - \frac{1}{2} \frac{\partial g_{lm}}{\partial x^i} \frac{dx^l}{ds} \frac{dx^m}{ds} = 0$$

or

$$g_{il} \frac{d^2 x^l}{ds^2} + \frac{1}{2} \left(2 \frac{\partial g_{il}}{\partial x^m} - \frac{\partial g_{lm}}{\partial x^i} \right) \frac{dx^l}{ds} \frac{dx^m}{ds} = 0$$

or

$$g_{il} \frac{d^2 x^l}{ds^2} + \frac{1}{2} \left(\frac{\partial g_{il}}{\partial x^m} + \frac{\partial g_{im}}{\partial x^l} - \frac{\partial g_{lm}}{\partial x^i} \right) \frac{dx^l}{ds} \frac{dx^m}{ds} = 0 \tag{3.99}$$

as

$$2 \frac{\partial g_{il}}{\partial x^m} \frac{dx^l}{ds} \frac{dx^m}{ds} = \frac{\partial g_{il}}{\partial x^m} \frac{dx^l}{ds} \frac{dx^m}{ds} + \frac{\partial g_{im}}{\partial x^l} \frac{dx^l}{ds} \frac{dx^m}{ds}$$

Using the definition of Christoffel symbol of first kind, Eq. (3.99) takes the form

$$g_{il} \frac{d^2 x^l}{ds^2} + \Gamma_{ilm} \frac{dx^l}{ds} \frac{dx^m}{ds} = 0$$

which on multiplication by g^{ki} reduces to

$$g^{ki} g_{il} \frac{d^2 x^l}{ds^2} + g^{ki} \Gamma_{ilm} \frac{dx^l}{ds} \frac{dx^m}{ds} = 0$$

or

$$\delta_l^k \frac{d^2 x^l}{ds^2} + \Gamma_{lm}^k \frac{dx^l}{ds} \frac{dx^m}{ds} = 0$$

or

$$\frac{d^2 x^k}{ds^2} + \Gamma_{lm}^k \frac{dx^l}{ds} \frac{dx^m}{ds} = 0 \qquad (3.100)$$

which is the required equation of geodesic [see also Eq. (3.24)].

EXERCISES

3.1 If ϕ is a scalar, prove that

$$\frac{\partial \phi}{\partial x^l}(g_{hj} g_{ik} - g_{hi} g_{jk}) g^{hl} = \frac{\partial \phi}{\partial x^j} g_{ik} - \frac{\partial \phi}{\partial x^i} g_{jk}.$$

3.2 Show that $g^{ij} \dfrac{\partial g_{ij}}{\partial x^k} + g_{ij} \dfrac{\partial g^{ij}}{\partial x^k} = 0.$

3.3 If ϕ is an invariant, show that $\dfrac{\partial^2 \phi}{\partial x^i \partial x^j}$ is not a tensor.

3.4 If A_i is a covariant vector, show that $\dfrac{\partial A_i}{\partial x^k}$ is not a tensor, but $\dfrac{\partial A_i}{\partial x^j} - \dfrac{\partial A_j}{\partial x^i}$ is a tensor.

3.5 Show that the quantities $\dfrac{\partial g_{ij}}{\partial x^k}, \dfrac{\partial g_{ij}}{\partial x^k} + \dfrac{\partial g_{ik}}{\partial x^j} - \dfrac{\partial g_{jk}}{\partial x^i}$ and $\dfrac{\partial^2 g_{ij}}{\partial x^k \partial x^l}$ are not tensors.

3.6 If A^{ij} are the components of a symmetric tensor and g_{ij} are the components of the metric tensor, prove that

$$A^{jk} \Gamma_{ijk} = \frac{1}{2} A^{jk} \frac{\partial g_{jk}}{\partial x^i}.$$

3.7 Obtain the equation of geodesic for the metrics:

(i) $ds^2 = (dx^1)^2 + [(x^2)^2 - (x^1)^2](dx^2)^2$

(ii) $ds^2 = f(x) dx^2 + dy^2 + dz^2 + \dfrac{1}{f(x)} dt^2$

(iii) $ds^2 = -dx^2 - dy^2 - dz^2 + f(x, y, z) dt^2$

3.8 For the metric $ds^2 = dr^2 + r^2 d\theta^2$, show that

(i) $r^2 \dfrac{d\theta}{ds} = R_0 = $ constant, $\left(\dfrac{dr}{ds}\right)^2 + r^2 \left(\dfrac{d\theta}{ds}\right)^2 = 1$ are the first integrals of the geodesic equation.

(ii) From (i), find a first-order differential equation for $r(\theta)$.

3.9 If F^{ij} is a skew symmetric tensor, show that $F^{ij}F_j^k$ is a symmetric tensor and calculate the number α so that the tensor $F^{ij}F_j^k - \alpha F_{pq}F^{pq}g^{ik}$ has zero trace. Also show that $\dfrac{\partial F_{ij}}{\partial x^k} + \dfrac{\partial F_{jk}}{\partial x^i} - \dfrac{\partial F_{ki}}{\partial x^j}$ is a rank three tensor.

3.10 Show that if a $\Gamma_{kl}^i \neq \Gamma_{lk}^i$ then the condition $g_{ik;l} \equiv 0$ implies that
$$\Gamma_{(kl)}^i = \frac{1}{2}g^{im}(g_{mk,l} + g_{ml,k} - g_{kl,m}) + g^{im}g_{kn}\Gamma_{[lm]}^n + g^{im}g_{ln}\Gamma_{[km]}^n.$$

3.11 Show that $F_{j,k}^i F_i^k = -F_{ji,l}F^{il}$, if F^{il} is skew symmetric.

3.12 Show that $T_{;j}^{ij} = 0$, where T^{ij} is the energy momentum tensor of the electromagnetic field (cf., Example 1.10 and Chapter 6).

3.13 If A^{ij} is skew symmetric, show that $A_{;i;j}^{ij} = 0$.

3.14 Show that the second derivative of a scalar field ϕ commutes (i.e., $\phi_{;ij} = \phi_{;ji}$). For the third derivative $\phi_{;ijk}$, show that
$$\phi_{;(ij)k} = \phi_{,ijk} - \phi_l \Gamma_{ij,k}^l.$$

3.15 If a vector A_i is orthogonal to family of hypersurfaces, then show that $A_{[i;j}A_{k]} = 0$.

3.16 Show that the covariant derivative of Levi-Civita covariant density of weight $W = -1$ is zero.

3.17 If the components of a vector A_i are $(\rho, z\sin\phi, e^\phi\cos z)$, prove that $\text{div}A_i = 2 + \dfrac{z}{\rho^2}\cos\phi - e^\phi\sin z$.

3.18 If in the coordinate system (r, θ, ϕ) the components of a vector A_i are (A_r, A_θ, A_ϕ), show that
$$A_{;i}^i = \frac{\partial A_r}{\partial\theta} + \frac{1}{r}\frac{\partial A_\theta}{\partial\theta} + \frac{1}{\sin\theta}\frac{\partial A_\phi}{\partial\phi} + \frac{2}{r}A_r + \frac{\cot\theta}{r}A_\theta.$$

3.19 If curl $A_i = 0$ then prove that A_i is gradient.

3.20 Find an expression for $\nabla^2\phi$ in cylindrical polar coordinates (r, θ, z).

3.21 For the metric $ds^2 = dx^2 + dy^2 - dz^2$, show that the null geodesics are given by
$$x = as + a', \quad y = bs + b', \quad z = cs + c'$$
where s is a parameter and a, b, c, a', b', c' are arbitrary constants satisfying $a^2 + b^2 - c^2 = 0$.

3.22 For the metric $ds^2 = -dx^2 - dy^2 - dz^2 + c^2dt^2$, show that every null curve can be expressed by
$$x = \int \sin\psi\sin\theta\cos\phi ds, y = \int \sin\psi\sin\theta\sin\phi ds$$
$$z = \int \sin\psi\cos\theta ds, t = \int \sin\psi ds \text{ (i.e., not every null curve is a null}$$
$$\text{geodesic).}$$

CHAPTER 4

The Riemann Curvature Tensor

4.1 Introduction

Through his general theory of relativity, Einstein redefined the gravity. From the classical point of view, gravity is the attractive force between massive objects in three-dimensional space. In general relativity, gravity manifests as curvature of four-dimensional spacetime. Conversely, curved space and time generate effects that are equivalent to gravitational effects. J.A. Wheelar has described the results by saying *"Matter tells spacetime how to bend and spacetime returns the complement by telling matter how to move."*

The general theory of relativity is thus a theory of gravitation in which gravitation emerges as the property of the spacetime structure through the metric tensor g_{ij}. The metric tensor determines another object (of tensorial nature) known as *Riemann curvature tensor*. At any given event this tensorial object provides all information about the gravitational field in the neighbourhood of the event. It may, in real sense, be interpreted as describing the curvature of the spacetime. It is for these reasons that a study of Riemann curvature tensor has been made here.

4.2 The Riemann Curvature Tensor

In this section, we shall construct a tensor from the metric tensor g_{ij} and its derivatives. If we use only g_{ij} and its first derivative, then, since at any point it is possible to find a coordinate system in which the first derivative of the metric tensor vanishes and so in this coordinate system the desired tensor must be equal to one of those that can be obtained from the metric tensor only (for example, g_{ij} or g^{ij} or $\epsilon^{ijkl}/\sqrt{g}$, etc.), and since this is an equality between tensors, so it must be true in all coordinate systems. Thus, we cannot construct new tensor from g_{ij} and its first derivative.

The next possibility is that we can consider g_{ij} and its first and second derivatives and try to find a tensor from it. For this purpose, consider

Eq. (3.44)

$$\frac{\partial^2 x'^r}{\partial x^l \partial x^k} = \frac{\partial x'^r}{\partial x^q} \Gamma_{lk}^q - \frac{\partial x'^i}{\partial x^l} \frac{\partial x'^j}{\partial x^k} \Gamma_{ij}'^r \tag{4.1}$$

Differentiate it partially with respect to x^a, to get

$$\frac{\partial^3 x'^r}{\partial x^a \partial x^l \partial x^k} = \Gamma_{lk}^a \left(\frac{\partial x'^r}{\partial x^b} \Gamma_{aq}^b - \frac{\partial x'^i}{\partial x^a} \frac{\partial x'^j}{\partial x^q} \Gamma_{ij}'^r \right)$$

$$- \Gamma_{ij}'^r \frac{\partial x'^i}{\partial x^l} \left(\frac{\partial x'^j}{\partial x^b} \Gamma_{ak}^b - \frac{\partial x'^b}{\partial x^a} \frac{\partial x'^c}{\partial x^k} \Gamma_{bc}'^j \right)$$

$$- \Gamma_{ij}'^r \frac{\partial x'^j}{\partial x^k} \left(\frac{\partial x'^i}{\partial x^b} \Gamma_{al}^b - \frac{\partial x'^b}{\partial x^a} \frac{\partial x'^c}{\partial x^l} \Gamma_{bc}'^i \right)$$

$$+ \frac{\partial x'^r}{\partial x^q} \frac{\partial \Gamma_{lk}^q}{\partial x^a} - \frac{\partial x'^i}{\partial x^l} \frac{\partial x'^j}{\partial x^k} \frac{\partial x'^b}{\partial x^a} \frac{\partial \Gamma_{ij}'^r}{\partial x'^b}$$

Collecting the similar terms and changing the dummy indices in the above equation, we get

$$\frac{\partial^3 x'^r}{\partial x^a \partial x^l \partial x^k} = \frac{\partial x'^r}{\partial x^q} \left(\frac{\partial \Gamma_{lk}^q}{\partial x^a} + \Gamma_{lk}^b \Gamma_{ab}^q \right)$$

$$- \frac{\partial x'^i}{\partial x^l} \frac{\partial x'^j}{\partial x^k} \frac{\partial x'^b}{\partial x^a} \left(\frac{\partial \Gamma_{ij}'^r}{\partial x'^b} - \Gamma_{iq}'^r \Gamma_{bj}'^q - \Gamma_{qj}'^r \Gamma_{bi}'^q \right)$$

$$- \Gamma_{ij}'^r \frac{\partial x'^j}{\partial x^q} \left(\Gamma_{lk}^q \frac{\partial x'^i}{\partial x^a} + \Gamma_{ak}^q \frac{\partial x'^i}{\partial x^l} + \Gamma_{al}^q \frac{\partial x'^i}{\partial x^k} \right) \tag{4.2}$$

Now interchanging the index k and a in the above equation and subtracting the resulting equation from Eq. (4.2), we get, after simplification

$$\frac{\partial x'^r}{\partial x^q} \left(\frac{\partial \Gamma_{lk}^q}{\partial x^a} - \frac{\partial \Gamma_{la}^q}{\partial x^k} + \Gamma_{lk}^b \Gamma_{ab}^q - \Gamma_{la}^b \Gamma_{kb}^q \right) - \frac{\partial x'^i}{\partial x^l} \frac{\partial x'^j}{\partial x^k} \frac{\partial x'^b}{\partial x^a}$$

$$\times \left(\frac{\partial \Gamma_{ij}'^r}{\partial x'^b} - \frac{\partial \Gamma_{ib}'^r}{\partial x'^j} - \Gamma_{qj}'^r \Gamma_{bi}'^q + \Gamma_{qb}'^r \Gamma_{ij}'^q \right) = 0$$

which yields

$$R_{ijb}'^r = \frac{\partial x'^r}{\partial x^q} \frac{\partial x^l}{\partial x'^i} \frac{\partial x^k}{\partial x'^j} \frac{\partial x^a}{\partial x'^b} R_{lka}^q \tag{4.3}$$

where

$$R_{lka}^q = \frac{\partial \Gamma_{lk}^q}{\partial x^a} - \frac{\partial \Gamma_{la}^q}{\partial x^k} + \Gamma_{lk}^b \Gamma_{ab}^q - \Gamma_{la}^b \Gamma_{kb}^q \tag{4.4}$$

Equation (4.3) is the transformation law of a rank four mixed tensor R^q_{lka}. This four rank tensor, given by Eq. (4.4), is known as *Riemann curvature tensor*. In some literature it is often referred to as *Riemann-Christoffel tensor*. This tensor was first discovered by Riemann (1826–1866) and after many years by Christoffel (1829–1900). The Riemann curvature tensor or curvature tensor plays a central role in the geometric structure of a Riemannian space. This tensor is not only important in describing the geometry of the curved spacetime, but also from this tensor we can construct other tensors which give a complete description of the gravitational field.

4.3 Commutation of Covariant Derivative: Another Way of Defining the Riemann Curvature Tensor

In ordinary calculus it is known that if $\phi(x)$ is a function of the variables x^i ($i = 1, 2, \ldots, n$) then, the order of the partial derivative is commutative, i.e.,

$$\frac{\partial^2 \phi}{\partial x^i \partial x^j} = \frac{\partial^2 \phi}{\partial x^j \partial x^i} \tag{4.5}$$

But when we talk about the tensors, in general, the order of the differentiation is not commutative; although the repeated application of covariant differentiation when applied to tensors will certainly produce tensors of higher rank.

Consider a covariant vector A_i, then from the definition of covariant differentiation [cf., Eq. (3.48)], we have

$$A_{i;j} = \frac{\partial A_i}{\partial x^j} - \Gamma^k_{ij} A_k \tag{4.6}$$

A further covariant differentiation of (4.6) yields

$$A_{i;j;l} = A_{i;jl} = \frac{\partial A_{i;j}}{\partial x^l} - \Gamma^k_{il} A_{k;j} - \Gamma^k_{jl} A_{i;k}$$

or

$$A_{i;jl} = \frac{\partial^2 A_i}{\partial x^l \partial x^j} - \frac{\partial}{\partial x^l}[\Gamma^k_{ij} A_k]$$

$$- \Gamma^k_{il} \left[\frac{\partial A_k}{\partial x^j} - \Gamma^m_{kj} A_m \right] - \Gamma^k_{jl} \left[\frac{\partial A_i}{\partial x^k} - \Gamma^m_{ik} A_m \right]$$

$$= \frac{\partial^2 A_i}{\partial x^l \partial x^j} - A_k \frac{\partial}{\partial x^l} \Gamma^k_{ij} - \Gamma^k_{ij} \frac{\partial A_k}{\partial x^l}$$

$$+ \Gamma^k_{il} \Gamma^m_{kj} A_m - \Gamma^k_{il} \frac{\partial A_k}{\partial x^j} + \Gamma^k_{jl} \Gamma^m_{ik} A_m - \Gamma^k_{jl} \frac{\partial A_i}{\partial x^k}$$

After rearranging, we get

$$A_{i;jl} = \frac{\partial^2 A_i}{\partial x^l \partial x^j} - \Gamma_{ij}^k \frac{\partial A_k}{\partial x^l} - \Gamma_{il}^k \frac{\partial A_k}{\partial x^j} - \Gamma_{jl}^k \frac{\partial A_i}{\partial x^k}$$

$$- A_k \frac{\partial}{\partial x^l} \Gamma_{ij}^k + A_m [\Gamma_{jl}^k \Gamma_{ik}^m + \Gamma_{il}^k \Gamma_{kj}^m] \qquad (4.7)$$

We now reverse the order of covariant differentiation, i.e., differentiate A_i first with respect to l and then with respect to j. This is obtained by interchanging j and l in Eq. (4.7). We thus get

$$A_{i;lj} = \frac{\partial^2 A_i}{\partial x^j \partial x^l} - \Gamma_{il}^k \frac{\partial A_k}{\partial x^j} - \Gamma_{ij}^k \frac{\partial A_k}{\partial x^l} - \Gamma_{lj}^k \frac{\partial A_i}{\partial x^k}$$

$$- A_k \frac{\partial}{\partial x^j} \Gamma_{il}^k + A_m [\Gamma_{lj}^k \Gamma_{ik}^m + \Gamma_{ij}^k \Gamma_{kl}^m] \qquad (4.8)$$

Subtracting Eqs. (4.7) and (4.8), we get

$$A_{i;jl} - A_{i;lj} = A_k \left[\frac{\partial}{\partial x^j} \Gamma_{il}^k - \frac{\partial}{\partial x^l} \Gamma_{ij}^k \right] + A_m [\Gamma_{il}^k \Gamma_{kj}^m - \Gamma_{ij}^k \Gamma_{kl}^m]$$

Interchanging the dummy suffix m and k in the last term, we get

$$A_{i;jl} - A_{i;lj} = \left[\frac{\partial}{\partial x^j} \Gamma_{il}^k - \frac{\partial}{\partial x^l} \Gamma_{ij}^k + \Gamma_{il}^m \Gamma_{mj}^k - \Gamma_{ij}^m \Gamma_{ml}^k \right] A_k$$

or

$$A_{i;jl} - A_{i;lj} = R_{ijl}^k A_k \qquad (4.9)$$

where

$$R_{ijl}^k = \frac{\partial}{\partial x^j} \Gamma_{il}^k - \frac{\partial}{\partial x^l} \Gamma_{ij}^k + \Gamma_{il}^m \Gamma_{mj}^k - \Gamma_{ij}^m \Gamma_{ml}^k \qquad (4.10)$$

or

$$R_{ijl}^k = \Gamma_{il,j}^k - \Gamma_{ij,l}^k + \Gamma_{il}^m \Gamma_{mj}^k - \Gamma_{ij}^m \Gamma_{ml}^k$$

where a comma denotes the partial differentiation. Now since the difference of two tensors is again a tensor, the expression on the left-hand side of Eq. (4.9) is a tensor, but since A_k is an arbitrary covariant tensor; it follows from the quotient law for tensors that R_{ijl}^k is a tensor of fourth rank (contravariant in k and covariant in ijl). This is the *Riemann curvature tensor* or simply the *Riemann tensor*.

In a similar way it can be shown that

$$A_{;k;l}^j - A_{;l;k}^j = -R_{ikl}^j A^i \qquad (4.11)$$

(see also Example 4.3). Similar formula holds for a mixed tensor of rank two and we have

$$A_{j;k;l}^i - A_{j;l;k}^i = A_j^a R_{akl}^i - A_a^i R_{jkl}^a \qquad (4.12)$$

An extension of Eq. (4.12) to the case of tensors of rank higher than two is given by

$$A^{ij\ldots}_{kl\ldots;m;n} - A^{ij\ldots}_{kl\ldots;n;m} = R^a_{kmn} A^{ij\ldots}_{al\ldots} + R^a_{lmn} A^{ij\ldots}_{ka\ldots} + \cdots$$

$$\cdots - R^i_{amn} A^{aj\ldots}_{kl\ldots} - R^j_{amn} A^{ia\ldots}_{kl\ldots} \tag{4.13}$$

Equation (4.13) is known as *Ricci identity* and it may be noted from this equation that if the Riemann tensor vanishes then the covariant derivative commutes. Moreover, from Eq. (4.10) it is seen that the Riemann curvature tensor is determined completely if the Christoffel symbols are known.

4.4 Covariant form of the Riemann Curvature Tensor

Here we shall derive the covariant form of the Riemann tensor so that various properties of this tensor can be studied conveniently. The mixed Riemann tensor R^k_{ijl} is [cf., Eq. (4.10)]

$$R^k_{ijl} = \frac{\partial}{\partial x^j} \Gamma^k_{il} - \frac{\partial}{\partial x^l} \Gamma^k_{ij} + \Gamma^m_{il} \Gamma^k_{mj} - \Gamma^m_{ij} \Gamma^k_{ml}$$

Multiplying both the sides of this equation by g_{hk}, we get

$$R_{hijl} = g_{hk} \frac{\partial}{\partial x^j} \Gamma^k_{il} - g_{hk} \frac{\partial}{\partial x^l} \Gamma^k_{ij} + g_{hk} \Gamma^m_{il} \Gamma^k_{mj} - g_{hk} \Gamma^m_{ij} \Gamma^k_{ml} \tag{4.14}$$

Further, since

$$g_{hk} \frac{\partial}{\partial x^j} \Gamma^k_{il} = \frac{\partial}{\partial x^j} (g_{hk} \Gamma^k_{il}) - \frac{\partial}{\partial x^j} (g_{hk}) \Gamma^k_{il}$$

$$= \frac{\partial}{\partial x^j} \Gamma_{hil} - \frac{\partial}{\partial x^j} (g_{hk}) \Gamma^k_{il} \tag{4.15}$$

etc., Eq. (4.14) thus becomes

$$R_{hijl} = \frac{\partial}{\partial x^j} \Gamma_{hil} - \frac{\partial}{\partial x^l} \Gamma_{hij} - \frac{\partial}{\partial x^j} (g_{hk}) \Gamma^k_{il}$$

$$+ \frac{\partial}{\partial x^l} (g_{hk}) \Gamma^k_{ij} + \Gamma^m_{il} \Gamma_{hmj} - \Gamma^m_{ij} \Gamma_{hml}$$

Changing the dummy suffix m in the last two terms to k, we get

$$R_{hijl} = \frac{\partial}{\partial x^j} \Gamma_{hil} - \frac{\partial}{\partial x^l} \Gamma_{hij} + \Gamma^k_{il} \left(\Gamma_{hkj} - \frac{\partial}{\partial x^j} g_{hk} \right) - \Gamma^k_{ij} \left(\Gamma_{hkl} - \frac{\partial}{\partial x^l} g_{hk} \right) \tag{4.16}$$

But, since

$$\frac{\partial}{\partial x^j} g_{hk} = \Gamma_{khj} + \Gamma_{hkj}$$

etc., Eq. (4.16) becomes

$$R_{hijl} = \frac{\partial}{\partial x^j}\Gamma_{hil} - \frac{\partial}{\partial x^l}\Gamma_{hij} + \Gamma_{ij}^k\Gamma_{khl} - \Gamma_{il}^k\Gamma_{khj}$$

$$= \frac{\partial}{\partial x^j}\Gamma_{hil} - \frac{\partial}{\partial x^l}\Gamma_{hij} + g_{km}(\Gamma_{ij}^k\Gamma_{hl}^m - \Gamma_{il}^k\Gamma_{hj}^m) \qquad (4.17)$$

On writing the first two terms on the right-hand side of Eq. (4.17) explicitly in terms of the partial derivatives of g_{il} and after simplifying, we get

$$R_{hijl} = \frac{1}{2}\left(\frac{\partial^2 g_{hl}}{\partial x^j \partial x^i} + \frac{\partial^2 g_{ij}}{\partial x^l \partial x^h} - \frac{\partial^2 g_{il}}{\partial x^j \partial x^h} - \frac{\partial^2 g_{hj}}{\partial x^l \partial x^i}\right) + g_{km}\left(\Gamma_{ij}^k\Gamma_{hl}^m - \Gamma_{il}^k\Gamma_{hj}^m\right)$$
$$(4.18)$$

which is the covariant form of the Riemann curvature tensor.

4.5   Properties of the Riemann Curvature Tensor

The Riemann tensor defined through Eqs. (4.18) and (4.10) has the following properties:

(i) R_{ijl}^h and R_{hijl} are skew symmetric in the last two indices, i.e.,

$$R_{ijl}^h = -R_{ilj}^h \qquad (4.19)$$

and

$$R_{hijl} = -R_{hilj} \qquad (4.20)$$

(ii) R_{hijl} is skew symmetric in the first two indices h and i, i.e.,

$$R_{hijl} = -R_{ihjl} \qquad (4.21)$$

(iii) R_{hijl} is symmetric with respect to an interchange of the first pair of indices (hi) and second pair of indices (jl), without changing the order of the indices in each pair, i.e.,

$$R_{hijl} = R_{jlhi} \qquad (4.22)$$

(iv) If we permute the last three indices (ijl) of Eqs. (4.10) and (4.18) in a cyclic order, then the sum thus obtained vanishes identically, i.e.,

$$R_{ijl}^k + R_{jli}^k + R_{lij}^k = 0 \qquad (4.23)$$

$$R_{hijl} + R_{hjli} + R_{hlij} = 0 \qquad (4.23a)$$

(v) The Riemann tensor also satisfies the identities

$$R_{hijk;l} + R_{hikl;j} + R_{hilj;k} = 0 \tag{4.24}$$

$$R^h_{ijk;l} + R^h_{ikl;j} + R^h_{ilj;k} = 0 \tag{4.24a}$$

Equations (4.24) are known as *Bianchi identities*.

The proofs of the above properties are as follows:

Proof (i) Interchanging the indices j and l in Eq. (4.10), we get

$$R^k_{ilj} = \frac{\partial}{\partial x^l}\Gamma^k_{ij} - \frac{\partial}{\partial x^j}\Gamma^k_{il} + \Gamma^m_{ij}\Gamma^k_{ml} - \Gamma^m_{il}\Gamma^k_{mjl} = -R^k_{ijl}$$

Multiplying this equation by g_{hk}, we have

$$g_{hk}R^k_{ilj} = -g_{hk}R^k_{ijl}$$

which leads to

$$R_{hilj} = -R_{hijl}$$

Proof (ii) Interchanging the indices h and i in Eq. (4.18), we get

$$R_{ihjl} = \frac{1}{2}\left(\frac{\partial^2 g_{il}}{\partial x^j \partial x^h} + \frac{\partial^2 g_{hj}}{\partial x^l \partial x^i} - \frac{\partial^2 g_{hl}}{\partial x^j \partial x^i} - \frac{\partial^2 g_{ij}}{\partial x^l \partial x^h}\right)$$

$$+ g_{km}(\Gamma^k_{hj}\Gamma^m_{il} - \Gamma^k_{hl}\Gamma^m_{ij}) = -R_{hijl}$$

Proof (iii) First interchange the indices h and j in Eq. (4.18), we get

$$R_{jihl} = \frac{1}{2}\left(\frac{\partial^2 g_{jl}}{\partial x^h \partial x^i} + \frac{\partial^2 g_{ih}}{\partial x^l \partial x^j} - \frac{\partial^2 g_{il}}{\partial x^h \partial x^j} - \frac{\partial^2 g_{jh}}{\partial x^l \partial x^i}\right) + g_{km}(\Gamma^k_{ih}\Gamma^m_{jl} - \Gamma^k_{il}\Gamma^m_{jh})$$

Now in this equation interchange the indices i and l, to get

$$R_{(jl)(hi)} = \frac{1}{2}\left(\frac{\partial^2 g_{ji}}{\partial x^h \partial x^l} + \frac{\partial^2 g_{lh}}{\partial x^i \partial x^j} - \frac{\partial^2 g_{li}}{\partial x^h \partial x^j} - \frac{\partial^2 g_{jh}}{\partial x^i \partial x^l}\right)$$

$$+ g_{km}(\Gamma^k_{lh}\Gamma^m_{ji} - \Gamma^k_{li}\Gamma^m_{jh}) = R_{(hi)(jl)}$$

Proof (iv) From Eq. (4.10), we have

$$R^k_{ijl} + R^k_{jli} + R^k_{lij} = \frac{\partial}{\partial x^j}\Gamma^k_{il} - \frac{\partial}{\partial x^l}\Gamma^k_{ij} + \Gamma^m_{il}\Gamma^k_{mj} - \Gamma^m_{ij}\Gamma^k_{ml}$$

$$+ \frac{\partial}{\partial x^l}\Gamma^k_{ji} - \frac{\partial}{\partial x^i}\Gamma^k_{jl} + \Gamma^m_{ji}\Gamma^k_{ml} - \Gamma^m_{jl}\Gamma^k_{mi}$$

$$+ \frac{\partial}{\partial x^i}\Gamma^k_{lj} - \frac{\partial}{\partial x^j}\Gamma^k_{li} + \Gamma^m_{lj}\Gamma^k_{mi} - \Gamma^m_{li}\Gamma^k_{mj}$$

$$= 0$$

Multiplying this equation by g_{hk}, we get

$$g_{hk}R^k_{ijl} + g_{hk}R^k_{jli} + g_{hk}R^k_{lij} = 0$$

or,

$$R_{hijl} + R_{hjli} + R_{hlij} = 0$$

Proof (v) The Bianchi identities can be proved easily if we make use of the geodesic coordinates system. In a geodesic coordinate system, Christoffel symbols are zero (and not their derivatives) at a given point. Thus, at this point Eq. (4.10) leads to

$$R^k_{ijl} = \frac{\partial}{\partial x^j}\Gamma^k_{il} - \frac{\partial}{\partial x^l}\Gamma^k_{ij}$$

In such a case, the covariant derivatives are just the ordinary derivatives and we have

$$R^k_{ijl;m} = \frac{\partial^2\Gamma^k_{il}}{\partial x^m \partial x^j} - \frac{\partial^2\Gamma^k_{ij}}{\partial x^m \partial x^l}$$

$$R^k_{ilm;j} = \frac{\partial^2\Gamma^k_{im}}{\partial x^l \partial x^j} - \frac{\partial^2\Gamma^k_{il}}{\partial x^m \partial x^j}$$

$$R^k_{imj;l} = \frac{\partial^2\Gamma^k_{ij}}{\partial x^m \partial x^l} - \frac{\partial^2\Gamma^k_{im}}{\partial x^j \partial x^l}$$

Adding these three equations, we get

$$R^k_{ijl;m} + R^k_{ilm;j} + R^k_{imj;l} = 0$$

Multiplying this equation by g_{hk}, we get

$$g_{hk}R^k_{ijl;m} + g_{hk}R^k_{ilm;j} + g_{hk}R^k_{imj;l} = 0$$

which leads to

$$R_{kijl;m} + R_{kilm;j} + R_{kimj;l} = 0$$

Since the terms in the Bianchi identities are the components of a tensor, this identity is true in all coordinate systems. Therefore, the Bianchi identities are the differential identities valid throughout the space.

EXAMPLE 4.1 Show that $R_{ijkl} = R_{klij}$ can be obtained from $R_{ijkl} = -R_{jikl} = -R_{ijlk}$ and $R_{ijkl} + R_{iklj} + R_{iljk} = 0$.

Solution   Given that

$$R_{ijkl} = -R_{jikl} = -R_{ijlk} \tag{4.25}$$

$$R_{ijkl} + R_{iklj} + R_{iljk} = 0 \tag{4.26}$$

From Eq. (4.26), we have

$$R_{klij} + R_{kijl} + R_{kjli} = 0$$

which leads to

$$R_{klij} = -R_{kijl} - R_{kjli}$$

$$= R_{ikjl} + R_{jkli} \quad \text{[from Eq. (4.25)]}$$

$$= R_{ikjl} - R_{jkil} \quad \text{[from Eq. (4.25)]}$$

$$= -(R_{ijlk} + R_{ilkj}) + (R_{jilk} + R_{jlki}) \quad \text{[from Eq. (4.26)]}$$

$$= R_{ijkl} + R_{iljk} - R_{ijlk} - R_{ljki} \quad \text{[from Eq. (4.25)]}$$

$$= R_{ijkl} + R_{iljk} + R_{ijkl} - R_{ljki} \quad \text{[from Eq. (4.25)]}$$

$$= 2R_{ijkl} + R_{iljk} + (R_{lkij} + R_{lijk}) \quad \text{[from Eq. (4.26)]}$$

$$= 2R_{ijkl} + R_{iljk} - R_{klij} - R_{iljk}) \quad \text{[from Eq. (4.25)]}$$

$$= 2R_{ijkl} - R_{klij}$$

Thus

$$R_{ijkl} = R_{klij}$$

EXAMPLE 4.2 Without using the geodesic coordinate system, prove Bianchi identities.

Solution From the definition of covariant derivative of a mixed tensor [cf., Eq. (3.52)], we have

$$R^h_{ijk;l} = \frac{\partial R^h_{ijk}}{\partial x^l} + \Gamma^h_{ml} R^m_{ijk} - \Gamma^m_{il} R^h_{mjk} - \Gamma^m_{jl} R^h_{imk} - \Gamma^m_{kl} R^h_{ijm}$$

$$R^h_{ijk;l} = \frac{\partial}{\partial x^l} \left[-\frac{\partial \Gamma^h_{ij}}{\partial x^k} + \frac{\partial \Gamma^h_{ik}}{\partial x^j} - \Gamma^p_{ij} \Gamma^h_{pk} + \Gamma^q_{ik} \Gamma^h_{qj} \right]$$

$$+ \Gamma^h_{ml} R^m_{ijk} - \Gamma^m_{il} R^h_{mjk} - \Gamma^m_{jl} R^h_{imk} - \Gamma^m_{kl} R^h_{ijm}$$

$$= -\frac{\partial^2 \Gamma^h_{ij}}{\partial x^l \partial x^k} + \frac{\partial^2 \Gamma^h_{ik}}{\partial x^l \partial x^j} - \frac{\partial \Gamma^p_{ij}}{\partial x^l} \Gamma^h_{pk} - \Gamma^p_{ij} \frac{\partial \Gamma^h_{pk}}{\partial x^l}$$

$$+ \frac{\partial \Gamma^q_{ik}}{\partial x^l} \Gamma^h_{qj} + \Gamma^q_{ik} \frac{\partial \Gamma^h_{qj}}{\partial x^l} + \Gamma^h_{ml} R^m_{ijk}$$

$$- \Gamma^m_{il} R^h_{mjk} - \Gamma^m_{jl} R^h_{mik} \Gamma^m_{kl} R^h_{ijm}$$

In a similar way, we can find $R^h_{ikl;j}$ and $R^h_{ilj;k}$. Now adding these three quantities, after a suitable change in dummy indices, we get

$$R^h_{ijk;l} + R^h_{ikl;j} + R^h_{ilj;k} = 0$$

Multiplying this equation by g_{th}, we get

$$g_{th}R^h_{ijk;l} + g_{th}R^h_{ikl;j} + g_{th}R^h_{ilj;k} = 0$$

Thus

$$R_{tijk;l} + R_{tikl;j} + R_{tilj;k} = 0$$

EXAMPLE 4.3   Prove that $A^i_{;j;k} - A^i_{;k;j} = -R^i_{mkj}A^m$.

Solution   We know that

$$A^i_{;j} = \frac{\partial A^i}{\partial x^j} - \Gamma^i_{jq}A^q$$

Differentiating this equation covaraintly, we get

$$A^i_{;j;k} = \frac{\partial A^i_{;j}}{\partial x^k} + \Gamma^i_{pk}A^p; j - \Gamma^p_{jk}A^i_{;pk}$$

$$= \frac{\partial}{\partial x^k}\left[\frac{\partial A^i}{\partial x^j} + \Gamma^i_{jq}A^q\right] + \Gamma^i_{pk}\left[\frac{\partial A^p}{\partial x^j} + \Gamma^p_{jm}A^m\right]$$

$$\quad - \Gamma^p_{jk}\left[\frac{\partial A^i}{\partial x^p} + \Gamma^i_{pl}A^l\right]$$

$$= \frac{\partial^2 A^i}{\partial x^k \partial x^j} + \frac{\partial \Gamma^i_{jq}}{\partial x^k}A^q + \Gamma^i_{jq}\frac{\partial A^q}{\partial x^k} + \Gamma^i_{pk}\frac{\partial A^p}{\partial x^j}$$

$$\quad + \Gamma^i_{pk}\Gamma^p_{jm}A^m - \Gamma^p_{jk}\frac{\partial A^i}{\partial x^p} - \Gamma^p_{jk}\Gamma^i_{pl}A^l \qquad (4.27)$$

Interchanging j and k in Eq. (4.27), we get

$$A^i_{;k;j} = \frac{\partial^2 A^i}{\partial x^j \partial x^k} + \frac{\partial \Gamma^i_{kq}}{\partial x^j}A^q + \Gamma^i_{kq}\frac{\partial A^q}{\partial x^j} + \Gamma^i_{pj}\frac{\partial A^p}{\partial x^k}$$

$$\quad + \Gamma^i_{pj}\Gamma^p_{km}A^m - \Gamma^p_{kj}\frac{\partial A^i}{\partial x^p} - \Gamma^p_{kj}\Gamma^i_{pl}A^l \qquad (4.28)$$

Subtracting Eq. (4.28) from Eq. (4.27), we get

$$A^i_{;j;k} - A^i_{;k;j} = \frac{\partial^2 A^i}{\partial x^k \partial x^j} - \frac{\partial^2 A^i}{\partial x^j \partial x^k} + \frac{\partial \Gamma^i_{jq}}{\partial x^k} A^q$$

$$- \frac{\partial \Gamma^i_{kq}}{\partial x^j} A^q + \Gamma^i_{pk} \Gamma^p_{jm} A^m - \Gamma^i_{pj} \Gamma^p_{km} A^m$$

$$= \frac{\partial^2 A^i}{\partial x^k \partial x^j} - \frac{\partial^2 A^i}{\partial x^j \partial x^k}$$

$$+ \left(\frac{\partial \Gamma^i_{jm}}{\partial x^k} - \frac{\partial \Gamma^i_{km}}{\partial x^j} + \Gamma^i_{pk} \Gamma^p_{jm} - \Gamma^i_{pj} \Gamma^p_{km} \right) A^m$$

or

$$A^i_{;j;k} - A^i_{;k;j} = \frac{\partial^2 A^i}{\partial x^k \partial x^j} - \frac{\partial^2 A^i}{\partial x^j \partial x^k} - R^i_{mkj} A^m \qquad (4.29)$$

Now if the partial derivatives commute, Eq. (4.29) then leads to

$$A^i_{;j;k} - A^i_{;k;j} = -R^i_{mkj} A^m = R^i_{mjk} A^m$$

4.6 Uniqueness of Riemann Curvature Tensor

Here we shall prove the following:

Theorem 4.1 The Riemann tensor is a unique tensor which can be constructed from the metric tensor and its first and second derivatives and is linear in the second derivative.

Proof Consider the coordinate system in which, at a point P, the Christoffel symbol Γ^i_{jk} vanishes; and the coordinate transformations that leave $\Gamma^i_{jk} = 0$, from Eq. (4.1), are the transformations $x^i \longrightarrow x'^i$ such that

$$\left(\frac{\partial^2 x'^r}{\partial x^l \partial x^k} \right)_P = 0 \qquad (4.30)$$

Any quantity which transforms as a tensor under a general tensor will also transform as a tensor according to the transformation under consideration. From Eq. (3.6), we have

$$\frac{\partial g_{ij}}{\partial x^k} = \Gamma^m_{ki} g_{mj} + \Gamma^m_{kj} g_{mi}$$

which leads to

$$\frac{\partial g_{ij}}{\partial x^k} + \frac{\partial g_{kj}}{\partial x^i} - \frac{\partial g_{ik}}{\partial x^j} = \Gamma^m_{ki}g_{mj} + \Gamma^m_{kj}g_{mi} + \Gamma^m_{ik}g_{mj}$$

$$+ \Gamma^m_{ij}g_{mk} - \Gamma^m_{ji}g_{mk} - \Gamma^m_{jk}g_{mi}$$

$$= \Gamma^m_{ki}g_{mj} + \Gamma^m_{ik}g_{mj}$$

$$= 2\Gamma^m_{ik}g_{mj} \qquad (4.31)$$

Since $\Gamma^i_{jk} = 0$, Eq. (4.31) shows that all the first derivatives of the metric tensor vanish and thus the tensor which we want to construct must be a linear combination of the second derivative of the metric tensor or, the first derivative of Γ^i_{jk}. But from Eq. (4.2), when Γ^i_{jk} and Γ'^l_{mn} are zero, we have at the point P

$$\frac{\partial^3 x'^r}{\partial x^a \partial x^l \partial x^k} = \frac{\partial x'^r}{\partial x^q} \frac{\partial \Gamma^q_{lk}}{\partial x^a} - \frac{\partial x'^i}{\partial x^l} \frac{\partial x'^j}{\partial x^k} \frac{\partial x'^b}{\partial x^a} \frac{\partial \Gamma'^r_{ij}}{\partial x'^b}$$

which gives

$$\frac{\partial x'^i}{\partial x^l} \frac{\partial x'^j}{\partial x^k} \frac{\partial x'^b}{\partial x^a} \frac{\partial \Gamma'^r_{ij}}{\partial x'^b} = \frac{\partial x'^r}{\partial x^q} \frac{\partial \Gamma^q_{lk}}{\partial x^a} - \frac{\partial^3 x'^r}{\partial x^a \partial x^l \partial x^k}$$

so that

$$\frac{\partial \Gamma'^r_{ij}}{\partial x'^b} = \frac{\partial x^l}{\partial x'^i} \frac{\partial x^k}{\partial x'^j} \frac{\partial x^a}{\partial x'^b} \frac{\partial x'^r}{\partial x^q} \frac{\partial \Gamma^q_{lk}}{\partial x^a} - \frac{\partial x^l}{\partial x'^i} \frac{\partial x^k}{\partial x'^j} \frac{\partial x^a}{\partial x'^b} \frac{\partial^3 x'^r}{\partial x^a \partial x^l \partial x^k} \qquad (4.32)$$

The quantity $\dfrac{\partial \Gamma}{\partial x}$ will transform as a tensor only when the second term in Eq. (4.32) vanishes and the only way to achieve this is to skew-symmetrize in a and k (or, in a and l) so that Eq. (4.32) from Eq. (4.30) leads to

$$\frac{\partial \Gamma'^r_{ij}}{\partial x'^b} - \frac{\partial \Gamma'^r_{ib}}{\partial x'^j} = \frac{\partial x^l}{\partial x'^i} \frac{\partial x^k}{\partial x'^j} \frac{\partial x^a}{\partial x'^b} \frac{\partial x'^r}{\partial x^q} \left(\frac{\partial \Gamma^q_{lk}}{\partial x^a} - \frac{\partial \Gamma^q_{la}}{\partial x^k} \right)$$

or

$$A'^r_{ijb} = \frac{\partial x^l}{\partial x'^i} \frac{\partial x^k}{\partial x'^j} \frac{\partial x^a}{\partial x'^b} \frac{\partial x'^r}{\partial x^q} A^q_{lka} \qquad (4.33)$$

where at P

$$A^q_{lka} = \frac{\partial \Gamma^q_{lk}}{\partial x^a} - \frac{\partial \Gamma^q_{la}}{\partial x^k} \qquad (4.34)$$

That is, when the Christoffel symbols Γ^i_{jk} vanishes, the desired tensor must be A^q_{lka} such that Eq. (4.34) is satisfied. But when $\Gamma^i_{jk} = 0$, the Riemann curvature tensor satisfies the Eq. (4.34) and therefore, $A^q_{lka} = R^q_{lka}$. Since this is an equality between tensors, it is valid in all coordinate systems. Hence the only tensor which can be constructed from the metric tensor and its first and second derivatives is the Riemann tensor. It is also linear in second derivative of metric tensor.

4.7 Number of Algebraically Independent Components of the Riemann Curvature Tensor

It is known that a general tensor of rank four has n^4 components in a n-dimensional space and for $n = 4$, the number of components is 256. However, in the case of Riemann tensor R_{hijl}, this number is greatly reduced, due to symmetry properties. In fact, the number of algebraically independent components of the Riemann tensor in a n-dimensional manifold, is

$$\frac{1}{12} n^2 (n^2 - 1)$$

To prove this, it may be noted that the components of R_{hijl} can be splitted into the following three categories:

(I) Components of the type R_{hihi}, i.e., those components where each index of the first pair has the same value as an index of the second pair, i.e., components like R_{1212}, etc.

(II) Components of the type R_{hihl}, i.e., those components where one of the indices in each pair is the same, i.e., components like R_{1213}, etc.

(III) Components of the type R_{hijl}, where all the four indices are different, like R_{1234}, etc.

The proof then consists in finding the number of independent components in each category and then adding these.

Let us consider the first category. Since only two of the indices are different here, then because of the symmetry property, the two pair of indices must be identical and be of the form R_{hihi}. The components R_{hiih} differ only in sign from R_{hihi}. The number of independent components of R_{hihi} is the same as the number of different index pairs (hi) with $h \neq i$. For a n-dimensional manifold there are n ways in which h can be chosen, and since $h \neq i$, for a given h, i can be chosen in $(n-1)$ ways. Further, whether the indices in a pair occur in the order (hi) or in (ih), is of no consequences, and the total number of different index pairs (hi) with $h \neq i$ is

$$N_{\mathrm{I}} = \frac{1}{2} n(n-1) \tag{4.35}$$

This number is not reduced by the presence of the cyclic identities (4.23a), because the identities are independent of the other algebraic identities only when all the four indices are different. Since, in the present case two of the four indices $hijl$ are equal, the cyclic identities (4.23a) have either the form:

$$R_{hihl} + R_{hhli} + R_{hlih} = 0 \tag{4.36}$$

$$R_{hijh} + R_{hjhi} + R_{hhij} = 0 \tag{4.37}$$

But, since

$$R_{hhli} = 0 = R_{hhij}$$

these expressions reduce to

$$R_{hihl} + R_{hlih} = 0 \tag{4.38}$$

$$R_{hijh} + R_{hjhi} = 0 \tag{4.39}$$

which are automatically satisfied because of the symmetry properties (4.21) and (4.22).

We now consider the second category where one index is repeated twice, i.e., three of the four indices $hijl$ are different. All such components can be put into the form R_{hihl}. Now, as shown above, the number of independent ways in which the indices of the pair (hi) can be chosen is

$$\frac{1}{2}n(n-1)$$

and the remaining third index can be chosen in $(n-2)$ ways. Hence, the total number of independent ways in which the indices $hihl$ can be chosen is

$$N_{\mathrm{II}} = \frac{1}{2}n(n-1)(n-2) \tag{4.40}$$

and is the number of independent components in category II.

Finally, consider category III, where all the four indices are different, i.e., R_{hijl}. Here the number of independent ways of choosing first pair (hi) is

$$\frac{1}{2}n(n-1)$$

and that of choosing the remaining pair (jl) is

$$\frac{1}{2}(n-2)(n-3)$$

But due to symmetry property (4.22), $R_{hijl} = R_{jlhi}$, i.e., since the order of the pairs is of no significance, the number of independent ways of choosing the four indices is

$$\frac{1}{2}n(n-1) \times \frac{1}{2}(n-2)(n-3) \times \frac{1}{2}$$

Further, from Eq. (4.23a), for a given set of four different indices, only two of the three components are independent; hence, the number of independent components with all four indices different are obtained on multiplying the above number by $\frac{2}{3}$, i.e.,

$$N_{\mathrm{III}} = \frac{2}{3} \times \frac{1}{8}n(n-1)(n-2)(n-3)$$

$$= \frac{1}{12}n(n-1)(n-2)(n-3) \tag{4.41}$$

Thus, the total number of independent components of the Riemann tensor R_{hijl}, from Eqs. (4.35), (4.40) and (4.41), is

$$N = N_{\mathrm{I}} + N_{\mathrm{II}} + N_{\mathrm{III}} = \frac{1}{12}n^2(n^2 - 1) \tag{4.42}$$

Hence, for $n = 4$, there are only 20 independent components of the Riemann tensor R_{hijl} instead of 256.

In four-dimensional space, the 20 independent components of the Riemann tensor R_{hijl} are obtained in the following manner:

Writing down the indices in the order $(hijl)$ we get the following scheme of 21 independent components:

$$
\begin{array}{ccccccc}
R_{1212} & R_{1223} & R_{1313} & R_{1324} & R_{1423} & R_{2323} & R_{2424} \\[4pt]
R_{1213} & R_{1224} & R_{1314} & R_{1334} & R_{1424} & R_{2324} & R_{2434} \\[4pt]
R_{1214} & R_{1234} & R_{1323} & R_{1414} & R_{1434} & R_{2334} & R_{3434}
\end{array} \tag{4.43}
$$

Of these, the three components with all the four indices different are connected through the cyclic identity (4.23a), viz.

$$R_{1234} + R_{1423} - R_{1324} = 0 \tag{4.44}$$

reducing thereby the number of independent components to 20.

4.8   The Ricci Tensor and the Scalar Curvature

The Riemann tensor can be used to obtain tensors of lower rank. Since Riemann tensor is a mixed tensor of rank four, there are three possible contraction that can be performed on Riemann tensor.

(i) Putting $k = i$ in Eq. (4.10), we get

$$
\begin{aligned}
R_{ijl}^i &= \frac{\partial \Gamma_{il}^i}{\partial x^j} - \frac{\partial \Gamma_{ij}^i}{\partial x^l} + \Gamma_{il}^m \Gamma_{mj}^i - \Gamma_{ij}^m \Gamma_{ml}^i \\[6pt]
&= \frac{\partial}{\partial x^j}\left(\frac{1}{\sqrt{g}}\frac{\partial \sqrt{g}}{\partial x^l}\right) - \frac{\partial}{\partial x^l}\left(\frac{1}{\sqrt{g}}\frac{\partial \sqrt{g}}{\partial x^j}\right) + \Gamma_{il}^i \Gamma_{mj}^m - \Gamma_{ij}^i \Gamma_{ml}^m \\[6pt]
&= 0
\end{aligned}
$$

(ii) Putting $k = j$ in Eq. (4.10), we get

$$
\begin{aligned}
R_{ijl}^j &= \frac{\partial \Gamma_{il}^j}{\partial x^j} - \frac{\partial \Gamma_{ij}^j}{\partial x^l} + \Gamma_{il}^m \Gamma_{mj}^j - \Gamma_{ij}^m \Gamma_{ml}^j \\[6pt]
&= -R_{ilj}^j \\[6pt]
&= -R_{il} \tag{4.45}
\end{aligned}
$$

(iii) Putting $k = l$ in Eq. (4.10), we get

$$R^l_{ijl} = R_{ij} = \frac{\partial \Gamma^l_{il}}{\partial x^j} - \frac{\partial \Gamma^l_{ij}}{\partial x^l} + \Gamma^m_{il}\Gamma^l_{mj} - \Gamma^m_{ij}\Gamma^l_{ml} \qquad (4.46)$$

Equation (4.46), obtained by the contraction of first contravariant index with the last covariant index of the Riemann tensor, defines a second rank tensor known as *Ricci tensor*, while Eq. (4.45) is just the negative of Ricci tensor. The Ricci tensor can also be expressed as

$$R_{ij} = g^{kl} R_{kilj}$$

From the symmetry property (4.22) it is seen that Ricci tensor is symmetric [this can also be seen by interchanging the indices i and j in Eq. (4.46)]. While from the skew-symmetry properties (4.20) and (4.21) it is observed that R_{ij} is the only second rank tensor that can be obtained from R_{kilj} since

$$R_{ij} = -g^{kl} R_{iklj} = -g^{kl} R_{kijl} = g^{kl} R_{ikjl}$$

and

$$g^{ki} R_{kilj} = g^{lj} R_{kilj} = 0$$

Further, from Ricci tensor we can construct a scalar as

$$R = g^{ij} R_{ij} \qquad (4.47)$$

This scalar R is called the *scalar curvature*. Also from the properties (4.20) and (4.21), the only way to construct R from R_{kilj} is

$$R \equiv g^{kl} g^{ij} R_{kilj} = -g^{kl} g^{ij} R_{iklj}$$

while

$$g^{ki} g^{lj} R_{kilj} = 0$$

Remarks

1. In one dimension, the Riemann tensor has the component R_{1111}, which from the symmetry properties is always zero [this can also be observed from Eq. (4.42)]. This is surprising that a curved line has zero curvature which clearly signifies that the Riemann curvature tensor reflects only the inner properties of the space; not how it is embedded in higher dimension.

2. In two dimensions, the Riemann tensor has only one component which may be taken as R_{1212}. But due to the symmetries of Riemann tensor, the other components related to R_{1212} are

$$R_{1212} = -R_{2112} = -R_{1221} = R_{2121}$$

and

$$R_{1111} = R_{1122} = R_{2211} = R_{2222} = 0$$

The Riemann tensor in two dimensions can be expressed in terms of the metric tensor and the scalar curvature. In any coordinate system, the relations among the components of Riemann tensor

$$R_{ijkl} = \alpha(g_{ik}g_{jl} - g_{il}g_{jk}). \quad i,j = 1,2 \tag{4.48}$$

But

$$R = g_{ij}R^{ij} = R^{ij}_{ij} = \alpha(g^i_i g^j_j - g^i_j g^j_i) = \alpha(4-2) = 2\alpha$$

Thus, in any coordinate system, Eq. (4.48) becomes

$$R_{ijkl} = \frac{1}{2}R(g_{ik}g_{jl} - g_{il}g_{jk}), \quad i,j = 1,2 \tag{4.49}$$

3. In three dimensions there are six independent components of Riemann tensor. The number of independent components of Ricci tensor is also six, and thus Riemann tensor can be expressed in terms of R_{ij} alone.

   To preserve the symmetry properties, we assume the following relation between Riemann and Ricci tensors:

$$R_{hijk} = g_{hj}T_{ik} + g_{ik}T_{hj} - g_{ij}T_{hk} - g_{hk}T_{ij} \tag{4.50}$$

Contracting the indices h and j in Eq. (4.50), we get

$$R_{ik} = T_{ik} + g_{ik}T \tag{4.51}$$

where $T = g^{hk}T_{hk}$. Multiplying Eq. (4.51) by g^{ik} and using $g^{ik}g_{ik} = 3$, we get $R = 4T$. Now put the value of T in Eq. (4.51), we get after simplification

$$T_{ik} = R_{ik} - \frac{1}{4}Rg_{ik}$$

When this value of T_{ik} is substituted in Eq. (4.50), we get Riemann tensor in terms of the Ricci tensor and scalar curvature as

$$R_{hijk} = (g_{hj}R_{ik} + g_{ik}R_{hj} - g_{ij}R_{hk} - g_{hk}R_{ij})$$

$$- \frac{R}{2}(g_{hj}g_{ik} - g_{hk}g_{ij}) \tag{4.52}$$

EXAMPLE 4.4 Calculate the components of Riemann tensor for the metric

$$ds^2 = dx^2 + G(x,y)dy^2$$

Solution Here

$$g_{11} = 1, \quad g_{22} = G(x,y) = G. \quad g^{11} = 1, \quad g^{22} = 1/G, \quad g_{ij} = 0, \quad \text{for} \, i \neq j$$

$$\Gamma^1_{11} = \Gamma^1_{12} = \Gamma^1_{21} = \Gamma^2_{11} = 0$$

$$\Gamma^2_{12} = \Gamma^2_{21} = \frac{1}{2G}\frac{\partial G}{\partial x}, \quad \Gamma^1_{22} = -\frac{1}{2}\frac{\partial G}{\partial x}, \quad \Gamma^2_{22} = \frac{1}{2G}\frac{\partial G}{\partial y}$$

In two dimensions, the only component of Riemann tensor is R_{1212} which can be calculated from Eq. (4.18), and we have

$$R_{1212} = \frac{1}{2}\left(\frac{\partial^2 g_{12}}{\partial x^1 \partial x^2} + \frac{\partial^2 g_{21}}{\partial x^2 \partial x^1} - \frac{\partial^2 g_{22}}{\partial x^1 \partial x^1} - \frac{\partial^2 g_{11}}{\partial x^2 \partial x^2}\right)$$

$$+ g_{km}(\Gamma_{21}^k \Gamma_{12}^m - \Gamma_{22}^k \Gamma_{11}^m)$$

$$= -\frac{1}{2}\left(\frac{\partial^2 G}{\partial x^2}\right) + g_{11}(\Gamma_{21}^1 \Gamma_{12}^1 - \Gamma_{22}^1 \Gamma_{11}^1)$$

$$+ g_{22}(\Gamma_{21}^2 \Gamma_{12}^2 - \Gamma_{22}^2 \Gamma_{11}^2)$$

$$= -\frac{1}{2}\left(\frac{\partial^2 G}{\partial x^2}\right) + \frac{1}{4G}\left(\frac{\partial G}{\partial x}\right)^2$$

EXAMPLE 4.5   For the metric $ds^2 = a^2 d\theta^2 + a^2 \sin^2 \theta d\phi^2$, calculate the components of Riemann tensor, Ricci tensor and scalar curvature.

Solution   Here

$$g_{11} = a^2, \quad g_{22} = a^2 \sin^2 \theta, \quad g^{11} = 1/a^2, \quad g^{22} = 1/a^2 \sin^2 \theta, \quad g_{ij} = 0$$

for $i \neq j$. The non-vanishing components of the Christoffel symbols are

$$\Gamma_{22}^1 = -\sin\theta\cos\theta, \quad \Gamma_{12}^2 = \Gamma_{21}^2 = \cot\theta$$

The only non-zero component of Riemann tensor is R_{1212} which can be calculated from Eq. (4.18), and we have

$$R_{1212} = -a^2 \sin^2 \theta$$

and the components of Ricci tensor, from Eq. (4.46), are

$$R_{11} = -1, \quad R_{22} = -\sin^2 \theta$$

while the scalar curvature, from Eq. (4.47), is

$$R = -\frac{2}{a^2}$$

Remarks

1. From the analytic geometry of surfaces, it is known that the scalar curvature given in Example 4.5 is equivalent to

$$R = \frac{2}{r_1 r_2}$$

where r_1 and r_2 are two principal radii of the curvature of the surface. On the sphere these radii coincide and are equal to the spherical radius. Thus the scalar curvature bears a simple relationship to the radius of curvature of the two-dimensional space on the spherical surface.

2. We have just seen the existence of curvature in two-dimensional space. Three-dimensional region with curvature do exist and to have an insight of it we proceed as follows:

The general space (in rectangular coordinate system) in which the curvature is constant is known to have the metric

$$ds^2 = dx^2 + dy^2 + dz^2 \left[1 + \frac{K}{4}(x^2 + y^2 + z^2) \right]^{-2} \qquad (4.53)$$

where K is the isotropic Gaussian curvature of the region. If $K \neq 0$ and (x, y, z) are replaced by $(\frac{x}{r}, \frac{y}{r}, \frac{z}{r})$, then the space coordinates in the above equation can be made isotropic. With this change, we have

$$ds^2 = r^2(dx^2 + dy^2 + dz^2) \left[1 + \frac{k}{4}(x^2 + y^2 + z^2) \right]^{-2} \qquad (4.54)$$

where $k = Kr^2$ and k may take values $1, -1$ or 0. Here r is not a function of coordinates. It has the character of the radius of curvature of three space, as we shall see in the later part of this discussion.

We shall now calculate the scalar curvature R and for this first let us write Eq. (4.54) in an easy to handle form as

$$ds^2 = F(dx^2 + dy^2 + dz^2) \qquad (4.55)$$

where

$$F \equiv r^2 \left[1 + \frac{k}{4}(x^2 + y^2 + z^2) \right]^{-2} \qquad (4.56)$$

The non-vanishing Christoffel symbols are

$$\Gamma_{11}^1 = -\Gamma_{22}^1 = -\Gamma_{33}^1 = \Gamma_{12}^2 = \Gamma_{13}^3 = \frac{F_x}{2F}$$

$$\Gamma_{12}^1 = -\Gamma_{11}^2 = \Gamma_{22}^2 = -\Gamma_{33}^2 = \Gamma_{23}^3 = \frac{F_y}{2F}$$

$$\Gamma_{13}^1 = \Gamma_{32}^2 = -\Gamma_{11}^3 = -\Gamma_{22}^3 = \Gamma_{33}^3 = \frac{F_z}{2F}$$

where

$$F_x = \frac{\partial F}{\partial x}, \quad F_y = \frac{\partial F}{\partial y}, \quad F_z = \frac{\partial F}{\partial z}$$

From the definition of Ricci tensor, we have

$$R_{11} = \frac{2F_{xx} + F_{yy} + F_{zz}}{2F} - \frac{4F_x^2 + F_y^2 + F_z^2}{4F^2}$$

$$R_{22} = \frac{2F_{yy} + F_{zz} + F_{xx}}{2F} - \frac{4F_y^2 + F_z^2 + F_x^2}{4F^2}$$

$$R_{33} = \frac{2F_{zz} + F_{xx} + F_{yy}}{2F} - \frac{4F_z^2 + F_x^2 + F_y^2}{4F^2}$$

Also

$$g^{ij} = \begin{bmatrix} 1/F & 0 & 0 \\ 0 & 1/F & 0 \\ 0 & 0 & 1/F \end{bmatrix}$$

and the scalar curvature is

$$R = g^{ij} R_{ij}$$

$$= g^{11} R_{11} + g^{22} R_{22} + g^{33} R_{33} + g^{44} R_{44}$$

$$= \frac{1}{F} \left[\frac{2(F_{xx} + F_{yy} + F_{zz})}{F} - \frac{3(F_x^2 + F_y^2 + F_z^2)}{2F^2} \right]$$

which from Eq. (4.56) takes the form

$$R = -\frac{6k}{r^2} \tag{4.57}$$

In a n-dimesional space, Eq. (4.57) becomes

$$R = -\frac{n(n-1)}{r^2} k$$

Thus the scalar curvature for the metric (4.54) is constant and proportional to the reciprocal square of the radius of curvature r of the region. It may be noted that in Eq. (4.54) x, y, z coordinates were defined as dimensionless fractions of the radius r. The coordinate space is spherical, flat or hyperbolic, according to $k = 1, 0$ or -1.

4.9   The Einstein Tensor

We shall now obtain an important identity from the Bianchi identities. Consider Eq. (4.24a)

$$R^k_{lij;m} + R^k_{ljm;i} + R^k_{lmi;j} = 0$$

and contract k and j to obtain

$$R_{li;m} + R^k_{lkm;i} + R^k_{lmi;k} = 0$$

which due to symmetry properties of Riemann tensor leads to

$$R_{li;m} - R^k_{lmk;i} + R^k_{lmi;k} = 0$$

or

$$R_{li;m} - R_{lm;i} + R^k_{lmi;k} = 0 \tag{4.58}$$

Now, multiplying Eq. (4.58) by g^{lh} and noting that the metric tensor is covariantly constant, we have

$$(g^{lh}R_{li})_{;m} - (g^{lh}R_{lm})_{;i} + (g^{lh}R^k_{lmi})_{;k} = 0$$

which yields

$$R^h_{i;m} - R^h_{m;i} + (g^{lh}R^k_{lmi})_{;k} = 0 \tag{4.59}$$

Also note that

$$g^{lh}R^k_{lmi} = g^{lh}g^{kn}R_{nlmi}$$

$$= g^{lh}g^{kn}R_{lnim}$$

$$= g^{kn}g^{lh}R_{lnim}$$

$$= g^{kn}R^h_{nim} \tag{4.60}$$

Substituting the last term in Eq. (4.59) from Eq. (4.60), we get

$$R^h_{i;m} - R^h_{m;i} + (g^{kn}R^h_{nim})_{;k} = 0$$

Contract h with m, to get

$$R^h_{i;h} - R^h_{h;i} + (g^{kn}R_{ni})_{;k} = 0$$

In the last term, changing the dummy index k to h, and since $g^{hn}R_{ni} = R^h_i$, we get

$$R^h_{i;h} - R^h_{h;i} + R^h_{i;h} = 0$$

or,

$$R^h_{i;h} - \frac{1}{2}R^h_{h;i} = 0 \tag{4.61}$$

But

$$R^h_{h;i} = \frac{\partial}{\partial x^i}R^h_h = \frac{\partial}{\partial x^j}(g^j_i R^h_h) \tag{4.62}$$

Changing the dummy suffix h in the first term of Eq. (4.61) to j, and using Eq. (4.62) for the second term, we finally get

$$\left(R^j_i - \frac{1}{2}g^j_i R\right)_{;j} = 0 \tag{4.63}$$

If we take

$$G^j_i = R^j_i - \frac{1}{2}g^j_i R \tag{4.64}$$

then Eq. (4.63) with Eq. (4.64) can be expressed as

$$G^j_{i;j} = 0 \qquad\qquad (4.65)$$

The tensor defined through Eq. (4.64) is called the *Einstein tensor*. Since Eq. (4.65) is obtained by contracting the Bianchi identities, it is some times also known as the *contracted Bianchi identities*. Moreover, Eq. (4.65) shows that the divergence of Einstein tensor vanishes. This tensor G^j_i plays a fundamental role in the general theory of relativity.

EXAMPLE 4.6   Obtain the non-vanishing components of Γ^i_{jk}, R_{ij}, R and G_{ij} for the most general static spherically symmetric metric

$$ds^2 = -e^\lambda dr^2 - r^2 d\theta^2 - r^2 \sin^2\theta d\phi^2 + e^\nu dt^2$$

where λ and ν are functions of r only.

Solution   Here

$$x^1 = r, \quad x^2 = \theta, \quad x^3 = \phi, \quad x^4 = t$$

$$g_{11} = -e^\lambda, \quad g_{22} = -r^2, \quad g_{33} = -r^2\sin^2\theta, \quad g_{44} = e^\nu$$

$$g^{11} = -e^{-\lambda}, \quad g^{22} = -\frac{1}{r^2}, \quad g^{33} = -\frac{1}{r^2\sin^2\theta}, \quad g^{44} = e^{-\nu}$$

$$g_{ij} = 0, \quad i \neq j, \quad \det g_{ij} = -e^{(\lambda+\nu)}r^4\sin^2\theta$$

From the definition of Christoffel symbol of second kind, we have

$$\Gamma^1_{11} = g^{1m}\Gamma_{m11} = g^{11}\Gamma_{111} + g^{12}\Gamma_{211} + g^{13}\Gamma_{311} + g^{14}\Gamma_{411}$$

$$= g^{11}\Gamma_{111}$$

$$= g^{11}\frac{1}{2}\left(\frac{\partial g_{11}}{\partial x^1} - \frac{\partial g_{11}}{\partial x^1} + \frac{\partial g_{11}}{\partial x^1}\right)$$

$$= \frac{1}{2}g^{11}\frac{\partial g_{11}}{\partial x^1}$$

$$= \frac{1}{2}(-e^{-\lambda})\frac{\partial}{\partial r}(-e^{-\lambda}).$$

$$= \frac{1}{2}\lambda'$$

In a similar manner, we can find the other components of Γ^i_{jk}, and all the non-vanishing components of Christoffel symbol of second kind are as follows:

$$\Gamma^1_{11} = \frac{1}{2}\lambda', \quad \Gamma^1_{22} = -re^{-\lambda}, \quad \Gamma^1_{33} = -r\sin^2\theta e^{-\lambda}, \quad \Gamma^1_{44} = \frac{1}{2}\nu'e^{\nu-\lambda}$$

$$\Gamma^2_{12} = \frac{1}{r}, \quad \Gamma^2_{33} = -\sin\theta\cos\theta, \quad \Gamma^3_{13} = \frac{1}{r}, \quad \Gamma^3_{23} = \cot\theta, \quad \Gamma^4_{14} = \frac{1}{2}\nu'$$

From the definition of the Ricci tensor, we have

$$R_{ij} = -\frac{\partial \Gamma_{ij}^a}{\partial x^a} + \frac{\partial \Gamma_{ia}^a}{\partial x^j} - \Gamma_{ij}^b \Gamma_{ba}^a + \Gamma_{ia}^b \Gamma_{bj}^a$$

which leads to

$$R_{11} = -\frac{\partial \Gamma_{11}^a}{\partial x^a} + \frac{\partial \Gamma_{1a}^a}{\partial x^1} - \Gamma_{11}^b \Gamma_{ba}^a + \Gamma_{1a}^b \Gamma_{b1}^a$$

$$= -\left(\frac{\partial \Gamma_{11}^1}{\partial x^1} + \frac{\partial \Gamma_{11}^2}{\partial x^2} + \frac{\partial \Gamma_{11}^3}{\partial x^3} + \frac{\partial \Gamma_{11}^4}{\partial x^4} \right)$$

$$+ \left(\frac{\partial \Gamma_{11}^1}{\partial x^1} + \frac{\partial \Gamma_{12}^2}{\partial x^1} + \frac{\partial \Gamma_{13}^3}{\partial x^1} + \frac{\partial \Gamma_{14}^4}{\partial x^1} \right)$$

$$- \left(\Gamma_{11}^1 \Gamma_{1a}^a + \Gamma_{11}^2 \Gamma_{2a}^a + \Gamma_{11}^3 \Gamma_{3a}^a + \Gamma_{11}^4 \Gamma_{4a}^a \right)$$

$$+ \left(\Gamma_{1a}^1 \Gamma_{11}^a + \Gamma_{1a}^2 \Gamma_{21}^a + \Gamma_{1a}^3 \Gamma_{31}^a + \Gamma_{1a}^4 \Gamma_{41}^a \right)$$

$$= \left(\frac{\partial \Gamma_{12}^2}{\partial x^1} + \frac{\partial \Gamma_{13}^3}{\partial x^1} + \frac{\partial \Gamma_{14}^4}{\partial x^1} \right)$$

$$- \left(\Gamma_{11}^1 \Gamma_{11}^1 + \Gamma_{11}^1 \Gamma_{12}^2 + \Gamma_{11}^1 \Gamma_{13}^3 + \Gamma_{11}^1 \Gamma_{14}^4 \right)$$

$$+ \left(\Gamma_{11}^1 \Gamma_{11}^1 + \Gamma_{12}^1 \Gamma_{11}^2 + \Gamma_{13}^1 \Gamma_{11}^3 + \Gamma_{14}^1 \Gamma_{11}^4 \right)$$

$$+ \left(\Gamma_{11}^2 \Gamma_{21}^1 + \Gamma_{12}^1 \Gamma_{21}^2 + \Gamma_{13}^2 \Gamma_{21}^3 + \Gamma_{14}^2 \Gamma_{21}^4 \right)$$

$$+ \left(\Gamma_{11}^3 \Gamma_{31}^1 + \Gamma_{12}^2 \Gamma_{31}^2 + \Gamma_{13}^3 \Gamma_{31}^3 + \Gamma_{14}^3 \Gamma_{31}^4 \right)$$

$$+ \left(\Gamma_{11}^4 \Gamma_{41}^1 + \Gamma_{12}^4 \Gamma_{41}^2 + \Gamma_{13}^4 \Gamma_{41}^3 + \Gamma_{14}^4 \Gamma_{41}^4 \right)$$

$$R_{11} = \frac{\partial \Gamma_{12}^2}{\partial x^1} + \frac{\partial \Gamma_{13}^3}{\partial x^1} + \frac{\partial \Gamma_{14}^4}{\partial x^1} - \Gamma_{11}^1 \Gamma_{12}^2 - \Gamma_{11}^1 \Gamma_{13}^3$$

$$- \Gamma_{11}^1 \Gamma_{14}^4 + \Gamma_{12}^2 \Gamma_{21}^1 + \Gamma_{13}^3 \Gamma_{31}^1 + \Gamma_{14}^4 \Gamma_{41}^4$$

$$= \frac{\partial}{\partial r}\left(\frac{1}{r} \right) + \frac{\partial}{\partial r}\left(\frac{1}{r} \right) + \frac{\partial}{\partial r}\left(\frac{1}{2}\nu' \right) - \frac{1}{2}\lambda'\frac{1}{r} - \frac{1}{2}\lambda'\frac{1}{r}$$

$$- \frac{1}{2}\lambda'\frac{1}{2}\nu' + \frac{1}{r^2} + \frac{1}{r^2} + \frac{1}{4}\nu'^2$$

$$- \frac{1}{r^2} - \frac{1}{r^2} + \frac{\nu''}{2} - \frac{\lambda'}{2r} - \frac{\lambda'}{2r} - \frac{1}{4}\lambda'\nu' + \frac{2}{r^2} + \frac{1}{4}\nu'^2$$

$$= \frac{\nu''}{2} - \frac{\lambda'\nu'}{4} + \frac{\nu'^2}{4} - \frac{\lambda'}{r}$$

In a similar way, we have

$$R_{22} = e^{-\lambda}\left[1 - \frac{r}{2}(\lambda' - \nu')\right] - 1$$

$$R_{33} = \left[e^{-\lambda}\left\{1 - \frac{r}{2}(\lambda' - \nu')\right\} - 1\right]\sin^2\theta$$

$$= R_{22}\sin^2\theta$$

$$R_{44} = e^{\nu-\lambda}\left[-\frac{\nu''}{2} + \frac{\nu'^2}{2} - \frac{\nu'\lambda'}{2} - \frac{\nu'\lambda'}{4} - \frac{\nu'}{r} - \frac{\nu'^2}{4}\right]$$

From the definition of scalar curvature, we have

$$R = g^{ij}R_{ij}$$

$$= g^{11}R_{11} + g^{22}R_{22} + g^{33}R_{33} + g^{44}R_{44}$$

$$R = -e^{-\lambda}\left(\frac{\nu''}{2} - \frac{\lambda'\nu'}{4} + \frac{\nu'^2}{4} - \frac{\lambda'}{r}\right)$$

$$+ \left(-\frac{1}{r^2}\right)\left[e^{-\lambda}\left\{1 - \frac{r}{2}(\lambda' - \nu')\right\} - 1\right]$$

$$+ \left(-\frac{1}{r^2\sin^2\theta}\right)\left[e^{-\lambda}\left\{1 - \frac{r}{2}(\lambda' - \nu')\right\} - 1\right]\sin^2\theta$$

$$+ e^{-\nu}e^{\nu-\lambda}\left[-\frac{\nu''}{2} + \frac{\lambda'\nu'}{4} - \frac{\nu'^2}{4} - \frac{\nu'}{r}\right]$$

$$= -2e^{-\lambda}\left[-\frac{\nu''}{2} - \frac{\lambda'\nu'}{4} + \frac{\nu'^2}{4} - \frac{(\lambda' - \nu')}{r} + \frac{1}{r^2}\right] - \frac{1}{r^2}$$

The definition of Einstein tensor leads to

$$G_{11} = R_{11} - \frac{1}{2}g_{11}R$$

$$= \left(\frac{\nu''}{2} - \frac{\lambda'\nu'}{4} + \frac{\nu'^2}{4} - \frac{\lambda'}{r}\right)$$

$$- \frac{1}{2}\left[-e^{\lambda}\left\{-e^{\lambda}\left(\nu'' - \frac{\lambda'\nu'}{2} + \frac{\nu'^2}{2} - \frac{\lambda'}{r} + \frac{\nu'}{r}\right)\right.\right.$$

$$\left.\left. - \frac{2}{r^2}\left(e^{-\lambda}\left[1 - \frac{r}{2}(\lambda' - \nu')\right] - 1\right)\right\}\right]$$

$$= \frac{\nu''}{2} - \frac{\lambda'\nu'}{4} + \frac{\nu'^2}{4} - \frac{\lambda'}{r}$$

$$- \frac{1}{2}\left(\nu'' - \frac{\lambda'\nu'}{2} + \frac{\nu'^2}{2} - \frac{\lambda'}{r} - \frac{\nu'}{r}\right)$$

$$- \frac{e^\lambda}{r^2}\left(e^{-\lambda}\left[1 - \frac{r}{2}(\lambda' - \nu')\right] - 1\right)$$

$$= -\frac{\lambda'}{2r} + \frac{\nu'}{r} - \frac{1}{r^2}\left(1 - \frac{r}{2}(\lambda' - \nu')\right) + \frac{e^\lambda}{r^2}$$

$$G_{22} = \left(e^{-\lambda}\left[1 - \frac{r}{2}(\lambda' - \nu')\right] - 1\right)$$

$$+ \frac{1}{2}r^2\left[-e^{-\lambda}\left(\nu'' - \frac{\lambda'\nu'}{2} + \frac{\nu'^2}{r} - \frac{\lambda'}{r} + \frac{\nu'}{r}\right)\right.$$

$$\left. - \frac{2}{r^2}\left(e^{-\lambda}\left[1 - \frac{r}{2}(\lambda' - \nu')\right] - 1\right)\right]$$

$$G_{33} = \left(e^{-\lambda}\left[1 - \frac{r}{2}(\lambda' - \nu')\right] - 1\right)\sin^2\theta$$

$$+ \frac{1}{2}r^2\sin^2\theta\left[-e^{-\lambda}\left(\nu'' - \frac{\lambda'\nu'}{2} + \frac{\nu'^2}{r} + \frac{\nu'}{r}\right)\right.$$

$$\left. - \frac{2}{r^2}\left(e^{-\lambda}\left[1 - \frac{r}{2}(\lambda' - \nu')\right] - 1\right)\right]$$

$$G_{44} = e^{\nu-\lambda}\left[-\frac{\nu'}{2} + \frac{\lambda'\nu'}{r} - \frac{\nu'^2}{4} - \frac{\nu'}{r}\right]$$

$$- \frac{1}{2}e^\nu\left[-e^{-\lambda}\left(\nu'' - \frac{\lambda'\nu'}{2} + \frac{\nu'^2}{2} - \frac{\lambda'}{r} + \frac{\nu'}{r}\right)\right]$$

$$+ \frac{1}{2}e^\nu\left[\frac{2}{r^2}\left(e^{-\lambda}\left[1 - \frac{r}{2}(\lambda' - \nu')\right] - 1\right)\right]$$

EXAMPLE 4.7 The metric of a four-dimensional non-static spherically symmetric spacetime is

$$ds^2 = -e^\lambda dr^2 - r^2 d\theta^2 - r^2\sin^2\theta d\phi^2 + e^\nu dt^2$$

where λ and ν are functions of r and t only. Calculate the non-vanishing components of $R^i_{jkl}, R_{ij}, R, G_{ij}$ and G^i_j.

Solution Here the coordinates are $(x^1, x^2, x^3, x^4) \longrightarrow (r, \theta, \phi, t)$.

$$g_{11} = -e^\lambda, \quad g_{22} = -r^2, \quad g_{33} = -r^2\sin^2\theta, \quad g_{44} = e^\nu$$

$$g^{11} = -e^{-\lambda}, \quad g^{22} = -\frac{1}{r^2}, \quad g^{33} = -\frac{1}{r^2 \sin^2 \theta}, \quad g^{44} = e^{-\nu},$$

$$g_{ij} = 0, \quad i \neq j, \quad \det g_{ij} = -e^{(\lambda + \nu)} r^4 \sin^2 \theta$$

From the definition and the symmetry property of Christoffel symbol of second kind, the non-vanishing components are as follows:

$$\Gamma^1_{11} = \tfrac{1}{2}\lambda' \quad \Gamma^1_{22} = -re^{-\lambda} \quad \Gamma^1_{33} = -r\sin^2\theta e^{-\lambda} \quad \Gamma^1_{44} = \tfrac{1}{2}\nu' e^{\nu - \lambda}$$

$$\Gamma^1_{41} = \tfrac{1}{2}\dot{\lambda} \quad \Gamma^2_{12} = \tfrac{1}{r} \quad \Gamma^2_{33} = -\sin\theta\cos\theta \quad \Gamma^3_{13} = \tfrac{1}{r}$$

$$\Gamma^3_{23} = \cot\theta \quad \Gamma^4_{11} = \tfrac{1}{2}e^{\lambda-\nu}\dot{\lambda} \quad \Gamma^4_{14} = \tfrac{1}{2}\nu' \quad \Gamma^4_{44} = -\tfrac{1}{2}\dot{\nu}$$

where a prime sign ($\prime$) denotes the differentiation with respect to r and a dot represents the differentiation with respect to t.

The non-zero components of Riemann tensor, from Eq. (4.10), are:

$$R^1_{212} = \frac{1}{2}r\lambda' e^{-\lambda},$$

$$R^1_{313} = \frac{1}{2}r\lambda' e^{-\lambda}\sin^2\theta,$$

$$R^2_{323} = -e^{-\lambda}\sin^2\theta + \sin^2\theta,$$

$$R^4_{212} = -\frac{1}{2}r\dot{\lambda}e^{-\nu},$$

$$R^4_{313} = -\frac{1}{2}r\dot{\lambda}e^{-\nu}\sin^2\theta,$$

$$R^4_{242} = -\frac{1}{2}r\nu' e^{-\lambda},$$

$$R^4_{343} = -\frac{1}{2}r\nu' e^{-\lambda}\sin^2\theta$$

$$R^4_{141} = -\frac{1}{2}\nu'' + \frac{1}{4}\dot{\lambda}^2 e^{\lambda-\nu} - \frac{1}{4}\dot{\lambda}\dot{\nu}e^{\lambda-\nu} + \frac{1}{2}\ddot{\lambda}e^{\lambda-\nu} - \frac{1}{4}\nu'^2 + \frac{1}{4}\nu'\lambda'$$

The non-zero components of Ricci tensor [using Eq. (4.46)] are:

$$R_{11} = -\frac{1}{2}\nu'' + \frac{1}{4}\dot{\lambda}e^{\lambda-\nu} - \frac{1}{4}\dot{\lambda}\dot{\nu}e^{\lambda-\nu} + \frac{1}{2}\ddot{\lambda}e^{\lambda-\nu} - \frac{1}{4}\nu'^2 + \frac{1}{4}\lambda'\nu' + r^{-1}\lambda'$$

$$R_{22} = -\frac{1}{2}r\nu' e^{-\lambda} + \frac{1}{2}r\lambda' e^{-\lambda} - e^{-\lambda} + 1$$

$$R_{33} = \sin^2\theta R_{22}$$

$$R_{41} = r^{-1}\dot{\lambda}$$

$$R_{44} = \frac{1}{2}\nu'' e^{\nu-\lambda} - \frac{1}{4}\dot{\lambda}^2 + \frac{1}{4}\dot{\lambda}\dot{\nu} - \frac{1}{2}\ddot{\lambda} + \frac{1}{4}\nu'^2 e^{\nu-\lambda} - \frac{1}{4}\lambda'\nu' e^{\nu-\lambda} + r^{-1}\nu' e^{\nu-\lambda}$$

while the scalar curvature is

$$R = g^{11}R_{11} + g^{22}R_{22} + g^{33}R_{33} + g^{44}R_{44}$$

$$= \nu'' e^{-\lambda} - \frac{1}{2}\dot{\lambda}^2 e^{-\nu} + \frac{1}{2}\dot{\lambda}\dot{\nu}e^{-\nu} - \ddot{\lambda}e^{-\nu} + \frac{1}{2}\nu'^2 e^{-\lambda} - \frac{1}{2}\lambda'\nu' e^{-\lambda} + 2r^{-1}\nu' e^{-\lambda}$$

$$- 2r^{-1}\lambda' e^{-\lambda} + 2r^{-2}e^{-\lambda} - 2r^{-2}$$

Also $G_{ij} = R_{ij} - \frac{1}{2}g_{ij}R$ leads to

$$G_{11} = r^{-1}\nu' - r^{-2}e^{\lambda} + r^{-2}$$

$$G_{22} = \frac{1}{2}r\nu' e^{-\lambda} - \frac{1}{2}r\lambda' e^{-\lambda} + \frac{1}{2}r^2\nu'' e^{-\lambda} - \frac{1}{4}r^2\dot{\lambda}^2 e^{-\nu} + \frac{1}{4}r^2\dot{\lambda}\dot{\nu}e^{-\nu}$$

$$- \frac{1}{2}r^2\ddot{\lambda}e^{-\nu} + \frac{1}{4}r^2\nu'^2 e^{-\lambda} - \frac{1}{4}r^2\nu'\lambda' e^{-\lambda}$$

$$G_{33} = \sin^2\theta G_{22}$$

$$G_{44} = r^{-1}\lambda' e^{\nu-\lambda} - r^{-2}e^{\nu-\lambda} + r^{-2}e^{\nu}$$

$$G_{41} = r^{-1}\dot{\lambda}$$

while $G^i_j = g^{ik}G_{kj}$ leads to

$$G^1_1 = r^{-1}\nu' e^{-\lambda} - r^{-2}e^{-\lambda} + r^{-2}$$

$$G^2_2 = \frac{1}{2}r^{-1}\lambda' e^{-\lambda} - \frac{1}{2}r^{-1}\nu' e^{-\lambda} - \frac{1}{2}\nu'' e^{-\lambda} + \frac{1}{4}\dot{\lambda}^2 e^{-\nu} - \frac{1}{4}\dot{\lambda}\dot{\nu}e^{-\nu}$$

$$+ \frac{1}{2}\ddot{\lambda}e^{-\nu} - \frac{1}{4}\nu'^2 e^{-\lambda} + \frac{1}{4}\nu'\lambda' e^{-\lambda}$$

$$G^3_3 = G^2_2$$

$$G^4_4 = r^{-1}\lambda' e^{-\lambda} - r^{-2}e^{-\lambda} + r^{-2}$$

$$G^4_1 = r^{-1}\dot{\lambda}e^{-\nu}$$

$$G^1_4 = r^{-1}\dot{\lambda}e^{-\lambda}$$

4.10 The Integrability of Riemann Tensor and the Flatness of the Space

In Euclidean geometry if a vector is parallely propagated from one point to another point, along any curve, the resulting vector is the same, i.e., independent of the path. The situation in curved space is, however, different. If we parallely transport a vector from one point to another along two different curves, we will get two different vectors. If somehow we can parallely propagate the vector from point A to point B (Figure 4.1) and the resulting vector is path independent, then the connection [Christoffel symbol of second kind having the transformation law as Eq. (3.15)] is said to be *integrable*. Thus, in order to have the usual concept of parallelism in a Riemannian space, the space should have an integrable connection.

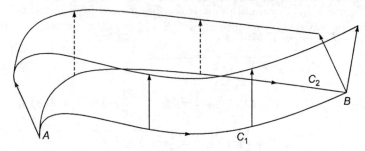

Figure 4.1 Parallel transport along two curves.

In this section, we shall prove the results which include the concepts of integrability, the vanishing of Riemann tensor and the flatness of the space. We have

Theorem 4.2 The necessary and sufficient condition for a connection to be integrable is that the Riemann tensor vanishes.

Proof First let the connection Γ^i_{jk} be integrable, then the vector A^i is parallely propagated. From the definition of parallel propagation, we have

$$A^i_{;j}\frac{dx^i}{dt} = 0$$

Since $\dfrac{dx^i}{dt}$ is arbitrary, this means that $A^i_{;j} = 0$, that is

$$A^i_{;j} = \frac{\partial A^i}{\partial x^j} + \Gamma^i_{jk}A^k = 0 \tag{4.66}$$

The necessary condition for this first order partial differential equation to have a solution is

$$\frac{\partial^2 A^i}{\partial x^j \partial x^k} = \frac{\partial^2 A^i}{\partial x^k \partial x^j} \tag{4.67}$$

But from Eq. (4.29) and the symmetry of Riemann tensor, we have

$$A^i_{;j;k} - A^i_{;k;j} = \frac{\partial^2 A^i}{\partial x^k \partial x^j} - \frac{\partial^2 A^i}{\partial x^j \partial x^k} - R^i_{mkj}A^m$$

$$= \frac{\partial^2 A^i}{\partial x^k \partial x^j} - \frac{\partial^2 A^i}{\partial x^j \partial x^k} + R^i_{mjk}A^m \tag{4.68}$$

From Eq. (4.66) the left-hand side of Eq. (4.68) vanishes. Thus, Eq. (4.67) will hold, if and only if

$$R^i_{mjk}A^m = 0$$

Since A^m is arbitrary at every point, therefore, the necessary condition for integrability is

$$R^i_{mjk} = 0$$

Now to prove the converse part, we consider the parallel propagation of a vector along an infinitesimal loop. Let P be the starting point and R the final point (Figure 4.2). This final point R can be reached from initial point P in two different ways, viz. one through PQR and the other through PSR.

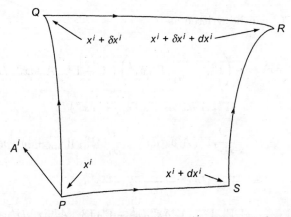

Figure 4.2 Parallel transport of the vector A^i along an infinitesimal loop.

We now propagate a vector A^i parallely along these two paths and compare the results. When the vector A^i at P is parallely propagated along PQ, i.e., from x^i to $x^i + \delta x^i$, we have [for parallel propagation, $dA^i = -\Gamma^i_{jk}A^k dx^j$, cf., Eq. (3.79a)]

$$(A^i)_Q = (A^i)_P + (\bar{\delta}A^i)_P$$

or

$$A^i(x + \delta x) = A^i(x) + \bar{\delta}A^i(x)$$

$$= A^i(x) - \Gamma^i_{jk}(x)A^j(x)\delta x^k$$

and when this vector is transported from Q to R, we have

$$(A^i)_R = (A^i)_Q + (\bar{\delta}A^i)_Q$$

or

$$A^i(x + \delta x + dx) = A^i(x + \delta x) + \bar{\delta}A^i(x + \delta x)$$

$$= A^i(x + \delta x) - \Gamma^i_{jk}(x + \delta x)A^j(x + \delta x)dx^k \qquad (4.69)$$

where

$$\bar{\delta}A^i(x+\delta x) = -\Gamma^i_{jk}(x+\delta x)A^j(x+\delta x)dx^k \qquad (4.70)$$

Since the curve is small, we can expand $\Gamma^i_{jk}(x)$ around some point $X = x$ on the curve, and we have

$$\Gamma^i_{jk}(x) = \Gamma^i_{jk}(X) + (x^l - X^l)\frac{\partial}{\partial x^l}\Gamma^i_{jk}(X) + \cdots$$

Thus, Eq. (4.70) can be written as

$$\bar{\delta}A^i(x+\delta x) = -\left(\Gamma^i_{jk} + \frac{\partial}{\partial x^l}\Gamma^i_{jk}\delta x^l\right)(A^j - \Gamma^j_{mn}A^m\delta x^n)dx^k$$

$$= (-\Gamma^i_{jk}A^j dx^k + \Gamma^i_{jk}\Gamma^j_{mn}A^m\delta x^n)dx^k$$

$$- \frac{\partial}{\partial x^l}\Gamma^i_{jk}A^j\delta x^l dx^k + \frac{\partial}{\partial x^l}(\Gamma^i_{jk})\Gamma^j_{mn}A^m\delta x^l\delta x^n dx^k$$

$$= -\Gamma^i_{jk}A^j dx^k - \frac{\partial}{\partial x^l}\Gamma^i_{jk}A^j\delta x^l dx^k$$

$$+ \Gamma^i_{jk}\Gamma^j_{mn}A^m\delta x^n dx^k + \Gamma^i_{jk}\Gamma^j_{mn}A^m\delta x^n dx^k$$

(neglecting the last term which is of third order). Equation (4.69) can now be written as (the vector A^i is parallely propagated along PQR)

$$A^i(x+\delta x+dx) = A^i - \Gamma^i_{jk}A^j\delta x^k - \Gamma^i_{jk}A^j dx^k$$

$$- \frac{\partial}{\partial x^l}\Gamma^i_{jk}A^j\delta x^l dx^k + \Gamma^i_{jk}\Gamma^j_{mn}A^m\delta x^n dx^k \qquad (4.71)$$

Similarly, we can parallely propagate the vector A^i along the path PSQ, by interchanging δx^i and dx^i in Eq. (4.71), and we have

$$A^i(x+dx+\delta x) = A^i - \Gamma^i_{jk}A^j dx^k - \Gamma^i_{jk}A^j\delta x^k$$

$$- \frac{\partial}{\partial x^l}\Gamma^i_{jk}A^j\delta x^k dx^l + \Gamma^i_{jk}\Gamma^j_{mn}A^m\delta x^k dx^n \qquad (4.72)$$

The difference of Eqs. (4.71) and (4.72) is the difference between the vectors on the left-hand side of Eqs. (4.71) and (4.72), and we have (after making suitable changes in dummy indices)

$$\bar{\delta}A^i(x + \delta x + dx) - A^i(x + dx + \delta x)$$

$$= -\frac{\partial}{\partial x^l}\Gamma^i_{jk}A^j\delta x^l dx^k + \frac{\partial}{\partial x^l}\Gamma^i_{jk}A^j dx^l \delta x^k$$

$$\quad - \Gamma^i_{jk}\Gamma^j_{mn}A^m\delta x^k dx^n + \Gamma^i_{jk}\Gamma^j_{mn}A^m\delta x^n dx^k$$

$$= \left(\frac{\partial\Gamma^i_{jk}}{\partial x^l} - \frac{\partial\Gamma^i_{jl}}{\partial x^k} + \Gamma^i_{ml}\Gamma^m_{jk} - \Gamma^i_{mk}\Gamma^m_{jl}\right)A^j\delta x^k dx^l$$

$$= -R^i_{jkl}A^j\delta x^k dx^l = R^i_{jlk}A^j\delta x^k dx^l \tag{4.73}$$

From Eq. (4.73) it is clear that the vector A^i will be same at R whether we travel along the path PQR or PSR only when $R^i_{jlk} = 0$. Thus, if the Riemann tensor vanishes then the vector A^i will not change when parallely propagated around any infinitesimal loop and hence the connection is integrable.

Theorem 4.3 The necessary and sufficient condition for a Riemannian space to be flat is that its Riemann tensor vanishes.

Proof If the space is flat then there exists a coordinate system in which the metric tensor is constant (or, the metric is diagonal with ± 1 diagonal elements). Since the metric is constant, therefore, the partial derivatives of the metric tensor vanish and so are the Christoffel symbols. But since Christoffel symbols are involved in the definition of Riemann tensor, therefore, Riemann tensor vanishes.

For the converse part, if the Riemann tensor vanishes, then from Theorem 4.2

$$A^i_{;j} = \frac{\partial A^i}{\partial x^j} + \Gamma^i_{jk}A^k = 0$$

which leads to

$$\frac{\partial A^i}{\partial x^j} = -\Gamma^i_{jk}A^k \tag{4.74}$$

Consider now the transformation law

$$dx^i = A^i dx'^i \tag{4.75}$$

then

$$ds^2 = g_{ab}dx^a dx^b$$

$$= g'_{ij}dx'^i dx'^j$$

which from Eq. (4.75) leads to

$$ds^2 = g_{ab}A^a dx'^a A^b dx'^b$$

$$= g'_{ij}dx'^i dx'^j$$

or

$$g'_{ij} = g_{ab}A^a A^b$$

Differentiating both sides of this equation partially with respect to x^k, we get

$$\frac{\partial g'_{ij}}{\partial x^k} = \frac{\partial g_{ab}}{\partial x^k}A^a A^b + g_{ab}\frac{\partial A^a}{\partial x^k}A^b + g_{ab}A^a\frac{\partial A^b}{\partial x^k}$$

which on using Eq. (4.74) becomes

$$\frac{\partial g'_{ij}}{\partial x^k} = \frac{\partial g_{ab}}{\partial x^k}A^a A^b + g_{ab}(-\Gamma^a_{ck}A^c)A^b + g_{ab}A^a(-\Gamma^b_{dk}A^d)$$

$$= \frac{\partial g_{ab}}{\partial x^k}A^a A^b - \Gamma_{bck}A^c A^b - \Gamma_{adk}A^a A^d$$

By using the definition of Γ_{ijk} and changing the dummy indices at the appropriate places, we get

$$\frac{\partial g'_{ij}}{\partial x^k} = \frac{\partial g_{ab}}{\partial x^k}A^a A^b - \frac{\partial g_{ab}}{\partial x^k}A^a A^b = 0$$

This shows that g'_{ij} are constants and hence the space is flat.

Note: Theorem 4.3 can be taken as the definition of the flat space.

The examples of flat space are the Euclidean space with line element $ds^2 = dx^2 + dy^2 + dz^2 + dw^2$ or a pseudo-Euclidean spacetime with the line-element $ds^2 = c^2 dt^2 - dx^2 - dy^2 - dz^2$. It may be noted that a flat space need not have the topology of a Euclidean space. For example, if we consider a plane, a subspace of a Euclidean space, and roll it to make a cylinder then on the surface of the cylinder we have a flat space.

Remarks

1. The justification of the word '*curvature*' in Riemann curvature tensor lies in the fact that when it disappears (vanishes) the space is flat, that is, the Cartesian coordinate system is introduced in the whole space.

2. The following statements are equivalent:

   The curvature tensor, defined by Eqs. (4.10) and (4.18), vanishes if and only if, the

   (i) space is flat.
   (ii) parallel transport of vectors is independent of path (or connection is integrable).
   (iii) covariant derivatives commute.

EXAMPLE 4.8 Show that the two-dimensional space $ds^2 = dv^2 - v^2 du^2$ is a flat space.

Solution   Here $g_{11} = 1, g_{22} = -v^2, g^{11} = 1, g^{22} = -1/v^2, g_{12} = g^{12} = 0,$ $g = -v^2$. Let $x^1 = v$ and $x^2 = u$, then the non-vanishing components of Christoffel symbol of second kind are:

$$\Gamma^1_{22} = v, \quad \Gamma^2_{12} = \Gamma^2_{21} = \frac{1}{v}$$

The only component of Riemann tensor in two dimensions is

$$R_{1212} = R^1_{212} = \Gamma^1_{22,1} - \Gamma^1_{12,2} + \Gamma^1_{1a}\Gamma^a_{22} - \Gamma^1_{2a}\Gamma^a_{21} = 0$$

which shows that the two-dimensional space of the problem is a flat space.

EXAMPLE 4.9   Show that $ds^2 = dt^2 - dr^2 - r^2 d\theta^2$ is the metric of a flat space.

Solution   For the given metric, we have

$$g_{11} = g^{11} = -1, \quad g_{22} = -r^2, \quad g^{22} = -r^{-22}, \quad g_{44} = g^{44} = 1$$
$$g_{ij} = g^{ij} = 0, \quad \text{for } i \neq j$$

The only non-vanishing derivative is $g_{22,1} = -2r$, while the non-vanishing components of Christoffel symbol of second kind are:

$$\Gamma^1_{22} = -r, \quad \Gamma^2_{12} = \Gamma^2_{21} = \frac{1}{r}$$

Also

$$\Gamma^1_{22,1} = -1, \quad \Gamma^2_{12,1} = \Gamma^2_{21,1} = -\frac{1}{r^2}$$

The definition of Riemann tensor yields

$$R_{1212} = R^1_{212} = \Gamma^1_{22,1} - \Gamma^1_{12,2} = 0$$

and the space is flat.

EXAMPLE 4.10   Show that the space with the metric $ds^2 = -dx^2 - dy^2 - dz^2 + e^{-t}dt^2$ is a flat space.

Solution   Here

$$x^1 = x, \quad x^2 = y, \quad x^3 = z, \quad x^4 = t, \quad g_{11} = g_{22} = g_{33} = -1, \quad g_{44} = e^{-t}$$

From the definition of Christoffel symbols, the only non-vanishing component is

$$\Gamma_{44}^4 = g^{4m}\Gamma_{m44}$$

$$= g^{44}\Gamma_{444}$$

$$= \frac{1}{2}g^{44}\left(\frac{\partial g_{44}}{\partial x^4}\right)$$

$$= \frac{1}{2}e^t\left(\frac{\partial e^{-t}}{\partial t}\right)$$

$$= -\frac{1}{2}$$

which is constant. Therefore, $R_{ijk}^h = 0$ and the space is flat.

4.11   Einstein Space

A Riemannian space $V_n(n > 2)$ is defined to be an *Einstein space* if its Ricci tensor has the form

$$R_{ij} = \alpha g_{ij} \tag{4.76}$$

where α is a scalar.

Multiplying Eq. (4.76) by g^{ij}, we get

$$g^{ij}R_{ij} = \alpha g^{ij}g_{ij}$$

which gives $R = \alpha n$ so that $\alpha = R/n$.

Thus, for an Einstein space, from Eq. (4.76), we have

$$R_{ij} = \frac{1}{n}Rg_{ij} \tag{4.77}$$

EXAMPLE 4.11   For the metric $ds^2 = g_{ij}dx^i dx^j, i, j = 1, 2$, obtain the values of gR_{ij} and gR.

Solution   Here

$$g^{ij} = \begin{bmatrix} g_{11} & g_{12} \\ g_{21} & g_{22} \end{bmatrix}, \quad g = g_{11}g_{22} - g_{12}g_{21}$$

$$g^{11} = \frac{g_{22}}{g}, \quad g^{22} = \frac{g_{11}}{g}, \quad g^{12} = -\frac{g_{12}}{g}$$

Also

$$R_{ij} = g^{lm}R_{mijl}$$

which leads to

$$R_{11} = g^{lm}R_{m11l}$$

$$= g^{11}R_{1111} + g^{12}R_{2111} + g^{21}R_{1112} + g^{22}R_{2112}$$

$$= g^{12}R_{2111} - g^{21}R_{1112} + g^{22}R_{2112}$$

$$= g^{22}R_{2112}$$

$$= \frac{g_{11}}{g}R_{2112}$$

$$= -\frac{g_{11}}{g}R_{1212}$$

In a similar way, we have

$$R_{22} = -\frac{g_{22}}{g}R_{1212}, \quad R_{12} = -\frac{g_{12}}{g}R_{1212} = R_{21}$$

Therefore

$$R_{ij} = -\frac{g_{ij}}{g}R_{1212}$$

which leads to

$$gR_{ij} = -g_{ij}R_{1212} \tag{4.78}$$

Also, from Eq. (4.78) we have

$$R = g^{ij}R_{ij}$$

$$= -g^{ij}\frac{g_{ij}}{g}R_{1212}$$

$$= -\frac{2}{g}R_{1212}$$

which leads to

$$gR = -2R_{1212} \tag{4.79}$$

From Eqs. (4.78) and (4.79), we thus have

$$R_{ij} = \frac{1}{2}Rg_{ij}$$

EXAMPLE 4.12 For a two-dimensional Riemannian space referred to an orthogonal system, show that

$$R_{12} = 0, \quad R_{11}g_{22} = R_{22}g_{11} = R_{1221}, \quad R = g^{ij}R_{ij} = \frac{2R_{1221}}{g_{11}g_{22}}, \quad R_{ij} = \frac{1}{2}Rg_{ij}$$

Solution For an orthogonal system $g_{12} = g_{21} = 0$ and the result follows from Example 4.11.

4.12   Curvature of a Riemannian Space

From any two vectors A^i and B^i at a point of a Riemannian space we can construct an invariant $R_{ijkl}A^iA^kB^jB^l$. Now replace these vectors by the following linear combinations:

$$X^i = \alpha A^i + \beta B^i, \quad Y^i = \gamma A^i + \delta B^i \qquad (4.80)$$

where α, β, γ and δ are scalars (invariants). From Eq. (4.80), we have

$$R_{ijkl}X^iX^kY^jY^l = R_{ijkl}(\alpha A^i + \beta B^i)(\alpha A^k + \beta B^k)(\gamma A^j + \delta B^j)(\gamma A^l + \delta B^l)$$

which using the symmetry properties of Riemann tensor leads to

$$R_{ijkl}X^iX^kY^jY^l = (\alpha\delta - \gamma\beta)^2 R_{ijkl}A^iA^kB^jB^l$$

Thus, $R_{ijkl}A^iA^kB^jB^l$, which is an invariant under coordinate transformation, is almost an invariant [due to the presence of the factor $(\alpha\delta - \gamma\beta)^2$] under linear transformation of vectors. In order to obtain an expression which is also invariant under linear transformation of vectors we now evaluate $(g_{ik}g_{jl} - g_{il}g_{jk})X^iX^kY^jY^l$ and from Eq. (4.80), we have

$$(g_{ik}g_{jl} - g_{il}g_{jk})X^iX^kY^jY^l = (g_{ik}g_{jl} - g_{il}g_{jk})(\alpha A^i + \beta B^i)(\alpha A^k + \beta B^k)$$

$$\times (\gamma A^j + \delta B^j)(\gamma A^l + \delta B^l)$$

$$= (\alpha\delta - \gamma\beta)^2(1 - \cos^2\theta)A^2B^2 \qquad (4.81)$$

where $A_iB^i = (A_jA^j)(B_kB^k)\cos\theta$, θ being the angle between A_i and B_i. Moreover

$$(g_{ik}g_{jl} - g_{il}g_{jk})A^iA^kB^jB^l = A^2B^2(1 - \cos\theta) \qquad (4.82)$$

From Eqs. (4.81) and (4.82), we have

$$(g_{ik}g_{jl} - g_{il}g_{jk})X^iX^kY^jY^l = (\alpha\delta - \gamma\beta)^2(g_{ik}g_{jl} - g_{il}g_{jk})A^iA^kB^jB^l$$

Since α, β, γ and δ are scalars, $(\alpha\delta - \gamma\beta)^2$ is also a scalar (invariant) and thus $(g_{ik}g_{jl} - g_{il}g_{jk})A^iA^kB^jB^l$ is an invariant under linear transformation of vectors. This means that the ratio of the two invariants $R_{ijkl}A^iA^kB^jB^l$ and $(g_{ik}g_{jl} - g_{il}g_{jk})A^iA^kB^jB^l$ is also an invariant, denote it by K, so that

$$K = \frac{R_{ijkl}A^iA^kB^jB^l}{(g_{ik}g_{jl} - g_{il}g_{jk})A^iA^kB^jB^l} \qquad (4.83)$$

This invariant is known as *Riemannian curvature* or *curvature* associated with the vectors A^i and B^i of the space. The above discussions can be summarized as:

Theorem 4.4 The (Riemannian) curvature associated with the contravariant vectors at a point of a Riemannian space V_n is invariant under linear transformation of vectors.

As an illustration as to how we can obtain the curvature of a space, consider a V_2 at every point of which there exists only two independent vectors. This means that the curvature of a V_2 is uniquely determined at each point. Its value can be obtained easily by choosing the vectors A^i and B^i with components $(1,0)$ and $(0,1)$, respectively. Also, from Remark 2 of Section 4.8, in a V_2 the only surviving component of Riemann tensor is R_{1212}. Thus, from Eq. (4.83), we have

$$K = \frac{R_{1212} A^1 A^1 B^2 B^2}{(g_{11}g_{22} - g_{12}g_{21}) A^1 A^1 B^2 B^2}$$

$$= \frac{R_{1212}}{g_{11}g_{22} - (g_{12})^2}$$

$$= \frac{R_{1212}}{g} \qquad (4.84)$$

Note: It may be noted that when the vectors A_i and B_i are unit orthogonal vectors, then (cf., Example 2.6)

$$(g_{ik}g_{jl} - g_{il}g_{jk}) A^i A^k B^j B^l = 1$$

and Eq. (4.83) leads to

$$K = R_{ijkl} A^i A^k B^j B^l \qquad (4.85)$$

The flatness of the space can now be defined in terms of the curvature of the space as:

"*A space is said to be flat if its curvature vanishes (i.e., $K = 0$) at every point of the space.*"

From Eq. (4.83), the necessary and sufficient condition for the flatness, for all vectors A^i and B^i, is

$$R_{ijkl} A^i A^k B^j B^l = 0$$

so that

$$R_{kjil} A^k A^i B^j B^l = 0$$

$$R_{klij} A^k A^i B^l B^j = 0$$

and

$$R_{ilkj} A^i A^k B^l B^j = 0$$

Since A^i and B^i are arbitrary vectors, addition of the above four equations yields

$$R_{ijkl} + R_{kjil} + R_{klij} + R_{ilkj} = 0$$

or

$$R_{ijkl} + R_{ilkj} + R_{ijkl} + R_{ilkj} = 0 \quad \text{[from Eq. (4.23)]}$$

or

$$2(R_{ijkl} + R_{ilkj}) = 0$$

or

$$R_{ijkl} = -R_{ilkj} = R_{iljk} \quad \text{[from Eq. (4.20)]}$$

Interchange j, k, l cyclically, to obtain

$$R_{iklj} = R_{ijkl}$$

which means that

$$R_{ijkl} = R_{iljk} = R_{iklj}$$

Using this in Eq. (4.23a), we obtain

$$R_{ijkl} = 0$$

which means that the space V_n is flat. Conversely, if $R_{ijkl} = 0$ then from Eq. (4.83) clearly $K = 0$. Thus we have

Theorem 4.5 The necessary and sufficient condition for a Riemannian space to be flat is that its curvature vanishes.

4.13   Spaces of Constant Curvature

In the previous section we have considered the curvature of the space associated with the contravariant vectors A^i and B^i, now we shall consider the spaces in which the curvature at every point does not depend upon the choice of the vectors A^i and B^i associated with the curvature. From Eq. (4.83), the necessary and sufficient condition is

$$[K(g_{ik}g_{jl} - g_{il}g_{jk}) - R_{ijkl}]A^i A^k B^j B^l = 0 \tag{4.86}$$

for all vectors A^i and B^i. This equation leads to

$$R_{ijkl} = K(g_{ik}g_{jl} - g_{il}g_{jk}) \tag{4.87}$$

where K is now a function of the coordinates x^i. Differentiating Eq. (4.87) covariantly, we get (since $g_{ij;k} = 0$)

$$R_{ijkl;t} = K_{;t}(g_{ik}g_{jl} - g_{il}g_{jk})$$

Similarly

$$R_{ijlt;k} = K_{;k}(g_{il}g_{jt} - g_{it}g_{jl})$$

$$R_{ijtk;l} = K_{;l}(g_{it}g_{jk} - g_{ik}g_{jt})$$

Adding these three equations, we get

$$R_{ijkl;t} + R_{ijlt;k} + R_{ijtk;l} = K_{;t}(g_{ik}g_{jl} - g_{il}g_{jk})$$

$$+ K_{;k}(g_{il}g_{jt} - g_{it}g_{jl}) + K_{;l}(g_{it}g_{jk} - g_{ik}g_{jt})$$

Since the left-hand side of this equation is zero due to Bianchi identity, we thus have

$$K_{;t}(g_{ik}g_{jl} - g_{il}g_{jk}) + K_{;k}(g_{il}g_{jt} - g_{it}g_{jl}) + K_{;l}(g_{it}g_{jk} - g_{ik}g_{jt}) = 0$$

Multiplying this equation by $g^{ik}g^{jl}$ and noting that $g^{ik}g_{ik} = n$, after simplification, we get

$$(1 - n)(2 - n)K_{;t} = 0$$

Hence, if $n > 2$, then $K_{;t} = \dfrac{\partial K}{\partial t} = 0$ which yields K as a constant. We thus have proved

Theorem 4.6 If at each point of a Riemannian space V_n $(n > 2)$, the Riemannian curvature is a function of the coordinates only then it is constant throughout V_n.

This theorem is known as *Schur's theorem* and a V_n in which this theorem holds is called a *space of constant curvature*.

Thus, for a space of constant curvature, we have

$$R_{ijkl} = K(g_{ik}g_{jl} - g_{il}g_{jk})$$

where K is a function of coordinates.

Remark

The significance of spaces of constant curvature is very well known in cosmology. The simplest cosmological model of the universe is obtained from the assumption that in the rest system of matter, there is no preferred point and no preferred direction, the three-dimensional space is being constituted in the same way everywhere. This cosmological principle, when translated into the language of Riemannian geometry, asserts that the three-dimensional position space is a space of maximal symmetry [a space is of maximal symmetry if it has maximum number of Killing vector fields and consequently, a space of constant curvature whose curvature can depend upon time (cf., Section 5.9)].

The cosmological solutions of Einstein equations which contain a three-dimensional space-like surface of a constant curvature are the Robertson-Walker metrics, while a four dimensional space of constant curvature is the deSitter model of the universe. deSitter universe possess a three-dimensional space of constant curvature and thus belongs to Robertson–Walker metrics (for details see Krammer, et al., 1980 and Stephani, 1982).

EXAMPLE 4.13 Show that a space of constant curvature is an Einstein space.

Solution For a space of constant curvature, we have

$$R_{ijkl} = K(g_{ik}g_{jl} - g_{il}g_{jk})$$

Multiplying this equation by g^{il} we get

$$R_{jk} = Kg_{jk}(1 - n) \tag{4.88}$$

Now multiplication of Eq. (4.88) by g^{jk} yields

$$R = Kn(1-n) \qquad (4.89)$$

From Eqs. (4.88) and (4.89), we have

$$R_{jk} = \frac{R}{n} g_{jk}$$

which shows that a space of constant curvature is an Einstein space.

EXAMPLE 4.14   Prove that a Riemannian space $(n > 2)$ satisfying

$$R^h_{ijk} = \alpha(\delta^h_j g_{ik} - \delta^h_k g_{ij})$$

is an Einstein space, where α is a constant. Also show that for Einstein spaces, the scalar curvature is constant.

Solution   Given that

$$R^h_{ijk} = \alpha(\delta^h_j g_{ik} - \delta^h_k g_{ij})$$

Contracting the indices h and k, we have

$$R_{ij} = a g_{ij} \qquad (4.90)$$

where $a = \alpha(1-n)$ is a scalar. Thus the given space is an Einstein space.

Now, multiplying Eq. (4.90) by g^{ij}, we get

$$R = g^{ij} R_{ij} = a g^{ij} g_{ij} = an$$

which shows that the scalar curvature is constant.

EXERCISES

4.1 The Minkowski line element is given by

$$ds^2 = dt^2 - dx^2 - dy^2 - dz^2$$

  (i) What is the signature of this metric?
  (ii) Is the metric flat?

4.2 The line element of R^3 in a particular coordinate system is

$$ds^2 = (dx^1)^2 + (x^1)^2 (dx^2)^2 + (x^1 \sin x^2)^2 (dx^3)^2$$

  (i) Identify the coordinates.
  (ii) Is the metric flat?

4.3 For any rank two tensor, prove that $T^{ij}_{;ij} = T^{ij}_{;ji}$.

4.4 Show that

$$A^i_{j;k;l} - A^i_{j;l;k} = R^i_{mkl} A^m_j + R^m_{jkl} A^i_m$$

4.5 Find the non-vanishing components of R_{hijk} for the metric

$$ds^2 = a^2 d\phi^2 + (b + a \sin \phi)^2 d\theta^2.$$

4.6 Show that $A_{i;jk} = \frac{1}{2} R_{ijkl} A^l$, where A_j satisfies the equation $A_{(j;k)} = 0$.

4.7 For the metric

$$ds^2 = e^{2\phi}(dx^4)^2 + e^{2\theta} dx^2 + dy^2 + dz^2$$

where θ and ϕ are functions of x only, show that the Riemann tensor vanishes if and only if $\phi'' - \theta'\phi' + \phi'^2 = 0$. where a prime denotes differentiation with respect to x. If $\theta = \phi$, prove that the spacetime is flat provided that $\phi = \log(ax + b)^{1/2}, a, b$ are constants.

4.8 If in a Riemannian space $R_{ij} = \frac{1}{2} R g_{ij}$, then show that $R_{ij} \equiv 0$.

4.9 If the identity

$$R_{ij;k} + R_{jk;i} + R_{ki;j} = 0$$

holds for a V_n, prove that R is constant.

4.10 The metric of a two-dimensional space is

$$ds^2 = g_{11}(dx^1)^2 + g_{22}(dx^2)^2$$

Show that $R_{11}g_{22} = R_{22}g_{11} = R_{1221}, R_{12} = 0$. If $R = g^{ij} R_{ij}$, show that $R g_{11} g_{22} = 2 R_{1221}$. Deduce that $2 R_{ij} = R g_{ij}$.

4.11 If the Ricci tensor of a four-dimensional space is such that $R_{ij} = \phi g_{ij}$, then show that ϕ is constant.

4.12 For the metric

$$ds^2 = e^{\phi}(dx^4)^2 - e^{-\phi}(x^2)^2(dx^3)^2 - e^{\lambda}[(dx^1)^2 + (dx^2)^2]$$

where ϕ and λ are functions of x^1 and x^2 only and $R_{ik} = 0$ for $i = k = 4$, show that

$$\frac{\partial^2 \phi}{(\partial x^1)^2} + \frac{\partial^2 \phi}{(\partial x^2)^2} + \frac{1}{x^2} \frac{\partial \phi}{\partial x^2} = 0.$$

4.13 For the metric $ds^2 = \frac{1}{1 - Kr^2} dr^2 + r^2 d\theta^2 + r^2 \sin^2 \theta d\phi^2$, show that $R_{ijkl} = a(g_{ik}g_{jl} - g_{il}g_{jk})$, where a is a constant and is related to the constant K.

4.14 In a Euclidean V_4, prove that the hypersphere $x^1 = c \sin \theta \sin \phi \sin \psi$, $x^2 = c \sin \theta \sin \phi \cos \psi, x^3 = c \sin \theta \cos \phi, x^4 = c \cos \theta$ is a V_3 of constant curvature $1/c^2$.

4.15 If $T_j^i = R_j^i + \delta_j^i(\alpha R + \beta)$, where α and β are scalars, find the value of α for which $T_{j;i}^i = 0$.

4.16 Show that for a V_4 the only covariant symmetric tensor of rank two whose components are linear in second derivatives of g_{ij} and involve also g_{ij} and their first derivatives are of the form $R_{ij} + g_{ij}(aR + b)$, where a and b are scalars.

4.17 For a flat $V_2, ds^2 = f(r)[(dx^1)^2 + (dx^2)^2]$ where $r^2 = (x^1)^2 + (x^2)^2$, show that $f(r) = c(r)^k$, where c and k are constants.

CHAPTER 5

Some Advanced Topics

5.1 Introduction

In the previous chapter, the algebraic and geometric properties of the Riemann curvature tensor were discussed. To have an idea about the physical importance of this tensor, it is worthwhile to quote Sachs (1964):

"The Riemann curvature tensor is the simplest non-trivial object one can build at a point; its vanishing is the criterion for the absence of genuine gravitational fields and its structure determines the relative motion of the neighbouring test particles via the equation of geodesic deviation."

Motivated by the all important roles played by the Riemann tensor in understanding the geometrical and physical properties of a space, this chapter includes a detailed study of Riemann tensor in the spacetime of general theory of relativity. The concept of Lie derivative and related results have also been discussed here. To know the relative motion of neighbouring test particles, we have

5.2 Geodesic Deviation

In a two-dimensional Euclidean space let there be two straight lines, then they are either parallel or intersect each other. The distance between these lines remains constant everywhere when they are parallel. But when they intersect, the distance (or separation) between them increases linearly as they move away from the point of intersection. Figure 5.1 illustrates two such straight lines I and II intersecting at point O and let θ be the small angle

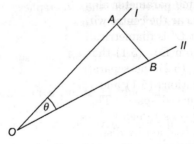

Figure 5.1 Intersecting lines in two-dimensional Euclidean space.

between them. Let A and B be any two points, respectively, on lines I and II such that $OA = OB = \alpha$. Assume that arc $AB = \beta$ is the measure of the separation between lines I and II at a distance α from O, then

$$\beta \simeq \theta\alpha \quad \text{and} \quad \frac{d^2\beta}{d\alpha^2} = 0 \tag{5.1}$$

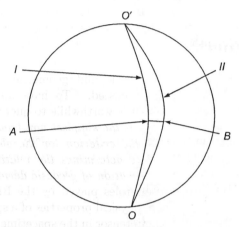

Figure 5.2 The deviation of two geodesics.

Now let us examine the corresponding situation on the surface of a two-dimensional sphere of unit radius (Figure 5.2). Let O be the pole. The two arcs of the great circles (i.e., geodesics) I and II are emanating from the pole O and θ is the angle between them. Let A and B be any two points on the geodesics I and II, respectively, such that $OA = OB = \alpha$. Also suppose that $\beta = AB$, the latitude arc joining A and B and is the measure of the separation between A and B along this arc, then

$$\beta \simeq \theta \sin \alpha \quad \text{and} \quad \frac{d^2\beta}{d\alpha^2} \neq 0 \tag{5.2}$$

Here the deviation between two geodesics on the surface of the sphere increases with respect to the affine parameter along them. It increases from O until it reaches its maximum near the centre with respect to O and then decreases to zero at point O' (point O' is diametrically opposite with respect to O).

It may be noted from Eq. (5.1) that the separation between the lines is linear while from Eq. (5.2) the separation between the geodesics does not increase linearly. Equations (5.1) and (5.2) also illustrate how a Euclidean space differs from a curved space. This situation can also be described as follows: if a particle is constrained to move on a surface which is a plane, or on a surface which is obtained by distortion of a plane, or part of plane (for example, cylinder, cone) then the geodesics are straight lines of this plane and the equations of motion can easily be integrated. But since both in flat and curved spaces, the geodesics are the paths (event histories) of free mass particles so if we are considering the curved spaces then how we can know the motion of the particle from the equations of motion or from the Christoffel symbols appearing in Eq. (3.24). That is how to measure the relative acceleration of two particles moving towards one another on neighbouring paths, or how to measure the separation of the neighbouring geodesics.

To handle such situations we consider a family $x^i = x^i(\alpha, \beta)$ of geodesics on a surface, where x^i are twice differentiable continuous functions of α and β. The parameter α is the affine parameter along each geodesic and the parameter β distinguishes between different geodesics. Let us form the partial derivatives

$$t^i = \frac{\partial x^i}{\partial \alpha}, \quad v^i = \frac{\partial x^i}{\partial \beta} \tag{5.3}$$

where t^i is the unit tangent vector to the geodesic given by β and v^i the separation (displacement) vector of the two neighbouring geodesics (at a common parameter value α). Then, from the definition of the intrinsic derivative (cf., Section 3.10), we have

$$\frac{\delta t^i}{\delta \beta} = t^i_{;j} \frac{\partial x^j}{\partial \beta}$$

$$= t^i_{;j} v^j$$

$$= \left(\frac{\partial t^i}{\partial x^j} + \Gamma^i_{kj} t^k \right) v^j$$

$$= \frac{\partial t^i}{\partial x^j} \frac{\partial x^j}{\partial \beta} + \Gamma^i_{kj} t^k v^j$$

$$= \frac{\partial t^i}{\partial \beta} + \Gamma^i_{kj} t^k v^j \tag{5.4}$$

$$= \frac{\partial}{\partial \beta} \left(\frac{\partial x^i}{\partial \alpha} \right) + \Gamma^i_{kj} t^k v^j$$

$$= \frac{\partial^2 x^i}{\partial \beta \partial \alpha} + \Gamma^i_{kj} t^k v^j$$

$$= \frac{\partial^2 x^i}{\partial \alpha \partial \beta} + \Gamma^i_{kj} v^j t^k$$

$$= \frac{\delta v^i}{\delta \alpha} \tag{5.5}$$

Since the geodesics are straight lines which do not change their direction as we move along them (cf., Section 3.4), this means that the rate of change of

t^i along itself is zero, that is (cf., Remark 5, Section 3.7)

$$t^i_{;j} t^j = 0 \tag{5.6}$$

Also

$$\frac{\delta^2 v^i}{\delta \alpha^2} = \frac{\delta}{\delta \alpha} \left(\frac{\delta v^i}{\delta \alpha} \right)$$

$$= \frac{\delta}{\delta \alpha} \left(\frac{\delta t^i}{\delta \beta} \right)$$

$$= \frac{\delta}{\delta \alpha} \left(t^i_{;k} \frac{\partial x^k}{\partial \beta} \right)$$

$$= \frac{\delta}{\delta \alpha} \left(\frac{\partial t^i}{\partial x^k} + \Gamma^i_{jk} t^j \right) \frac{\partial x^k}{\partial \beta}$$

$$= \frac{\delta}{\delta \alpha} \left(\frac{\partial t^i}{\partial \beta} + \Gamma^i_{jk} t^j \frac{\partial x^k}{\partial \beta} \right)$$

$$= \frac{\delta}{\delta \alpha} \left(\frac{\partial t^i}{\partial \beta} + \Gamma^i_{jk} t^j v^k \right)$$

$$= \left[\frac{\partial t^i}{\partial \beta} + \Gamma^i_{jk} t^j v^k \right]_{;l} \left(\frac{\partial x^l}{\partial \alpha} \right)$$

$$= \frac{\partial}{\partial x^l} \left(\frac{\partial t^i}{\partial \beta} \right) \frac{\partial x^l}{\partial \alpha} + \Gamma^i_{jk,l} t^j v^k \frac{\partial x^l}{\partial \alpha}$$

$$\quad + \Gamma^i_{jk} t^j_{;l} v^k \frac{\partial x^l}{\partial \alpha} + \Gamma^i_{jk} t^j v^k_{;l} \frac{\partial x^l}{\partial \alpha}$$

$$= \frac{\partial^2 t^i}{\partial \alpha \partial \beta} + \Gamma^i_{jk,l} t^j v^k t^l + \Gamma^i_{jk} \left(\frac{\partial t^j}{\partial x^l} + \Gamma^j_{lm} t^m \right) v^k \frac{\partial x^l}{\partial \alpha}$$

$$\quad + \Gamma^i_{jk} t^j \left(\frac{\partial v^k}{\partial x^l} + \Gamma^k_{ln} v^n \right) \frac{\partial x^l}{\partial \alpha}$$

$$= \frac{\partial^2 t^i}{\partial \alpha \partial \beta} + \Gamma^i_{jk,l} t^l t^j v^k + \Gamma^i_{jk} \left(\frac{\partial t^j}{\partial \alpha} v^k + t^j \frac{\partial v^k}{\partial \alpha} \right)$$

$$\quad + \Gamma^i_{jk} \Gamma^j_{lm} t^m t^l v^k + \Gamma^i_{jk} \Gamma^k_{ln} t^j t^l v^n \tag{5.7}$$

Moreover, from Eq. (5.6), we have

$$0 = \frac{\delta}{\delta \beta} \left(\frac{\delta t^i}{\delta \alpha} \right)$$

$$= \frac{\delta}{\delta \beta} \left(t^i_{;k} \frac{\partial x^k}{\partial \alpha} \right)$$

$$= \frac{\delta}{\delta\beta}\left(\frac{\partial t^i}{\partial x^k} + \Gamma^i_{jk}t^j\right)\frac{\partial x^k}{\partial \alpha}$$

$$= \left[\frac{\partial t^i}{\partial \alpha} + \Gamma^i_{jk}t^j t^k\right]_{;l}\left(\frac{\partial x^l}{\partial \beta}\right)$$

$$= \frac{\partial}{\partial x^l}\left(\frac{\partial t^i}{\partial \alpha}\right)\frac{\partial x^l}{\partial \beta} + \Gamma^i_{jk,l}t^j t^k v^l + \Gamma^i_{jk}t^j_{;l}t^k v^l + \Gamma^i_{jk}t^j t^k_{;l}v^l$$

$$= \frac{\partial^2 t^i}{\partial \alpha \partial \beta} + \Gamma^i_{jk,l}t^j t^k v^l + \Gamma^i_{jk}\left(\frac{\partial t^j}{\partial x^l} + \Gamma^j_{lm}t^m\right)t^k v^l$$

$$\quad + \Gamma^i_{jk}t^j\left(\frac{\partial t^k}{\partial x^l} + \Gamma^k_{ln}t^n\right)v^l$$

$$= \frac{\partial^2 t^i}{\partial \alpha \partial \beta} + \Gamma^i_{jk,l}t^j t^k v^l + \Gamma^i_{jk}\left(\frac{\partial t^j}{\partial \beta}t^k + t^j\frac{\partial t^k}{\partial \beta}\right)$$

$$\quad + \Gamma^i_{jk}\Gamma^j_{lm}t^m t^k v^l + \Gamma^i_{jk}\Gamma^k_{ln}t^j t^n v^l$$

This equation leads to

$$\frac{\partial^2 t^i}{\partial \alpha \partial \beta} = -\left[\Gamma^i_{jk,l}t^j t^k v^l + \Gamma^i_{jk}\left(\frac{\partial t^j}{\partial \beta}t^k + t^j\frac{\partial t^k}{\partial \beta}\right)\right.$$

$$\left. + \Gamma^i_{jk}\Gamma^j_{lm}t^m t^k v^l + \Gamma^i_{jk}\Gamma^k_{ln}t^j t^n v^l\right]$$

Substituting this value in Eq. (5.7) and using Eqs. (5.3) and (5.5), after a suitable change of dummy indices, we have

$$\frac{\delta^2 v^i}{\delta \alpha^2} = [-\Gamma^i_{jk,l} + \Gamma^i_{jl,k} - \Gamma^i_{ml}\Gamma^m_{kj} + \Gamma^i_{mk}\Gamma^m_{lj}]t^j t^l v^k$$

which, using Eq. (4.10) reduces to

$$\frac{\delta^2 v^i}{\delta \alpha^2} = R^i_{jkl}t^j t^l v^k \tag{5.8}$$

The right-hand side of this equation represents the measure of the change in separation of neighbouring geodesics, or measure of the relative acceleration of two particles moving towards one another on neighbouring paths. This equation is called the *equation of geodesic deviation*.

5.3   Decomposition of Riemann Curvature Tensor

From the Riemann curvature tensor R_{ijkl} and the metric tensor, we can construct another rank four tensor known as Weyl conformal curvature tensor. In n-dimensions, the Riemann tensor can be decomposed into its irreducible component. This decomposition can be achieved by assuming the expression

$$R_{ijkl} = C_{ijkl} + P(g_{ik}R_{jl} + g_{jl}R_{ik} - g_{il}R_{jk} - g_{jk}R_{il}) + Q(g_{il}g_{jk} - g_{ik}g_{jl})R \tag{5.9}$$

where P and Q are some constants to be determined, C_{ijkl} is the Weyl tensor, R_{ij} the Ricci tensor and R the scalar curvature. The Weyl tensor has the same symmetries as that of Riemann tensor, i.e.,

$$C_{ijkl} = -C_{jikl} = -C_{ijlk}, C_{ijkl} = C_{klij} \tag{5.10}$$

$$C_{ijkl} + C_{iklj} + C_{iljk} = 0 \tag{5.11}$$

The Weyl tensor is also traceless, i.e.,

$$C^m_{imj} = g^{mn}C_{nimj} = 0 \tag{5.12}$$

which shows that the Weyl tensor is irreducible (cf., Section 1.9).

Multiplying Eq. (5.9) by g^{ik}, using Eq. (5.12) and $g^{ij}g_{ij} = n$, we get

$$R_{jl} = P(n-2)R_{jl} + [P + Q(1-n)]g_{jl}R$$

Comparing the coefficients of R_{jl} and $g_{jl}R$ on both sides of this equation, we get

$$P = \frac{1}{n-2}, \quad Q = \frac{1}{(n-1)(n-2)}$$

Thus, from Eq. (5.9), we have the following decomposition of Riemann tensor (for $n > 2$)

$$R_{ijkl} = C_{ijkl} + \frac{1}{n-2}(g_{ik}R_{jl} + g_{jl}R_{ik} - g_{il}R_{jk} - g_{jk}R_{il})$$

$$+ \frac{1}{(n-1)(n-2)}(g_{il}g_{jk} - g_{ik}g_{jl})R \tag{5.13}$$

which is the defining equation for the *Weyl curvature tensor* (or *Weyl conformal curvature tensor*) for a n-dimensional Riemannian space.

Therefore, in a V_4 (a Riemannian space of dimension four) which is a space of interest in general theory of relativity, Eq. (5.13) becomes

$$R_{ijkl} = C_{ijkl} + \frac{1}{2}(g_{ik}R_{jl} + g_{jl}R_{ik} - g_{il}R_{jk} - g_{jk}R_{il})$$

$$+ \frac{R}{6}(g_{il}g_{jk} - g_{ik}g_{jl}) \tag{5.14}$$

This equation can also be expressed as

$$R_{ijkl} = C_{ijkl} + E_{ijkl} + G_{ijkl} \tag{5.15}$$

where E_{ijkl} is the Einstein curvature tensor defined as

$$E_{ijkl} = \frac{1}{2}(g_{ik}S_{jl} + g_{jl}S_{ik} - g_{il}S_{jk} - g_{jk}S_{il}) \qquad (5.16)$$

with S_{ij} being the traceless tensor, defined as

$$S_{ij} = R_{ij} - \frac{1}{4}Rg_{ij} \qquad (5.17)$$

$\left(\text{here } S = S_i^i = g^{ij}S_{ij} = g^{ij}R_{ij} - \frac{1}{4}g^{ij}g_{ij}R = 0\right)$ and

$$G_{ijkl} \equiv \frac{R}{12}(g_{ik}g_{jl} - g_{il}g_{jk}) \qquad (5.18)$$

It may be noted that Eq. (5.14) is a more frequent decomposition and may be regarded as the definition of the *Weyl tensor* in four-dimensional Riemannian space, all of the other quantities may be computed directly if the metric tensor is given.

Before discussing the properties of the quantities that appear in the decomposition (5.15), first let us examine that why the Weyl curvature tensor is known as Weyl conformal curvature tensor.

Definition 5.1 If V and $\tilde{V}$ are two Riemannian spaces with $g_{ij}(x)$ and $\tilde{g}_{ij}(x)$ being their metric tensors related through equation

$$\tilde{g}_{ij}(x) = e^{2\phi}g_{ij}(x) \qquad (5.19)$$

where ϕ is a real function of coordinates, then V and $\tilde{V}$ are called *conformal spaces* and the correspondence between V and $\tilde{V}$ is known as *conformal mapping*.

If the coordinate system of both V and $\tilde{V}$ is same then the line elements of V and $\tilde{V}$ are connected by the equation $d\tilde{s}^2 = e^{2\phi}ds^2$. We know that [cf., Eqs. (2.29) and (2.30)] the angle between two real vectors A^i and B^i is

$$\cos\theta = \frac{A_iB^i}{\sqrt{(A_iA^i)(B_iB^i)}} = \frac{g_{ij}A^jB^j}{\sqrt{(g_{ij}A^iA^j)(g_{ij}B^iB^j)}} \qquad (5.20)$$

which [using Eq. (5.19)] shows that under a conformal mapping, angles are preserved (see also Example 2.8). Also from Eq. (5.19), we have

$$\tilde{g}^{ij}(x) = e^{-2\phi}g^{ij}(x) \qquad (5.21)$$

From Eq. (3.1), the Christoffel symbol of first kind for $\tilde{V}$ is

$$\tilde{\Gamma}_{kij} = \frac{1}{2}\left(\frac{\partial\tilde{g}_{ki}}{\partial x^j} + \frac{\partial\tilde{g}_{jk}}{\partial x^i} - \frac{\partial\tilde{g}_{ij}}{\partial x^k}\right)$$

which [using Eq. (5.19)] becomes

$$\tilde{\Gamma}_{kij} = \frac{1}{2}e^{2\phi}\left(\frac{\partial g_{ki}}{\partial x^j} + \frac{\partial g_{jk}}{\partial x^i} - \frac{\partial g_{ij}}{\partial x^k}\right)$$

$$+ e^{2\phi}\left(\frac{\partial \phi}{\partial x^j}g_{ki} + \frac{\partial \phi}{\partial x^i}g_{jk} - \frac{\partial \phi}{\partial x^k}g_{ij}\right)$$

$$= e^{2\phi}\left[\Gamma_{kij} + \left(g_{ki}\frac{\partial \phi}{\partial x^j} + g_{jk}\frac{\partial \phi}{\partial x^i} - g_{ij}\frac{\partial \phi}{\partial x^k}\right)\right] \qquad (5.22)$$

Equation (5.22) gives the relationship between Christoffel symbols of first kind of two conformal spaces.

In a similar way, using Eqs. (5.19) and (5.21), the Christoffel symbols of second kind of two spaces V and $\tilde{V}$ are related through the equation

$$\tilde{\Gamma}^k_{ij} = \tilde{g}^{kl}\tilde{\Gamma}_{lij} = \Gamma^k_{ij} + \left(\delta^k_i\frac{\partial \phi}{\partial x^j} + \delta^k_l\frac{\partial \phi}{\partial x^i} - g_{ij}g^{kl}\frac{\partial \phi}{\partial x^l}\right) \qquad (5.23)$$

We now prove the following:

Theorem 5.1 The Weyl tensor is preserved under conformal mapping.

Proof To prove the theorem, it is necessary to find the Riemann tensor $\tilde{R}_{ijkl}$, the Ricci tensor $\tilde{R}_{ij}$ and the scalar curvature $\tilde{R}$ for the space $\tilde{V}$; and then use the decomposition (14). First we find $\tilde{R}_{ijkl}$. This can be done by using Eqs. (5.19) and (5.23) in Eq. (4.18) and we have

$$\tilde{R}_{ijkl} = \frac{1}{2}\left(\frac{\partial^2 \tilde{g}_{il}}{\partial x^k \partial x^j} + \frac{\partial^2 \tilde{g}_{jk}}{\partial x^l \partial x^i} - \frac{\partial^2 \tilde{g}_{jl}}{\partial x^k \partial x^i} - \frac{\partial^2 \tilde{g}_{ik}}{\partial x^l \partial x^j}\right)$$

$$+ \tilde{g}_{mn}(\tilde{\Gamma}^m_{jk}\tilde{\Gamma}^n_{il} - \tilde{\Gamma}^m_{jl}\tilde{\Gamma}^n_{ik})$$

$$= e^{2\phi}\left[R_{ijkl} + \left\{g_{il}\left(\frac{\partial^2 \phi}{\partial x^j \partial x^k} - \frac{\partial \phi}{\partial x^j}\frac{\partial \phi}{\partial x^k}\right)\right.\right.$$

$$+ g_{jk}\left(\frac{\partial^2 \phi}{\partial x^i \partial x^l} - \frac{\partial \phi}{\partial x^i}\frac{\partial \phi}{\partial x^l}\right) - g_{ik}\left(\frac{\partial^2 \phi}{\partial x^j \partial x^l} - \frac{\partial \phi}{\partial x^j}\frac{\partial \phi}{\partial x^l}\right)$$

$$\left.- g_{jl}\left(\frac{\partial^2 \phi}{\partial x^i \partial x^k} - \frac{\partial \phi}{\partial x^i}\frac{\partial \phi}{\partial x^k}\right)\right\}$$

$$+ \left.\left\{g_{il}g_{jk}\left(g^{mn}\frac{\partial \phi}{\partial x^m}\frac{\partial \phi}{\partial x^n}\right) - g_{ik}g_{jl}\left(g^{mn}\frac{\partial \phi}{\partial x^m}\frac{\partial \phi}{\partial x^n}\right)\right\}\right]$$

$$= e^{2\phi}[R_{ijkl} + (g_{il}\phi_{jk} + g_{jk}\phi_{il} - g_{ik}\phi_{jl} - g_{jl}\phi_{ik})$$

$$+ (g_{il}g_{jk} - g_{ik}g_{jl})(g^{mn}\phi_{,m}\phi_{,n})] \qquad (5.24)$$

where

$$\phi_{ij} = \phi_{ji} = \frac{\partial^2 \phi}{\partial x^i \partial x^j} - \frac{\partial \phi}{\partial x^i}\frac{\partial \phi}{\partial x^j} \tag{5.25}$$

$$g^{mn}\phi_{,m}\phi_{,n} = g^{mn}\frac{\partial \phi}{\partial x^m}\frac{\partial \phi}{\partial x^n} \tag{5.26}$$

We now find the Ricci tensor $\tilde{R}_{ij}$ for $\tilde{V}$. Multiplying both sides of Eq. (5.24) by $\tilde{g}^{ik}$ and using Eq. (5.21), we get

$$\tilde{g}^{ik}\tilde{R}_{ijkl} = \tilde{R}_{jl}$$

$$= R_{jl} + (\delta_l^k \phi_{jk} + \delta_j^i \phi_{il} - 4\phi_{jl} - g_{jl}g^{ik}\phi_{ik})$$

$$+ (\delta_l^k g_{jk} - 4g_{jl})(g^{mn}\phi_{,m}\phi_{,n})$$

$$= R_{jl} - 2\phi_{jl} - g_{jl}\phi - 3g_{jl}g^{mn}\phi_{,m}\phi_{,n}$$

But from Eqs. (5.25) and (5.26), we have

$$\phi = g^{mn}\phi_{mn} = g^{mn}\frac{\partial^2 \phi}{\partial x^m \partial x^n} - g^{mn}\phi_{,m}\phi_{,n}$$

Thus, the above equation can be expressed as

$$\tilde{R}_{jl} = R_{jl} - 2\phi_{jl} - g_{jl}g^{mn}\frac{\partial^2 \phi}{\partial x^m \partial x^n} - 2g_{jl}g^{mn}\phi_{,m}\phi_{,n} \tag{5.27}$$

Finally, to obtain $\tilde{R}$, we multiply Eq. (5.27) by $\tilde{g}^{jl}$ and use Eq. (5.21) to get

$$\tilde{R} = e^{-2\phi}\left[R - 6g^{mn}\frac{\partial^2 \phi}{\partial x^m \partial x^n} - 6g^{mn}\phi_{,m}\phi_{,n}\right] \tag{5.28}$$

From Eq. (5.27), we have

$$\phi_{jl} = -\frac{1}{2}\tilde{R}_{jl} + \frac{1}{2}R_{jl} - \frac{1}{2}g_{jl}g^{mn}\frac{\partial^2 \phi}{\partial x^m \partial x^n} - 2g_{jl}g^{mn}\phi_{,m}\phi_{,n} \tag{5.29}$$

But from Eq. (5.28), using Eq. (5.19), we have

$$g_{jl}g^{mn}\frac{\partial^2 \phi}{\partial x^m \partial x^n} = -\frac{1}{6}\tilde{R}\tilde{g}_{jl} + \frac{1}{6}Rg_{jl} - g_{jl}g^{mn}\phi_{,m}\phi_{,n}$$

Substituting this value in Eq. (5.29), we get

$$\phi_{jl} = -\frac{1}{2}(\tilde{R}_{jl} - R_{jl}) + \frac{1}{12}(\tilde{R}\tilde{g}_{jl} - Rg_{jl}) - \frac{1}{2}g_{jl}g^{mn}\phi_{,m}\phi_{,n} \tag{5.30}$$

From Eq. (5.24), raising the first index of Riemann tensor, we have

$$\tilde{R}^p_{jkl} = R^p_{jkl} + \delta_l^p \phi_{jk} - \delta_k^p \phi_{jl} + g^{ip}(g_{jk}\phi_{il} - g_{jl}\phi_{ik})$$

$$+ (\delta_l^p g_{jk} - \delta_k^p g_{jl})(g^{mn}\phi_{,m}\phi_{,n}) \tag{5.31}$$

Now using the value of ϕ_{jl}, etc. from Eq. (5.30) in Eq. (5.31), we get, after simplification

$$\tilde{R}^p_{jkl} - \frac{1}{2}(\delta^p_k \tilde{R}_{jl} + \tilde{g}_{jl}\tilde{R}^p_k - \delta^p_l \tilde{R}_{jk} - \tilde{g}_{jk}\tilde{R}^p_l) - \frac{\tilde{R}}{6}(\delta^p_l \tilde{g}_{jk} - \delta^p_k \tilde{g}_{jl})$$

$$= R^p_{jkl} - \frac{1}{2}(\delta^p_k R_{jl} + g_{jl}R^p_k - \delta^p_l R_{jk} - g_{jk}R^p_l) - \frac{R}{6}(\delta^p_l g_{jk} - \delta^p_k g_{jl})$$

(5.32)

which is a relation between the Riemann tensor, Ricci tensor and the scalar curvature of the two spaces V and $\tilde{V}$.

Hence, from Eq. (5.14) after raising the first index, Eq. (5.32) leads to

$$\tilde{C}^p_{jkl} = C^p_{jkl}$$

which shows that the Weyl tensor is preserved under conformal mapping. This completes the proof.

Remarks

1. Since the Weyl tensor remains invariant under conformal mapping, therefore this tensor is known as Weyl conformal curvature tensor.

2. A space for which Weyl conformal tensor vanishes is called a *conformally flat space*.

EXAMPLE 5.1 Show that a four-dimensional space is conformally flat if the Riemann curvature tensor satisfies the relation

$$R_{ijkl} = \alpha(g_{ik}g_{jl} - g_{il}g_{jk})$$

Solution   Given that

$$R_{ijkl} = \alpha(g_{ik}g_{jl} - g_{il}g_{jk})$$

Contract this equation twice to get

$$R_{jl} = 3\alpha g_{jl} \quad \text{and} \quad R = 12\alpha$$

Now substitute these values of R_{ijkl}, R_{jl} and R in the defining Eq. (5.14) of the Weyl conformal tensor, we get

$$C_{ijkl} = 0$$

and the space is conformally flat.

Note. This example also indicates that a conformally flat space is a space of constant curvature (cf., Section 4.13).

The duals of C_{ijkl}, E_{ijkl} and G_{ijkl} are defined as follows:

$$C^*_{ijkl} = \frac{1}{2}\epsilon_{ijmn}C^{mn}_{kl}, \quad C^*_{ijkl} = \frac{1}{2}\epsilon_{klrs}C^{rs}_{ij}$$

(5.32a)

$$E^*_{ijkl} = \frac{1}{2}\epsilon_{ijmn}E^{mn}_{kl}, \quad E^*_{ijkl} = \frac{1}{2}\epsilon_{klrs}E^{rs}_{ij} \tag{5.33}$$

and

$$G^*_{ijkl} = \frac{1}{2}\epsilon_{ijmn}G^{mn}_{kl}, \quad G^*_{ijkl} = \frac{1}{2}\epsilon_{klrs}G^{rs}_{ij} \tag{5.34}$$

Properties of C_{ijkl}, E_{ijkl} and G_{ijkl}

The Weyl conformal curvature tensor C_{ijkl}, the Einstein curvature tensor E_{ijkl} and the tensor G_{ijkl} appearing in the decomposition (5.15) have the following properties:

(i) $E_{ijkl} = -E_{jikl}, \quad E_{ijkl} = -E_{ijlk}, \quad E_{ijkl} = E_{klij}$

$\quad E_{ijkl} + E_{iklj} + E_{iljk} = 0$

$\quad E_{jk} \equiv E^i_{jki} = S_{jk} = R_{jk} - \frac{1}{4}g_{jk}R, \quad E^j_j = E^{ij}_{ji} = E^{ij}_{ij} = 0$

(ii) $G_{ijkl} = -G_{jikl}, \quad G_{ijkl} = -G_{ijlk}, \quad G_{ijkl} = G_{klij}$

$\quad G_{ijkl} + G_{iklj} + G_{iljk} = 0$

$\quad G_{jk} \equiv G^i_{jki} = \frac{1}{4}g_{jk}R, \quad G^j_j = G^{ij}_{ji} = -G^{ij}_{ij} = R$

(iii) $C^{**}_{ijkl} = -C_{ijkl}$

(iv) $E^{**}_{ijkl} = E_{ijkl}$

(v) $C^*_{ijkl} = C^*_{ijkl}$

(vi) $E^*_{ijkl} = -E^*_{ijkl}$

(vii) The quantity $E^{(+)}_{ijkl} \equiv E_{ijkl} + iE^*_{ijkl}$ is self-dual, on the first (second) pair of indices, upto a factor of $-i(+i)$, that is

$$E^{(+)*}_{ijkl} = -iE^{(+)}_{ijkl} \quad \text{and} \quad E^{(+)*}_{ijkl} = +iE^{(+)}_{ijkl}$$

(viii) $C^{ij*}_{ij} = 0$

(ix) $E^{ij*}_{ij} = 0$

(x) $C^*_{ijkl} = C^*_{klij}$

(xi) $E^*_{ijkl}E^{ijkl} = 0$

(xii) $E_{ijrs}E^{rs}_{kl}E^{ijkl} = 0$

(xiii) $E^*_{ijrs}E^{rs}_{mn}E^{mnpq}E^{ij}_{pq} = 0$

The proofs of the above mentioned properties are as follows:

Proof (i) and (ii)   Follow directly from Eqs. (5.16) and (5.18).

Proof (iii)   Consider

$$C^{*\dot{k}l}_{ij} = \frac{1}{4}\epsilon^{klrs}\epsilon_{ijmn}C^{mn}_{rs}$$

Using Eq. (2.42) we obtain, on lowering the indices k and l,

$$C^*_{ijkl} = -(C_{ik}g_{jl} - C_{il}g_{jk} - C_{jk}g_{il} + C_{jl}g_{ik} + C_{ijkl}) \tag{5.35}$$

But since the Weyl tensor is traceless, we thus have

$$C^{**}_{ijkl} = -C_{ijkl}$$

Proof (iv)   Here we can use Eq. (5.35) and write

$$E^{**}_{ijkl} = -(E_{ik}g_{jl} - E_{il}g_{jk} - E_{jk}g_{il} + E_{jl}g_{ik} + E_{ijkl})$$

which on using property (i) leads to

$$E^{**}_{ijkl} = -(S_{ik}g_{jl} - S_{il}g_{jk} - S_{jk}g_{il} + S_{jl}g_{ik} + E_{ijkl})$$

$$= -(-2E_{ijkl} + E_{ijkl}) = E_{ijkl}$$

Remark

Observe that, in proving property (iv), we had to use the explicit definition of E_{ijkl} [cf., Eq. (5.16)]. It may easily be seen that if we take

$$E_{ijkl} = \frac{1}{2}(g_{il}R_{jk} + g_{jk}R_{il} - g_{ik}R_{jl} - g_{jl}R_{ik})$$

as the definition of the Einstein curvature tensor [cf., Eq. (5.14)], then we cannot obtain Property (iv). This suggests that the decomposition (5.15) is more basic than the decomposition (5.14).

Proof (v)   We have

$$C^{**}_{ijkl} = -C_{ijkl}$$

or

$$\overset{*}{C}{}^{**}_{ijkl} = -C^{*}_{ijkl}$$

or

$$-C^{*}_{ijkl} = -C^{*}_{ijkl}$$

or

$$C^{*}_{ijkl} = C^{*}_{ijkl}$$

Proof (vi)   We have

$$E^{**}_{ijkl} = E_{ijkl}$$

or

$$\overset{*}{E}{}^{**}_{ijkl} = E^{*}_{ijkl}$$

or

$$-E^{*}_{ijkl} = E^{*}_{ijkl}$$

Proof (vii)   Obvious.

Proof (viii)   Since $C^{ij*}_{kl} = \frac{1}{2}\epsilon_{klrs}C^{ijrs}$, therefore

$$C^{ij*}_{ij} = \frac{1}{2}\epsilon_{ijrs}C^{ijrs} = 0$$

because $C_{ijkl} + C_{iklj} + C_{iljk} = 0$.

Proof (ix) Same as property (viii).

Proof (x) Consider

$$C^{**}_{ijkl} = -C_{ijkl} = -C_{klij}$$

or

$$C^{*\overset{*}{*}}_{ijkl} = -C^{*}_{klij}$$

or

$$-C^{*}_{ijkl} = -C^{*}_{klij}$$

Thus

$$C^{*}_{ijkl} = C^{*}_{klij}$$

Proof (xi) We have

$$E^{*}_{ijkl}E^{ijkl} = -E^{*}_{ijkl}E^{ijkl}$$

$$= -E^{*}_{klij}E^{klij}$$

$$= -E^{*}_{klij}E^{ijkl}$$

$$= -E_{klij}E^{\overset{*}{*}ijkl}$$

$$= -E_{ijkl}E^{\overset{*}{*}ijkl}$$

$$= -E^{*}_{ijkl}E^{ijkl}$$

$$= 0$$

Proof (xii) We have

$$E_{ijrs}E^{rs}_{kl}E^{ijkl} = E^{**}_{ijrs}E^{rs}_{kl}E^{ijkl}$$

$$= E_{ijrs}E^{\overset{*}{*}rs}_{kl}E^{\overset{*}{*}ijkl}$$

$$= -E_{ijrs}E^{*rs}_{kl}E^{\overset{*}{*}ijkl}$$

$$= E_{ijrs}E^{rs}_{kl}E^{\overset{*}{*}\overset{*}{*}ijkl}$$

$$= -E_{ijrs}E^{rs}_{kl}E^{ijkl}$$

$$= 0$$

Note: This is an important property satisfied by the Einstein curvature tensor.

Proof (xiii) We have

$$E^*_{ijrs}E^{rs}_{mn}E^{mnpq}E^{ij}_{pq} = -E^*_{ijrs}E^{rs}_{mn}E^{mnpq}E^{ij}_{pq}$$

$$= -E^*_{rsij}E^{ij}_{mn}E^{mnpq}E^{rs}_{pq}$$

$$= -E_{rsij}\overset{*}{E}{}^{ij}_{mn}E^{mnpq}E^{rs}_{pq}$$

$$= -E_{ijrs}E^{rs}_{pq}E^{mnpq}\overset{*}{E}{}^{ij}_{mn}$$

$$= -E_{ijrs}E^{rs}_{pq}E^{pqmn}\overset{*}{E}{}^{ij}_{mn}$$

$$= -E^*_{ijrs}E^{rs}_{pq}E^{pqmn}E^{ij}_{mn}$$

$$= -E^*_{ijrs}E^{rs}_{pq}E^{pqmn}E^{ij}_{mn}$$

$$= 0$$

Remarks

1. The field equations of general relativity, known as *Einstein field equations,* are given by

$$R_{ij} - \frac{1}{2}g_{ij}R = -kT_{ij} \tag{5.36}$$

where R_{ij} is the Ricci tensor, g_{ij} the metric tensor, T_{ij} the energy-momentum tensor, R the scalar curvature and k is a constant.

Multiplying Eq. (5.36) by g^{ij} and using $g^{ij}g_{ij} = 4$, we get $R = kT$. Substitute it in Eq. (5.36), to get

$$R_{ij} = -k(T_{ij} - \frac{1}{2}g_{ij}T) \tag{5.37}$$

If $T_{ij} = 0$, then $T = g^{ij}T_{ij} = 0$ and Eq. (5.37) leads to

$$R_{ij} = 0 \tag{5.38}$$

which are the field equations for empty spacetime. This is also known as *Einstein law of gravitation.* The word *'empty'* here means that there is no matter present and also no physical fields except, the gravitational field. The gravitational field does not disturb the emptiness of the space, while the other fields do. For the space between the planets in the solar system, the condition of emptiness holds in a good approximation and Eq. (5.38) is applied in such a case.

The condition (5.38) is obviously satisfied for flat spaces. In this case the geodesics are the straight lines and the particle move along these straight lines. When the space is not flat, then the Einstein law puts restriction on the curvature of the space.

2. In Section 4.7, it is shown that the number of independent components of Riemann tensor in n-dimension is $\dfrac{1}{12}n^2(n^2-1)$. Thus

   (i) for $n=1$, $R_{ijkl}=0$.

   (ii) for $n=2$, R_{ijkl} has only one independent component, namely

$$R_{1212}=\frac{1}{2}gR$$

   (iii) for $n=3$, R_{ijkl} has six independent components. The Ricci tensor has also six independent components and thus R_{ijkl} can be expressed in terms of Ricci tensor as

$$R_{ijkl}=g_{ik}R_{jl}+g_{jl}R_{ik}-g_{il}R_{jk}-g_{jk}R_{il}-\frac{R}{2}(g_{ik}g_{jl}-g_{il}g_{jk})$$

   (iv) for $n=4$, R_{ijkl} has twenty independent components-ten of which are given by Ricci tensor and the remaining ten by the Weyl tensor C_{ijkl}, which is given by equation

$$C_{ijkl}=R_{ijkl}-\frac{1}{2}(g_{ik}R_{jl}+g_{jl}R_{ik}-g_{il}R_{jk}-g_{jk}R_{il})$$

$$-\frac{R}{6}(g_{il}g_{jk}-g_{ik}g_{jl})$$

If $R_{ij}=0$, then this equation leads to $R_{ijkl}=C_{ijkl}$. Since R_{ijkl} characterize the gravitational field, therefore, it is the Weyl tensor which describes the true gravitational fields in a vacuum region.

Thus, for empty spacetime of dimension two or three, from (ii) and (iii) above, the Riemann curvature tensor R_{ijkl} vanishes and consequently there is no gravitational field. It is only in four or more dimensions that genuine gravitational field can exist in empty space.

Therefore, according to general theory of relativity: *if we lived in a universe where the spacetime has only three dimensions, gravity could not exist in a vacuum region.*

5.4   Electric and Magnetic Parts of the Riemann and Weyl Tensors

The similarities between electromagnetism and gravitation are very rich and detailed. Some of these similarities are still uncovered while some are further developed. One of the similarity is reflected in the Maxwell-like form of the gravitational field tensor (the Weyl tensor), the super-energy-momentum tensor (the Bel-Robinson tensor) and the dynamical Equations (the Bianchi identities) (cf., Ahsan, 1999 and Kramer et al., 1980).

In Chapter 2, we have seen that the electromagnetic field can be decomposed into its electric and magnetic parts [cf., Eq. (2.54)]. Similar type of decomposition can be adapted in general relativity and the Weyl tensor can be decomposed into electric and magnetic parts.

An observer moving with time-like 4-velocity u^a in a relativistic electromagnetic field measures the electric and magnetic components of the field, respectively, by (cf., Remark 4, Section 2.6)

$$E_a = F_{ab}u^b, \quad H_a = F_{ab}^* u^b \tag{5.39}$$

Here $F_{ab} = -F_{ba}$ is the Maxwell stress tensor with dual $F_{ab}^* = \frac{1}{2}\epsilon_{abcd}F^{cd}$, and the 4-velocity of the observer is normalized so that $u_c u^c = -1$.

The observer's measurement of the spacetime curvature components has some analogies with the electromagnetic measurements described above. The gravitational stress tensor, or Riemann curvature tensor R_{abcd}, is skew symmetric in both the first and last pair of its indices. By analogy with the definition in (5.39), the electric and magnetic parts of the Riemann curvature tensor can be defined (Ahsan, 1999) respectively, by

$$\hat{E}_{ac} = R_{abcd}u^b u^d, \quad \hat{H}_{ac} = {}^* R_{abcd}u^b u^d \tag{5.40}$$

where the dual is defined to be

$$^* R_{abcd} = \frac{1}{2}\epsilon_{abef}R_{cd}^{ef} \tag{5.41}$$

The Riemann curvature tensor is said to be *purely electric* if $\hat{H}_{ac} = 0$ and *purely magnetic* if $\hat{E}_{ac} = 0$.

Despite the remarkable analogies between the mathematical properties of electromagnetic and gravitational stress tensor, there is an important distinction between them whereas the Maxwell tensor is irreducible, the Riemann tensor has separable traces. Hence, one may consider the electric and magnetic components of the trace-free part, the Weyl tensor C_{abcd}, of the curvature tensor, as well as the electric and magnetic parts of the Riemann tensor. Indeed, these are distinct objects in general. An observer with time-like 4-velocity vector u is said (Ahsan, 1999 and Kramer et al., 1980) to measure the electric and magnetic components, E_{ac} and H_{ac}, respectively, of the Weyl tensor C_{abcd} by

$$E_{ac} = C_{abcd}u^b u^d, \quad H_{ac} = {}^* C_{abcd}u^b u^d \tag{5.42}$$

where the dual is defined to be

$$^* C_{abcd} = \frac{1}{2}\epsilon_{abef}C_{cd}^{ef}$$

Also

$$E_{ab} + iH_{ab} = Q_{ab} = \bar{C}_{abcd}u^b u^d \tag{5.43}$$

where

$$Q_{ab} = Q_{ba}, \quad Q_a^a = Q_{ab}u^b = 0$$

$$\bar{C}_{abcd} = C_{abcd} + i^* C_{abcd} \tag{5.44}$$

and

$$E_{ab} = E_{ba}, \quad E_{ab}u^b = 0, \quad E_{ab}g^{ab} = E_t^t = 0$$

$$H_{ab} = H_{ba}, \quad H_{ab}u^b = 0, \quad H_{ab}g^{ab} = H_t^t = 0 \tag{5.45}$$

The Weyl tensor is said to be *purely electric* if $H_{ac} = 0$ and *purely magnetic* if $E_{ac} = 0$. It is known that (Kramer et al., 1980) the Weyl tensor in terms of E and H can be decomposed as

$$C_{ab}^{cd} = 2u_{[a}E_{b]}^{[c}u^{d]} + \delta_{[a}^{[c}E_{b]}^{d]} - \epsilon_{abef}u^e H^{f[c}u^{d]} - \epsilon^{cdef}u_e H_{f[a}u_{b]} \tag{5.46}$$

which equivalently can be written as

$$C^{abcd} = (\epsilon^{acef}\epsilon^{bdpq} - g^{acef}g^{bdpq})u_e u_p E_{fq}$$

$$+ (\epsilon^{acef}g^{bdpq} - g^{acef}\epsilon^{bdpq})u_e u_p H_{fq} \tag{5.46a}$$

or

$$C_{abcd} = 2u_a u_c E_{bd} + 2u_b u_d E_{ac} - 2u_a u_d E_{bc} - 2u_b u_c E_{ad}$$

$$+ g_{ad}E_{bc} + g_{bc}E_{ad} - g_{ac}E_{bd} - g_{bd}E_{ac} + \epsilon_{ab}^{pq}u_p u_d H_{qc}$$

$$- \epsilon_{ab}^{pq}u_p u_c H_{qd} + \epsilon_{cd}^{pq}u_b u_p H_{aq} - \epsilon_{cd}^{pq}u_a u_p H_{bq} \tag{5.47}$$

5.5   Classification of Gravitational Fields

Since a gravitational field is characterized by the Riemann curvature tensor and, in vacuum Riemann tensor reduces to Weyl tensor. Therefore, in order to have a classification of vacuum gravitational field, it is sufficient to classify the Weyl tensor. There are essentially three main approaches for the classification of Weyl tensor, namely, the matrix method, the spinor method and the tensor method. The tensor method is equivalent to the other two methods. The spinor method is the shortest and elegant route to Petrov classification, while the tensor method is useful in many calculations. The matrix method suffers particularly from the fact that it does not bring out the hierarchy of types in Penrose diagram so well as the other methods do, nor it is convenient in calculations but it does have slight advantages in some of the simplest physical interpretation.

The classification of gravitational fields, commonly known as *Petrov classification*, is of great importance in the theory of general relativity, especially in the study of gravitational radiation. The different types of gravitational fields that have been resulted from the Petrov classification scheme are designated as *Petrov types* I, II, D, N, III. Petrov type I gravitational field is called an *algebraically general* gravitational field; while

Petrov types II, D, N and III are known as *algebraically special* gravitational fields. It is also known that gravitational fields belonging to Petrov types N and III correspond to the state of gravitational radiation (cf., Kramer et al., 1980; Petrov, 1969; Pirani, 1965; and Stephani, 1982).

The Riemann curvature has also been classified, among others, by Sharma and Husain (1969) according to the number of eigenvalues of a complex six-dimensional tensor defined in terms of curvature tensor. The different cases that have been arrived at are summarized as follows:

Case I: When all the eigenvalues are different, the matrix for R_{ijkl} reduces to

$$R_{ijkl} = \begin{bmatrix} a_1 & 0 & 0 & b_1 & 0 & 0 \\ 0 & a_2 & 0 & 0 & b_2 & 0 \\ 0 & 0 & a_3 & 0 & 0 & b_3 \\ b_1 & 0 & 0 & -a_1 & 0 & 0 \\ 0 & b_2 & 0 & 0 & -a_2 & 0 \\ 0 & 0 & b_3 & 0 & 0 & -a_3 \end{bmatrix}$$

Case II: When two of the three eigenvalues are equal, we have the following two sub-cases:

Case II(a)

$$R_{ijkl} = \begin{bmatrix} a_1 & 0 & 0 & b_1 & 0 & 0 \\ 0 & a_1 & 0 & 0 & b_1 & 0 \\ 0 & 0 & -2a_1 & 0 & 0 & -2b_1 \\ b_1 & 0 & 0 & -a_1 & 0 & 0 \\ 0 & b_1 & 0 & 0 & -a_1 & 0 \\ 0 & 0 & 2b_1 & 0 & 0 & -2a_1 \end{bmatrix}$$

Case II(b)

$$R_{ijkl} = \begin{bmatrix} 2a & 0 & 0 & 2b & 0 & 0 \\ 0 & -(a+d) & -c & 0 & (b-c) & -d \\ 0 & -c & -(a-d) & 0 & -d & (b+c) \\ 2b & 0 & 0 & -2a & 0 & 0 \\ 0 & (b-c) & -d & 0 & (a+d) & c \\ 0 & -d & (b+c) & 0 & c & (a-d) \end{bmatrix}$$

Case III: When all the three eigenvalues are equal, we then have the following possibilities:

Case III(a)

$$R_{ijkl} = \begin{bmatrix} 0 & -a & -b & 0 & -b & a \\ -a & 0 & 0 & -b & 0 & 0 \\ -b & 0 & 0 & a & 0 & 0 \\ 0 & -b & a & 0 & a & b \\ -b & 0 & 0 & a & 0 & 0 \\ a & 0 & 0 & b & 0 & 0 \end{bmatrix}$$

Case III(b)

$$R_{ijkl} = \begin{bmatrix} 0 & 0 & 0 & 0 & 0 & 0 \\ 0 & a & -b & 0 & b & a \\ 0 & -b & -a & 0 & a & -b \\ 0 & 0 & 0 & 0 & 0 & 0 \\ 0 & b & a & 0 & -a & b \\ 0 & a & -b & 0 & b & a \end{bmatrix}$$

The Cases I, II(b) and III(a) correspond to the Petrov types I, II and III, respectively. It has been shown by Sharma and Husain (1969) that Cases III(a) and III(b) correspond to the case of gravitational radiation and further that they are characterized by the following covariant conditions:

(i) A necessary and sufficient condition in order that R_{ijkl} may belong to Case III(a) is that there exists a null vector l^i such that

$$R_{ijkl}l^i l^k = 0 \quad \text{and} \quad R^*_{ijkl}l^i l^k = 0$$

(ii) A necessary and sufficient condition in order that R_{ijkl} may belong to Case III(b) is that there exists a null vector l^i such that

$$R_{ijkl}l^i = 0 \quad \text{and} \quad R^*_{ijkl}l^i = 0$$

5.6 Invariants of the Riemann Tensor

It is known that the number of independent components of the Riemann tensor in n-dimensions is $\frac{1}{12}n^2(n^2-1)$. These components of the Riemann tensor describe the curvature of a n-dimensional space, but they do not do it in an invariant manner. This invariant characterization of curved space must be in terms of scalars which are constructed from the Riemann tensor and the metric tensor. These scalars can be constructed as follows (cf., [Weinberg, 1972]):

For a general transformation $x^i \longrightarrow x'^i$, the n^2 quantities $\dfrac{\partial x'^i}{\partial x^j}$ can be made anything we want to like at a given point of the space,. i.e., at this point $\frac{1}{12}n^2(n^2-1)$ independent components of the Riemann tensor and $\frac{1}{2}n(n+1)$

components of the metric tensor may by general coordinate transformation be subjected to n^2 algebraic conditions. Thus, the number of scalars that can be constructed from the Riemann tensor and the metric tensor is

$$\frac{1}{12}n^2(n^2-1) + \frac{1}{2}n(n+1) - n^2 = \frac{1}{12}n(n-1)(n-2)(n+3), \quad \text{for } n \geq 3 \tag{5.48}$$

For $n = 3$, Eq. (5.48) leads to three curvature scalars, namely, $R, R^{ij}R_{ij}, \dfrac{\det R}{\det g}$, while for $n = 4$, Eq. (5.48) suggests that there are fourteen invariants of the Riemann curvature tensor. There is the Ricci scalar R. There are four invariants of the Weyl tensor C_{ijkl}. There are three invariants of the Einstein curvature tensor E_{ijkl} and six invariants of the combined Weyl and Einstein curvature tensors. The component forms of these invariants are given by (cf., Greenberg, 1972)

$$A_1 = C_{ijkl}C^{ijkl}, \quad A_2 = C^*_{ijkl}C^{ijkl} \tag{5.49}$$

$$B_1 = \frac{4}{3}C_{ijmn}C^{mnrs}C^{ij}_{rs}, \quad B_2 = \frac{4}{3}C^*_{ijmn}C^{mnrs}C^{ij}_{rs} \tag{5.49a}$$

$$E = 2E_{ijkl}E^{ijkl} \tag{5.49b}$$

$$F = 4E_{ijrs}E^{rs}_{mn}E^{mnpq}E^{ij}_{pq} - \frac{1}{2}E^2 \tag{5.49c}$$

$$3G = 32E_{ijrs}E^{rs}_{mn}E^{mnpq}E_{uvpq}E^{uvxy}E^{ij}_{xy} - 3EF - E^3 \tag{5.49d}$$

$$K_1 = \frac{1}{4}C_{ijrs}E^{rs}_{mn}E^{ijmn}, \quad K_2 = \frac{1}{4}C^*_{ijrs}E^{rs}_{mr}E^{ijmn} \tag{5.49e}$$

$$2L_1 = 32C_{ijrs}E^{rs}_{mn}E^{pqmn}C_{pqxy}E^{xyuv}E^{ij}_{uv} - K_1^2 + K_2^2 \tag{5.49f}$$

$$2L_2 = 32C^*_{ijrs}E^{rs}_{mn}E^{pqmn}C_{pqxy}E^{xyuv}E^{ij}_{uv} - 2K_1K_2 \tag{5.49g}$$

$$3M_1 = 256C_{ijrs}E^{rsmn}E_{ijmn}C^{ijkl}E_{klpq}E^{uvpq}C_{uvwx}E^{wxyz}$$
$$E^{ij}_{yz} - K_1^3 + 3K_1K_2^2 - 18K_1L_1 + 18K_2L_2 \tag{5.49h}$$

$$3M_2 = 256C^*_{ijrs}E^{rsmn}E_{ijmn}C^{ijkl}E_{klpq}E^{uvpq}C_{uvwx}$$
$$E^{wxyz}E^{ij}_{yz} - 18K_1L_2 - 18K_2L_1 - 3K_1^2K_2 + K_2^3 \tag{5.49i}$$

It is known that at a point of spacetime, the Einstein curvature tensor is related in an algebraic way to the distribution of matter and energy density through the Einstein's field equations

$$R_{ij} - \frac{1}{2}g_{ij}R = -\frac{8\pi G}{c^4}T_{ij} \tag{5.50}$$

which, in alternate form, may be expressed as

$$S_{ij} = R_{ij} - \frac{1}{4}g_{ij}R = -\frac{8\pi G}{c^4}\left(T_{ij} - \frac{1}{4}g_{ij}T\right) \tag{5.51}$$

When the Einstein field equations are written in the form (5.51) it may be noted that S_{ij} is related to the trace-free part of the energy-momentum or stress-energy tensor T_{ij}.

The invariants of S_{ij} (Greenberg, 1972) are given by

$$e = \frac{1}{2} S_{ij} S^{ij}, \quad f = \frac{1}{2} S_{ij} S^{jk} S^i_k, \quad g = \frac{1}{4} S_{ip} S^{pq} S_{qr} S^{ri} - \frac{1}{2} e^2 \qquad (5.52)$$

A relation between the invariants of S_{ij} and E_{ijkl} is given by

$$E = 8e, \quad F = -16e^2 - 64g, \quad G = 64f^2 \qquad (5.53)$$

From Eq. (5.53) it may be noted that the number of summations implied is considerably reduced when compared with the expressions of E, F and G [cf., Eqs. (5.49b) and (5.49c)], and thus provides a computational advantage. Also, this equation provides a coordinate independent relation between the quantities which describe the geometry and the quantities which describe the matter content. Moreover, Eq. (5.53) shows that G is a non-negative quantity, a fact which is not clear from Eq. (5.49d).

The study of these scalar invariants is important in general theory of relativity since they allow a manifestation of coordinate invariants characterization of certain geometrical properties of spacetimes. For example, the behaviour of the scalar $R_{ijkl} R^{ijkl}$ is studied in connection with the existence of any geometrical singularity. Based on an analogy with the state of electromagnetic radiation in terms of the invariants of the electromagnetic field (cf., Chapter 6), we shall now formulate a criterion for the existence of gravitational radiation in terms of the invariants of the Riemann curvature tensor.

If in the decomposition (5.14), we set $R_{ij} = 0$ then Riemann tensor reduces to Weyl tensor; and in this case there are four invariants of Riemann tensor which are given by

$$A_1 = R_{ijkl} R^{ijkl}, \quad A_2 = R^*_{ijkl} R^{ijkl}$$

$$B_1 = \frac{4}{3} R_{ijmn} R^{mnrs} R^{ij}_{rs}, \quad B_2 = \frac{4}{3} R^*_{ijmn} R^{mnrs} R^{ij}_{rs}$$

These invariants have been calculated by Ahsan and Husain (1977) for the classification of Riemann tensor due to Sharma and Husain (1969) and Petrov (1957). It is found that all these four invariants vanish for Cases III(a), III(b) and Petrov types N and III; and this leads to the following criterion for the existence of gravitational radiation:

"*If $R_{abcd} \neq 0$ and $A_1 = A_2 = B_1 = B_2 = 0$, then the gravitational radiation is present; otherwise there is no gravitational radiation.*"

The validity of this assertion has also been checked by considering the following of spacetime solutions (Ahsan and Husain, 1977):

(i) *Takeno's plane wave solution*

$$ds^2 = -A dx^2 - 2D dx dy - B dy^2 - dz^2 + dt^2$$

(ii) *Einstein–Rosen metric*

$$ds^2 = e^{2\gamma - 2\psi}(dt^2 - dr^2) - r^2 e^{-2\psi} d\phi^2 - e^{2\psi} dz^2$$

where γ and ψ are functions of r and t only, $\psi = 0$ and $\gamma = \gamma(r - t)$.

(iii) *The Peres metric*

$$ds^2 = -dx_1^2 - dx_2^2 - dx_3^2 - 2f(dx_4 + dx_3)^2 + dx_4^2$$

(iv) *The Schwarzchild exterior solution*

$$ds^2 = -\left(1 - \frac{2m}{r}\right)^{-1} dr^2 - r^2 d\theta^2 - r^2 \sin^2\theta d\phi^2 + \left(1 - \frac{2m}{r}\right) dt^2$$

It is found that for the metrics (i)–(iii), all the four invariants of the Riemann tensor vanish and thus correspond to the state of gravitational radiation. While for the Schwarzchild exterior solution $A_1 \neq 0$, $B_1 \neq 0$, $A_2 = 0, B_2 = 0$; and Schwarzchild solution, being a Petrov type D solution, is known to be non-radiative.

5.7 Lie Derivative

In the previous chapters, we have discussed that how quantities change under coordinate transformation. It is interesting to explore the situation when a quantity remains invariant under coordinate transformation. For example, under which coordinate transformation the metric tensor remains invariant. Such type of coordinate transformations are of great importance as they provide informations about the symmetries of the Riemaninan manifold. In Euclidean space, the two types of transformations are: (a) discrete, such as reflection, and (b) continuous, such as translation and rotation. The continuous transformations are important and find their applications in general theory of relativity. In this section, we shall not only discuss a different type of transformation that will lead to the symmetries of the spacetime but also introduce a new type of derivative called Lie derivative.

Consider the coordinate transformation

$$x'^i = x'^i(\epsilon; x^j) \tag{5.54}$$

where

$$x^i = x'^i(0; x^j) \tag{5.55}$$

and ϵ is a parameter. Equation (5.54) describes a *one-parameter set of transformations* $x^i \longrightarrow x'^i$ which can be explained as follows:

Let a given point A be labelled by the set of four coordinates x^i. To this point A assign another point B of the spacetime in the same coordinate system which was used to label the first point A. This point B is labelled by the four coordinates x'^i. Thus to each point of the spacetime we can assign another point of the spacetime using the same coordinate system; and as a consequence, Eq. (5.54) describes a mapping of the spacetime onto itself.

Consider the special case of the infinitesimal transformation

$$x^i \longrightarrow x'^i = x^i + \epsilon \xi^i(x) \tag{5.56}$$

where ϵ is a parameter (small and arbitrary) and $\xi^i(x)$ is a continuous vector field, which may be defined as

$$\xi^i(x) = \left(\frac{\partial x'^i}{\partial \epsilon} \right)_{\epsilon=0} \tag{5.57}$$

The transformation defined by Eq. (5.56) is called an *infinitesimal mapping* which means that "to each point A (with coordinates x^i) of the spacetime there corresponds another point B [with coordinates $x'^i = x^i + \epsilon \xi^i(x)$], when the same coordinate system is used".

Now let there be a tensor field $T(x)$ defined in the spacetime under consideration. This tensor field $T(x)$ can be evaluated at point B in two different manners, viz., first, the value $T(x')$ of $T(x)$ at point B and secondly, the value $T'(x')$ of the transformed tensor T' (using the usual transformation laws of tensors) at point B. The difference between these two values of the tensor field T evaluated at the point B with the coordinates x' leads to the concept of Lie derivative of T. This process is illustrated by defining the Lie derivatives of the scalar field $\phi(x)$ (a tensor of rank zero), a contravariant vector A^i (a tensor of rank one) and a covariant vector A_i (a tensor of rank one).

First consider a scalar field $\phi(x)$. The value of ϕ at point B is $\phi(x')$. Then using the infinitesimal expansion [cf., Eq. (5.56)] the value of $\phi(x')$ at point x^i can be written. We have

$$\phi(x') = \phi(x + \epsilon\xi) = \phi(x) + \epsilon \frac{\partial \phi(x)}{\partial x^k} \xi^k \tag{5.58}$$

Since ϕ is a scalar, it remains invariant under the coordinate transformation (5.56), and we have

$$\phi'(x') = \phi(x) \tag{5.59}$$

where ϕ' is a function evaluated at point B whose coordinates are x'^i and ϕ is a function evaluated at point A whose coordinates are x^i. Then the *Lie derivative of the scalar function $\phi(x)$, with respect to the vector ξ^i*, denoted by $\mathcal{L}_\xi \phi(x)$, is defined as [from Eqs. (5.58) and (5.59)]

$$\mathcal{L}_\xi \phi(x) = \lim_{\epsilon \to 0} \frac{\phi(x') - \phi'(x')}{\epsilon}$$

$$= \lim_{\epsilon \to 0} \left\{ \frac{[\phi(x) + \epsilon \frac{\partial \phi(x)}{\partial x^k} \xi^k] - \phi(x)}{\epsilon} \right\}$$

$$= \xi^k \frac{\partial \phi(x)}{\partial x^k} \tag{5.60}$$

We thus have

Theorem 5.2 The Lie derivative of a scalar ϕ with respect to the vector ξ^i is the scalar product of the vector ξ^i with the gradient of the scalar ϕ.

Since ϕ is a scalar, the partial derivative in Eq. (5.60) may be replaced by covariant derivative and we have

$$\mathcal{L}_\xi \phi(x) = \xi^k \phi_{;k} \tag{5.61}$$

as the Lie derivative of a scalar function.

Remark

Equation (5.60) can also be obtained if we evaluate all functions under consideration at the same point A. Thus $\phi'(x')$ can be written as

$$\phi'(x') = \phi'(x + \epsilon\xi) = \phi'(x) + \epsilon\xi^k(x)\frac{\partial\phi'(x)}{\partial x^k} \tag{5.62}$$

Also, neglecting the terms of second and higher order in ϵ, we can replace $\phi'(x)$ by $\phi(x)$ in all terms containing ϵ and Eq. (5.62) can then be written as

$$\phi'(x') = \phi'(x) + \epsilon\xi^k(x)\frac{\partial\phi(x)}{\partial x^k}$$

This equation leads to

$$\phi'(x) = \phi'(x') - \epsilon\xi^k(x)\frac{\partial\phi(x)}{\partial x^k} = \phi(x) - \epsilon\xi^k(x)\frac{\partial\phi(x)}{\partial x^k}$$

[from Eq. (5.58)]. From this equation, the Lie derivative of a scalar function ϕ is

$$\mathcal{L}_\xi \phi(x) = \lim_{\epsilon \to 0} \frac{\phi(x) - \phi'(x)}{\epsilon}$$

$$= \lim_{\epsilon \to 0} \left\{ \frac{\phi(x) - [\phi(x) - \epsilon\xi^k(x)\frac{\partial\phi(x)}{\partial x^k}]}{\epsilon} \right\}$$

$$= \xi^k \frac{\partial\phi(x)}{\partial x^k} \tag{5.63}$$

Following Eq. (5.63), the *Lie derivative of a general tensor field* $T(x)$ *with respect to* ξ^i is defined as

$$\mathcal{L}_\xi T(x) = \lim_{\epsilon \to 0} \frac{T(x) - T'(x)}{\epsilon} \tag{5.64}$$

We also have

Theorem 5.3 The Lie derivative of a contravariant vector A^i with respect to the vector ξ is

$$\mathcal{L}_\xi A^i = \xi^k A^i_{;k} - A^k \xi^i_{;k}$$

Proof Consider a contravariant vector A^i which transforms according to the law

$$A'^i(x') = \frac{\partial x'^i}{\partial x^k} A^k(x) \tag{5.65}$$

But from Eq. (5.56), we have

$$\frac{\partial x'^i}{\partial x^k} = \frac{\partial x^i}{\partial x^k} + \epsilon \frac{\partial \xi^i(x)}{\partial x^k} = \delta^i_k + \epsilon \frac{\partial \xi^i(x)}{\partial x^k} \tag{5.66}$$

Using Eq. (5.66) in Eq. (5.65), we get

$$A'^i(x') = A^i(x) + \epsilon A^k(x) \frac{\partial \xi^i(x)}{\partial x^k} \tag{5.67}$$

Expanding A'^i around the point x^i and neglecting the terms of second and higher order in ϵ, we get

$$A'^i(x') = A'^i(x) + \epsilon \xi^k(x) \frac{\partial A^i(x)}{\partial x^k} \tag{5.68}$$

Equations (5.67) and (5.68) now lead to

$$A'^i = A^i + \epsilon \left(A^k \frac{\partial \xi^i}{\partial x^k} - \xi^k \frac{\partial A^i}{\partial x^k} \right) \tag{5.69}$$

where all the functions are evaluated at point A.

Therefore, from Eqs. (5.64) and (5.69), the Lie derivative of a contravariant vector A^i with respect to the vector ξ is

$$\mathcal{L}_\xi A^i = \lim_{\epsilon \to 0} \frac{A^i(x) - A'^i(x)}{\epsilon} = \xi^k \frac{\partial A^i}{\partial x^k} - A^k \frac{\partial \xi^i}{\partial x^k} \tag{5.70}$$

Since the Christoffel symbols are not used in the derivation of this equation, therefore, from the definition of covariant differentiation of contarvariant vector [cf., Eq. (3.46)], the partial derivatives in Eq. (5.70) can be replaced by covariant derivatives. Hence, the Lie derivative of a contravariant vector A^i is given by

$$\mathcal{L}_\xi A^i = \xi^k A^i_{;k} - A^k \xi^i_{;k} \tag{5.71}$$

Theorem 5.4 The Lie derivative of a covariant vector A_i with respect to the vector ξ is

$$\mathcal{L}_\xi A_j = \xi^i A_{j;i} + A_i \xi^i_{;j}$$

Proof The covariant vector A_i transforms as

$$A'_j(x') = \frac{\partial x^i}{\partial x'^j} A_i(x) \tag{5.72}$$

Now differentiating Eq. (5.56) with respect to x'^j, we get

$$\frac{\partial x'^i}{\partial x'^j} = \frac{\partial x^i}{\partial x'^j} + \epsilon \frac{\partial \xi^i(x)}{\partial x'^j}$$

or

$$\delta^i_j = \frac{\partial x^i}{\partial x'^j} + \epsilon \frac{\partial \xi^i(x)}{\partial x'^j}$$

or

$$\frac{\partial x^i}{\partial x'^j} = \delta^i_j - \epsilon \frac{\partial \xi^i(x)}{\partial x'^j} \tag{5.73}$$

(to the first order in ϵ). Using Eq. (5.73) in Eq. (5.72), we have

$$A'_j(x') = \left[\delta^i_j - \epsilon \frac{\partial \xi^i(x)}{\partial x'^j} \right] A_i(x)$$

$$= A_j(x) - \epsilon A_i(x) \frac{\partial \xi^i(x)}{\partial x^j} \tag{5.74}$$

Expanding $A'_j(x')$ around point A, we get, after neglecting the higher order terms in ϵ

$$A'_j(x') = A'_j(x) + \epsilon \xi^i(x) \frac{\partial A_j(x)}{\partial x^i} \tag{5.75}$$

A comparison of Eqs. (5.74) and (5.75) leads to

$$A'_j = A_j - \epsilon \left(A_i \frac{\partial \xi^i}{\partial x^j} + \xi^i \frac{\partial A_j}{\partial x^i} \right) \tag{5.76}$$

Thus, using Eq. (5.64) and replacing the partial derivatives by covariant derivatives, we get

$$\mathcal{L}_\xi A_j = \xi^i A_{j;i} + A_i \xi^i_{;j} \tag{5.77}$$

Theorem 5.5 The Lie derivative of a covariant tensor A_{ij} of rank two is

$$\mathcal{L}_\xi A_{ij} = \xi^m A_{ij;m} + A_{il} \xi^l_{;j} + A_{kj} \xi^k_{;i}$$

Proof Consider a covariant tensor A_{ij} of rank two for which the transformation law is

$$A'_{ij}(x') = \frac{\partial x^k}{\partial x'^i} \frac{\partial x^l}{\partial x'^j} A_{kl}(x) \tag{5.78}$$

which from Eq. (5.73) reduces to

$$A'_{ij} = A_{ij} - \epsilon \left(A_{il}\frac{\partial \xi^l}{\partial x^j} + A_{kj}\frac{\partial \xi^k}{\partial x^i} \right) \tag{5.79}$$

where the terms containing ϵ^2 has been neglected.

Now expanding $A'_{ij}(x')$ around the point x'^i and neglecting the higher order terms in ϵ, we have

$$A'_{ij}(x') = A'_{ij}(x + \epsilon\xi) = A'_{ij}(x) + \epsilon\xi^m \frac{\partial A_{ij}(x)}{\partial x^m} \tag{5.80}$$

From Eqs. (5.79) and (5.80), we have

$$A'_{ij} = A_{ij} - \epsilon \left(\xi^m \frac{\partial A_{ij}}{\partial x^m} + A_{il}\frac{\partial \xi^l}{\partial x^j} + A_{kj}\frac{\partial \xi^k}{\partial x^i} \right) \tag{5.81}$$

which from Eq. (5.64) leads to

$$\mathcal{L}_\xi A_{ij} = \lim_{\epsilon \to 0} \frac{A_{ij}(x) - A'_{ij}(x)}{\epsilon}$$

$$= \xi^m \frac{\partial A_{ij}}{\partial x^m} + A_{il}\frac{\partial \xi^l}{\partial x^j} + A_{kj}\frac{\partial \xi^k}{\partial x^i} \tag{5.82}$$

Equation (5.82) in terms of covariant derivatives may be expressed as

$$\mathcal{L}_\xi A_{ij} = \xi^m A_{ij;m} + A_{il}\xi^l_{;j} + A_{kj}\xi^k_{;i} \tag{5.83}$$

This completes the proof.

Theorem 5.6   The Lie derivative of a contravariant tensor A^{ij} of rank two is

$$\mathcal{L}_\xi A^{ij} = \xi^m \frac{\partial A^{ij}}{\partial x^m} - A^{il}\frac{\partial \xi^j}{\partial x^l} - A_{kj}\frac{\partial \xi^i}{\partial x^k} \tag{5.84}$$

and in terms of covariant derivatives

$$\mathcal{L}_\xi A^{ij} = \xi^m A^{ij}_{;m} - A^{il}\xi^j_{;l} - A^{kj}\xi^i_{;k} \tag{5.85}$$

Proof   Follow on similar lines as that of Theorem 5.5.

Remarks

1. Since the covariant derivative of metric tensor vanishes, Eq. (5.83) leads to

$$\mathcal{L}_\xi g_{ij} = g_{il}\xi^l_{;j} + g_{kj}\xi^k_{;i}$$

$$= \xi_{i;j} + \xi_{j;i}$$

$$= 2\xi_{(i;j)} \tag{5.86}$$

Equation (5.86), in view of Eq. (5.82), is completely equivalent to equation

$$\mathcal{L}_\xi g_{ij} = \xi^m \frac{\partial g_{ij}}{\partial x^m} + g_{il} \frac{\partial \xi^l}{\partial x^j} + g_{kj} \frac{\partial \xi^k}{\partial x^i} \tag{5.87}$$

2. For the Lie derivative of g^{ij}, Eqs. (5.84) and (5.85), respectively, can take the forms

$$\mathcal{L}_\xi g^{ij} = \xi^m \frac{\partial g^{ij}}{\partial x^m} - g^{il} \frac{\partial \xi^j}{\partial x^l} - g^{kj} \frac{\partial \xi^i}{\partial x^k} \tag{5.88}$$

and

$$\begin{aligned} \mathcal{L}_\xi g^{ij} &= -g^{il} \xi^j_{;l} - g^{kj} \xi^i_{;k} \\ &= -(\xi^{i;j} + \xi^{j;i}) \\ &= -2\xi^{(i;j)} \end{aligned} \tag{5.89}$$

Theorem 5.7 The Lie derivative of the product of two tensors X and Y satisfies the Leibnitz rule of the products of derivatives, that is

$$\mathcal{L}_\xi(XY) = X\mathcal{L}_\xi Y + Y\mathcal{L}_\xi X \tag{5.90}$$

Proof Let $X = A^i$ and $Y = B_{ij}$, then $XY = A^i B_{ij}$ is a covariant vector and thus from Eq. (5.78), the Lie derivative of the covariant vector $A^i B_{ij}$ is

$$\begin{aligned} \mathcal{L}_\xi(A^i B_{ij}) &= \xi^k(A^i B_{ij})_{;k} + A^i B_{ik} \xi^k_{;j} \\ &= \xi^k(A^i_{;k} B_{ij} + A^i B_{ij;k}) + A^i B_{ik} \xi^k_{;j} \\ &= \xi^k A^i_{;k} B_{ij} + \xi^k A^i B_{ij;k} + A^i B_{ik} \xi^k_{;j} - B_{ij} A^k \xi^i_{;k} + B_{ij} A^k \xi^i_{;k} \end{aligned}$$

Changing the dummy indices in the last term on the right-hand side of this equation, we get

$$\begin{aligned} \mathcal{L}_\xi(A^i B_{ij}) &= \xi^k A^i_{;k} B_{ij} + \xi^k A^i B_{ij;k} + A^i B_{ik} \xi^k_{;j} - B_{ij} A^k \xi^i_{;k} + B_{kj} A^i \xi^k_{;i} \\ &= A^i(\xi^k B_{ij;k} + B_{ik} \xi^k_{;j} + B_{kj} \xi^k_{;i}) + B_{ij}(\xi^k A^i_{;k} - A^k \xi^i_{;k}) \\ &= A^i \mathcal{L}_\xi B_{ij} + B_{ij} \mathcal{L}_\xi A^i \end{aligned}$$

[from Eqs. (5.71) and (5.83)]. Therefore

$$\mathcal{L}_\xi(XY) = X\mathcal{L}_\xi Y + Y\mathcal{L}_\xi X$$

Remark

From the above discussions, it is easy to show that Lie differentiation satisfies the following properties:

(i) It is linear. Thus, for example

$$\mathcal{L}_\xi(\alpha A^i + \beta B^i) = \alpha \mathcal{L}_\xi A^i + \beta \mathcal{L}_\xi B^i$$

(ii) The Lie derivative of a tensor of type (p,q) is again a tensor of the same type (p,q), where p and q indicate the covariant and contravariant nature of the tensor.

(iii) The Lie derivative commutes with the operation of contraction. The operation of contraction can be considered as the multiplication by the mixed fundamental tensor δ^i_j and thus

$$\mathcal{L}_\xi(\delta^i_j T^i_j) = (\mathcal{L}_\xi \delta^i_j)T^i_j + \delta^i_j(\mathcal{L}_\xi T^i_j)$$
$$= (\delta^i_{j;k}\xi^k + \delta^i_k \xi^k_{;j} - \delta^k_j \xi^i_{;k})T^i_j + \delta^i_j(\mathcal{L}_\xi T^i_j)$$
$$= \delta^i_j(\mathcal{L}_\xi T^i_j)$$

(iv) The Lie derivative can also be applied to arbitrary, linear geometric objects, for example, to Christoffel symbols.

(v) The Lie derivative commutes with the partial derivative, that is

$$\frac{\partial}{\partial x^k}(\mathcal{L}_\xi X) = \mathcal{L}_\xi \frac{\partial X}{\partial x^k}$$

The Lie derivative of a general tensor $T^{i\cdots}_{j\cdots}$ with respect to the vector ξ can be obtained as follows:

First partially differentiate the tensor $T^{i\cdots}_{j\cdots}$ and contract it with the vector ξ. Then write an additional term for each index of the form of the last two terms in Eqs. (5.71) and (5.77) where for the contravariant and covariant indexes the sign, respectively, is negative and positive, that is

$$\mathcal{L}_\xi T^{i\cdots}_{j\cdots} = \xi^k T^{i\cdots}_{j\cdots;k} - T^{k\cdots}_{j\cdots}\xi^i_{;k} - \cdots + T^{i\cdots}_{k\cdots}\xi^k_{;j} + \cdots \qquad (5.91)$$

Thus, for example, according to this prescription, the Lie derivative of the Riemann curvature tensor is

$$\mathcal{L}_\xi R^i_{jkl} = \xi^h R^i_{jkl;h} - R^h_{jkl}\xi^i_{;h} + R^i_{hkl}\xi^h_{;j} + R^i_{jhl}\xi^h_{;k} + R^i_{jkh}\xi^h_{;l} \qquad (5.92)$$

Consider now the Lie derivative of the Levi-Civita tensor [cf., Eqs. (2.38) and (2.39)] which will lead to a completely skew symmetric tensor. But since all such tensors are proportional to ϵ_{ijkl}, we can express the Lie derivative of ϵ_{ijkl} as

$$\mathcal{L}_\xi \epsilon_{ijkl} = -\theta \epsilon_{ijkl} \qquad (5.93)$$

where θ is a scalar and depends only on ξ. This scalar can be obtained as follows:

From Eq. (5.91), we have

$$\mathcal{L}_\xi \epsilon_{ijkl} = \xi^m \epsilon_{ijkl;m} + \epsilon_{mjkl}\xi^m_{;i} + \epsilon_{imkl}\xi^m_{;j} + \epsilon_{ijml}\xi^m_{;k} + \epsilon_{ijkm}\xi^m_{;l}$$

But $\epsilon_{ijkl;m} = 0$. Using Eq. (5.93) the above equation leads to

$$-\theta\epsilon_{ijkl} = \epsilon_{mjkl}\xi^m_{;i} + \epsilon_{imkl}\xi^m_{;j} + \epsilon_{ijml}\xi^m_{;k} + \epsilon_{ijkm}\xi^m_{;l}$$

Multiplying this equation by ϵ^{ijkl} and using Eqs. (2.45) and (2.46), we get

$$-\theta = \xi^a_{;a} \tag{5.94}$$

Equation (5.93) can thus be expressed as

$$\mathcal{L}_\xi \epsilon_{ijkl} = \xi^a_{;a}\epsilon_{ijkl} \tag{5.95}$$

From Eq. (5.94) it may be noted that the scalar field θ is simply the divergence of the vector ξ. It is usually termed as the *expansion* and has number of applications in general relativity and cosmology (Kramer et al., 1980 and Ludvigsen, 1999, see also Section 6.5).

5.8 The Killing Equation

When we are considering physical systems, symmetric properties of the system are often helpful in understanding the system. In this section, we shall apply the concept of Lie differentiation in studying the geometric structure of the spacetime under consideration. Since the geometry of the spacetime is described by the metric tensor g_{ij}, it is therefore worthwhile to see whether or not the metric tensor changes its value under infinitesimal coordinate transformation.

A mapping of the spacetime onto itself of the form (5.56) is called an *isometric mapping* if the Lie derivative of the metric tensor associated with it vanishes, i.e.,

$$\mathcal{L}_\xi g_{ij} = 0 \tag{5.96}$$

Equation (5.96) shows that the metric tensor is invariant under the transformation (5.56) if $g'_{ij}(x) = g_{ij}(x)$ for all coordinates x^k. Thus, if a point transformation in a Riemannian space does not change the length of any curve in the space, we say that the transformation does not change the metric and the transformation is said to define a *motion* or an *isometry*.

The condition (5.96), from Eq. (5.87), is equivalent to

$$\xi^m \frac{\partial g_{ij}}{\partial x^m} + g_{il}\frac{\partial \xi^l}{\partial x^j} + g_{kj}\frac{\partial \xi^k}{\partial x^i} = 0 \tag{5.97}$$

For a given metric, Eq. (5.97) represents a system of differential equations which determines the vector field $\xi^i(x)$. If this equation has no solution then the space has no symmetry. Equation (97) can be regarded as the covariant characterization of the symmetries present, although it involves partial derivatives. This can be seen by replacing the partial derivatives with the covariant derivatives in Eq. (5.97), considering Eq. (5.96) with Eq. (5.82), we have the covariant equation as

$$\mathcal{L}_\xi g_{ij} = \xi_{i;j} + \xi_{j;i} = 0 \tag{5.98}$$

Equation (5.98), a system of first order differential equations, is called the *Killing equation,* named after Wilhelm Karl Joseph Killing (1847–1923)—a German mathematician who made important contributions to the theories of Lie algebras, Lie groups, and non-Euclidean geometry. The vectors $\xi^i(x)$, which are the solutions of this equation, are called the *Killing vectors;* and characterize the symmetry properties of the Riemannian space in an invariant manner. The number and types of solutions of these ten equations depend upon the nature of the metric and hence vary from space to space. If for a spacetime Eq. (5.98) is satisfied, then the spacetime is said to admit a motion or an isometry.

Killing Eq. (5.98) and Lie differentiation play an important role in the classification of gravitational fields (Weinberg, 1972). A gravitational field is said to be *stationary* if it admits a time-like Killing vector field $\xi^i(x)$, that is, there exists a solution to the Killing Eq. (5.98), where $\xi_i = g_{ij}\xi^j$ and $\xi^2 = \xi_i\xi^i > 0$.

If we choose the coordinate system such that the Killing vector ξ^i has the component

$$\xi^i = (0, 0, 0, 1) \tag{5.99}$$

then Eq. (5.97) reduces to

$$\frac{\partial g_{ij}}{\partial x^4} = 0 \tag{5.100}$$

Thus, in this coordinate system, all the components of the metric tensor are independent of the spacetime coordinate x^4. An important example of the stationary gravitational field is the Kerr metric (Kramer et al., 1980) (see also Section 6.6).

If in a stationary spacetime the trajectories of the Killing vector ξ^i are orthogonal to a family of hypersurfaces, then the spacetime is said to be *static.* In such a spacetime there exists a coordinate system which is adapted to the Killing vector field $\xi^i(x)$ such that

$$\frac{\partial g_{ij}}{\partial x^4} = 0, \quad g_{4\mu} = 0, \quad \mu = 1, 2, 3 \tag{5.101}$$

A static solution of the Einstein field equations is the Schwarzschild exterior solution (cf., Section 6.6) which is of great importance in general theory of relativity (Ludvigsen, 1999).

EXAMPLE 5.2   Obtain the Killing vectors for Minkowski space.

Solution   For the Minkowski space, we have

$$g_{11} = g_{22} = g_{33} = -1, \quad g_{44} = 1, \quad g_{ij} = 0, \quad i \neq j \tag{5.102}$$

The Killing Eq. (5.98) in such case is

$$\frac{\partial \xi_i}{\partial x^j} + \frac{\partial \xi_j}{\partial x^i} = 0 \tag{5.103}$$

When $i, j = 1, 2, 3, 4$, Eq. (5.103) yields

$$\frac{\partial \xi_1}{\partial x^1} = \frac{\partial \xi_2}{\partial x^2} = \frac{\partial \xi_3}{\partial x^3} = \frac{\partial \xi_4}{\partial x^4} = 0 \tag{5.104}$$

The Killing vector ξ_i also satisfies the equation

$$\frac{\partial \xi_4}{\partial x^\nu} + \frac{\partial \xi_\nu}{\partial x^4} = 0, \quad \frac{\partial \xi_\mu}{\partial x^\nu} + \frac{\partial \xi_\nu}{\partial x^\mu} = 0 \tag{5.105}$$

where $\mu, \nu = 1, 2, 3$ and $\mu \neq \nu$.

The solution of Eq. (5.104) is

$$\xi_1 = \xi_1(x^2, x^3, x^4), \quad \xi_2 = \xi_2(x^1, x^3, x^4) \tag{5.106}$$

$$\xi_3 = \xi_3(x^1, x^2, x^4), \quad \xi_4 = \xi_4(x^1, x^2, x^3) \tag{5.106a}$$

while the solution of Eq. (5.105) is

$$\xi_i = c_i + \epsilon_{ij} x^j \tag{5.107}$$

where c_i and ϵ_{ij} are some constants and $\epsilon_{ij} = -\epsilon_{ji}$.

The set of four constants (parameters) describes the four translations in Minkowski spacetime; while the six constants ϵ_{ij} correspond to six *generalized rotations* called *Lorentz rotations*. Thus, each one of the six constants ϵ_{ij} describes either a three-dimensional *rotation* (three spatial rotation) or a homogeneous Lorentz transformation. Therefore, a Minkowski space admits ten linearly independent Killing vectors.

EXAMPLE 5.3   Obtain the Killing vectors for the surface of a unit sphere in a two-dimensional Riemannian space.

Solution   Here the metric is (cf., Example 3.2)

$$ds^2 = d\theta^2 + \sin^2 \theta d\phi^2$$

and

$$x^1 = \theta, \quad x^2 = \phi, \quad g_{11} = 1, \quad g_{22} = \sin^2 \theta, \quad g_{ij} = 0, \quad i \neq j$$

From Eq. (5.97), we have

$$\frac{\partial \xi^1}{\partial \theta} = 0 \tag{5.108}$$

$$\frac{\partial \xi^1}{\partial \phi} + \sin^2 \theta \frac{\partial \xi^2}{\partial \theta} = 0 \tag{5.109}$$

$$\frac{\partial \xi^2}{\partial \phi} + \xi^1 \cot \theta = 0 \tag{5.110}$$

Equation (5.108) leads to

$$\xi^1 = f(\phi) \tag{5.111}$$

where f is an arbitrary function of ϕ. Equation (5.109) now gives

$$\sin^2 \theta \frac{\partial \xi^2}{\partial \theta} = -f'(\phi)$$

which when solved leads to

$$\xi^2 = f'(\phi) \cot \theta + g(\phi) \tag{5.112}$$

where $f'(\phi)$ denotes the differentiation with respect to ϕ and $g(\phi)$ is an arbitrary function of ϕ. From Eqs. (5.111) and (5.112), Eq. (5.110) becomes

$$[f''(\phi) + f(\phi)] \cot \theta + g'(\phi) = 0 \tag{5.113}$$

Equation (5.129) is satisfied only when

$$f''(\phi) + f(\phi) = 0, \quad g'(\phi) = 0$$

which has the solution as

$$f(\phi) = c_1 \sin \phi + c_2 \cos \phi, \quad g(\phi) = c_3$$

Also

$$f'(\phi) = c_1 \cos \phi - c_2 \sin \phi$$

Therefore, the most general solution of the Killing equation, from Eqs. (5.111) and (5.112), is

$$\xi^1 = c_1 \sin \phi + c_2 \cos \phi \tag{5.114}$$

$$\xi^2 = (c_1 \cos \phi - c_2 \sin \phi) \cot \theta + c_3 \tag{5.114a}$$

where c_1, c_2 and c_3 are arbitrary constants. Thus

$$\bar{\xi} = (c_1 \sin \phi + c_2 \cos \phi) \frac{\partial}{\partial \theta} + [c_3 + \cot \theta (c_1 \cos \phi - c_2 \sin \phi)] \frac{\partial}{\partial \phi} \tag{5.115}$$

is the most general Killing vector. It is a linear combination of three Killing vectors

$$\frac{\partial}{\partial \phi}, \quad \left(\cos \phi \frac{\partial}{\partial \theta} - \cot \theta \sin \phi \frac{\partial}{\partial \phi} \right), \quad \left(\sin \phi \frac{\partial}{\partial \theta} + \cot \theta \cos \phi \frac{\partial}{\partial \phi} \right) \quad (5.116)$$

which can also be expressed as

$$\xi_1^i = (\sin \phi, \cos \phi \cot \theta)$$

$$\xi_2^i = (\cos \phi, - \sin \phi \cot \theta) \quad (5.117)$$

$$\xi_3^i = (0, 1)$$

These are three linearly independent Killing vectors on the surface of the unit sphere.

5.9 The Curvature Tensor and Killing Vectors

In this section we shall find the spaces which possess maximum number of Killing vectors and thus provide an explanation to the Remark of Section 4.13. In fact, we shall prove a number of results connecting the Riemann curvature tensor and Killing vectors and we have

Theorem 5.8 For any Killing vector ξ^i,

$$\xi_{;k}^{j;k} + R_m^j \xi^m = 0 \quad (5.118)$$

Proof For any vector field ξ^i, from Eq. (4.9), we have

$$\xi_{i;jk} - \xi_{i;kj} = R_{imkj}\xi^m$$

Contracting this equation with i and k, we get

$$\xi_{;k}^{j;k} + R_m^j \xi^m = -(\xi_{;i}^i)^{;j}$$

If ξ^i is a Killing vector, then the right-hand side of this equation vanishes due to Eq. (5.98); and hence Eq. (5.118) is proved.

Theorem 5.9 For any Killing vector ξ^i,

$$\xi_{i;jk} = R_{kji}^l \xi_l \quad (5.119)$$

Proof From Eq. (4.9), for any vector field ξ, we have

$$\xi_{k;ji} - \xi_{k;ij} = R_{kji}^l \xi_l \quad (5.120)$$

and

$$\xi_{j;ik} - \xi_{j;ki} = R_{jik}^l \xi_l \quad (5.121)$$

$$\xi_{i;kj} - \xi_{i;jk} = R_{ikj}^l \xi_l \quad (5.122)$$

Adding Eqs. (5.120)–(5.122), we get

$$(\xi_{k;ji} - \xi_{k;ij}) + (\xi_{j;ik} - \xi_{j;ki}) + (\xi_{i;kj} - \xi_{i;jk}) = (R^l_{kji} + R^l_{jik} + R^l_{ikj})\xi_l$$

From the cyclic property (4.23) this equation leads to

$$\xi_{k;ji} - \xi_{k;ij} + \xi_{i;kj} - \xi_{i;jk} + \xi_{j;ik} - \xi_{j;ki} = 0 \qquad (5.123)$$

Since ξ^i is given to be a Killing vector field, Eq. (5.123) leads to

$$\xi_{k;ji} - \xi_{k;ij} - \xi_{i;jk} = 0 \qquad (5.124)$$

which when substituted in Eq. (5.120) yields the required result.

We shall now find the integrability condition for Eq. (5.119). For every $\xi_{i;j}$, from Eq. (5.119), we have

$$\xi_{i;j;k;m} = \xi_{i;jkm} = (R^l_{kji}\xi_l)_{;m} = R^l_{kji;m}\xi_l + R^l_{kji}\xi_{l;m}$$

and

$$\xi_{i;j;m;k} = \xi_{i;jmk} = (R^l_{mji}\xi_l)_{;k} = R^l_{mji;k}\xi_l + R^l_{mji}\xi_{l;k}$$

Subtraction of these two equations yields

$$\xi_{i;jkm} - \xi_{i;jmk} = (R^l_{kji;m} - R^l_{mji;k})\xi_l + R^l_{kji}\xi_{l;m} - R^l_{mji}\xi_{l;k} \qquad (5.125)$$

Moreover, from the general formula for the commutators of tensors we have

$$\xi_{i;jkm} - \xi_{i;jmk} = R^l_{ikm}\xi_{l;j} + R^l_{jkm}\xi_{l;i} \qquad (5.126)$$

with this, Eq. (5.125) becomes

$$R^l_{ikm}\xi_{l;j} + R^l_{jkm}\xi_{l;i} = (R^l_{kji;m} - R^l_{mji;k})\xi_l + R^l_{kji}\xi_{l;m} - R^l_{mji}\xi_{l;k}$$

which, on using ξ_i to be a Killing vector, reduces to

$$(R^l_{kji;m} - R^l_{mji;k})\xi_l + (R^l_{kji}\delta^n_m - R^l_{mji}\delta^n_k + R^l_{jkm}\delta^n_i - R^l_{ikm}\delta^n_j)\xi_{l;n} = 0 \qquad (5.127)$$

Equations (5.127) are the integrability conditions and impose conditions on ξ_i and $\xi_{i;j}$ about the existence of number of Killing vectors at a point. Thus, if we know the nature of the Killing vector of some unknown metric then we can have some informations about the curvature tensor of that spacetime (for further detail, see Weinberg, 1972).

Equation (5.119) indicates that from the Killing vectors ξ_i and its first derivative $\xi_{i;k}$ all higher derivatives can be found in a given Riemannian space. Therefore, if we can specify the values of ξ_i and $\xi_{i;k}$ at one point, the Killing vectors can be determined uniquely. Moreover, since ξ_i is a Killing vector then in a N-dimensional Riemannian space there are exactly $\dfrac{N}{2}(N+1)$ such initial values. Thus, in a N-dimensional Riemannian space, the maximum number of linearly independent Killing vectors are $\dfrac{N(N+1)}{2}$. If $N = 4$, the maximum number of linearly independent Killing vectors are ten.

If a space has maximum number of Killing vectors then it is said to be *maximally symmetric space*. For such spaces, we have

Theorem 5.10 A maximally symmetric space is a space of constant curvature.

Proof Here we have to identify the maximally symmetric spaces, that is, the spaces which possess maximum number $\dfrac{N(N+1)}{2}$ of Killing vectors. For such space there will be no restriction on the values of Killing vectors ξ_i and $\xi_{i;k}$ and in such case from Eq. (5.127), we have

$$R^l_{kji;m} = R^l_{mji;k} \tag{5.128}$$

and the coefficient of $\xi_{l;n}$ must have a vanishing skew symmetric part, that is

$$R^l_{kji}\delta^n_m - R^n_{kji}\delta^l_m - R^l_{mji}\delta^n_k + R^n_{mji}\delta^l_k + R^l_{jkm}\delta^n_i$$
$$- R^n_{jkm}\delta^l_i - R^l_{ikm}\delta^n_j + R^n_{ikm}\delta^l_j = 0 \tag{5.129}$$

Put $n = m$, remembering that $\delta^n_n = N$ (the dimension of the space), to get

$$(N-1)R^l_{kji} + (R^l_{kij} + R^l_{ijk} + R^l_{jki}) - \delta^l_i R_{jk} + \delta^l_j R_{ik} = 0$$

Using the skew symmetric and cyclic properties of the Riemann tensor, we get

$$(N-1)R^l_{kji} = \delta^l_i R_{jk} - \delta^l_j R_{ik} \tag{5.130}$$

Multiplying this equation by g^{kj}, we get, after simplification

$$R^l_i = \frac{R}{N}\delta^l_i$$

which on multiplication with g_{lp} leads to

$$R_{ip} = \frac{R}{N}g_{ip} \tag{5.131}$$

With this value of Ricci tensor, Eq. (5.130) becomes

$$R^l_{kji} = \frac{R}{N(N-1)}(\delta^l_i g_{jk} - \delta^l_j g_{ik}) \tag{5.132}$$

Multiply this equation by g_{pl} to get

$$R_{pkji} = \frac{R}{N(N-1)}(g_{pi}g_{jk} - g_{pj}g_{ik}) \tag{5.133}$$

But from Eq. (5.128), the scalar curvature must be constant; and from Eq. (4.89) this scalar curvature R is

$$R = -KN(N-1) \tag{5.134}$$

Using this value of R in Eqs. (5.131) and (5.133), we get

$$R_{ip} = -K(N-1)g_{ip} \tag{5.135}$$

and

$$R_{pkji} = K(g_{pj}g_{ik} - g_{pi}g_{jk}) \tag{5.136}$$

Spaces satisfying Eq. (5.136) are known to be spaces of constant curvature (cf., Section 4.13). Hence, a maximally symmetric space is a space of constant curvature.

Remarks

1. From Eq. (5.131) it is clear that a maximally symmetric space is an Einstein space.

2. To obtain a model of the universe, certain simplifying assumptions have to be made and one such assumption is that the universe is isotropic and homogeneous. This is known as *cosmological principle*. By *isotropy* we mean that all spatial directions are equivalent, while *homogeneity* means that it is impossible to distinguish one place in the universe from the other (for further details, see Stephani, 1982 and Weinberg, 1972). In the spaces of constant curvature no points and no directions are preferred, that is, the spaces of constant curvature are isotropic and homogeneous and thus these spaces find their applications in cosmology.

EXAMPLE 5.4 If u^i is tangent to a geodesic and ξ_i is a Killing vector, show that $\xi_i u^i$ is constant along the geodesic.

Solution If u^i is tangent to a geodesic, then from Eq. (2.24), we have

$$u^k_{;l}u^l = 0 \tag{5.137}$$

Moreover, given that ξ_i is a Killing vector, that is

$$\xi_{(i;j)} = 0 \tag{5.138}$$

The change in $u^i\xi_i$ along the geodesic is given by

$$u^i(\xi_k u^k)_{;i} = u^i\xi_{k;i}u^k + u^i\xi_k u^k_{;i} = 0$$

[from Eqs. (5.137) and (138)]. Thus $\xi_i u^i$ is constant along the geodesic.

EXAMPLE 5.5 If ξ_i is a Killing vector and G^{ij} is the Einstein tensor then show that $J^i = G^{ij}\xi_j$ is divergence free.

Solution The divergence of J^i is

$$J^i_{;i} = (G^{ij}\xi_j)_{;i} = G^{ij}_{;i}\xi_j + G^{ij}\xi_{(j;i)} = 0$$

from Eq. (4.65) and the fact that ξ_i is a Killing vector.

Remarks

1. If G^{ij} defines the energy-momentum tensor and J^i the current, then the conserved quantity J^i (as $J^i_{;i} = 0$) is related to the matter content of the spacetime through Einstein field equations [cf., Eqs. (5.36), (5.37) and (4.64)].

2. If ξ_i is a Killing vector, then

$$\xi_{i;j} + \xi_{j;i} = \xi_{(i;j)} = 0$$

implies that $\xi_{i;j}$ is a skew symmetric tensor. If we denote it as

$$F_{ij} = \xi_{i;j} \qquad (5.139)$$

then with this F_{ij} we can define the *conserved current* as

$$J_i = F^{;k}_{ik} \qquad (5.140)$$

If F_{ij} is identified as the electromagnetic field tensor then Eq. (5.140) is one of the Maxwell's equation with current density as J^i (see also Section 6.2). The other Maxwell's equation is

$$F_{[ij;k]} = 0$$

In this way, we thus have obtained a relationship between the Killing vectors and the electromagnetic fields.

5.10 Curvature Tensors Involving Riemann Tensor

So far we have discussed the geometric and physical properties of the Riemann tensor and it is seen that this tensor plays a key role in general theory of relativity. There are some other fourth rank tensors which involve Riemann tensor. One such tensor is the Weyl conformal tensor (see Section 5.3); and some of the other tensors are projective curvature tensor, conharmonic curvature tensor, concircular curvature tensor and space-matter tensor. These tensors have their importance in differential geometry as well as in relativity. This section deals with a brief study of such tensors (for details see Ahsan, 1977a, 1976b, 1978, 1996, 1998; Ahsan and Siddiqui, 2009, 2010; Siddiqui and Ahsan, 2010).

(a) Projective curvature tensor

Consider a n-dimensional differentiable manifold of class C^∞ and assume that there is given in M an affine connection ∇ without torsion whose local parameters are Γ_{ji}^h. Then the so called paths or autoparallel curves are defined as curves $x^h = x^h(t)$ which satisfiy the system of differential equations

$$\frac{d^2 x^h}{dt^2} + \Gamma_{ji}^h \frac{dx^j}{dt} \frac{dx^i}{dt} = \alpha(t) \frac{dx^h}{dt} \tag{5.141}$$

$\alpha(t)$ being a function defined along the curves, or

$$\frac{d^2 x^h}{ds^2} + \Gamma_{ji}^h \frac{dx^j}{ds} \frac{dx^i}{ds} = 0 \tag{5.142}$$

where s being the so called affine parameter on paths (cf., Sections 3.4, 3.5 and 3.11).

If there is given another connection ∇^* without torsion whose local parameters are Γ_{ji}^{*h}, and if the affine connections ∇ and ∇^* give the same system of paths, we must have

$$H(X, Y) = \pi(X)Y + \pi(Y)X \tag{5.143}$$

where

$$H(X, Y) = (\nabla^* - \nabla)(X, Y) = (\nabla_X^* - \nabla_X)Y \tag{5.144}$$

π being a certain 1-form, or

$$\Gamma_{ji}^{*h} - \Gamma_{ji}^h = \delta_j^h p_i + \delta_i^h p_j \tag{5.144a}$$

where π is the local component of p_i. The change of ∇ given by the above equation is called a projective change of ∇. We aslo say that ∇^* and ∇ are projectively related (cf., Yano, 1970). It may be noted that under a projective change, the geodesics are preserved.

In a Riemannian manifold V_n of dimension n, the curvature tensor which remain unchanged under a projective change is called the projective curvature tensor. It is denoted by $W(X, Y, Z)$ and is defined by (Mishra, 1984; Yano, 1970)

$$W(X, Y, Z) = R(X, Y, Z) - \frac{1}{n-1}[X\,Ric(Y, Z) - Y\,Ric(X, Z)] \tag{5.145}$$

so that for a V_4

$$W(X, Y, Z) = R(X, Y, Z) - \frac{1}{3}[X\,Ric(Y, Z) - Y\,Ric(X, Z)] \tag{5.145a}$$

where $R(X, Y, Z)$ denotes the Riemann curvature tensor. In local coordinates, this equation can be written as

$$W_{bcd}^h = R_{bcd}^h - \frac{1}{3}(R_{bc}\delta_d^h - R_{bd}\delta_c^h) \tag{5.146}$$

It may be noted that the contraction of W^h_{bcd} over h and d vanishes. Also

$$W_{abcd} = R_{abcd} - \frac{1}{3}(R_{bc}g_{ad} - R_{bd}g_{ac}) \qquad (5.147)$$

The projective curvature satisfies the following properties:

(i) $W(X,Y,Z) = -W(Y,X,Z)$

(ii) $W(X,Y,Z) + W(Y,Z,X) + W(Z,X,Y)$

Moreover, if the tensor W^h_{bcd} of a Riemannian manifold of dimension $n > 2$ vanishes, the manifold is said to be projectively flat. From Eq. (5.145) it is evident that a projectively flat manifold is a space of constant curvature, and thus the projective curvature tensor represents the deviation of the manifold from projective flatness. This measure of deviation from projective flatness can be obtained from the quantity

$$W = \sup_A \frac{|W_{abcd}A^{ab}A^{cd}|}{A_{bc}A^{bc}}, \quad (A_{bc} = -A_{cb})$$

(b) Conharmonic curvature tensor

We know that two Riemannian spaces are conformally related through the equation

$$\tilde{g}_{ij} = e^{2\phi}g_{ij} \qquad (5.148)$$

where $\tilde{g}_{ij}$ and g_{ij} are the metric tensors of the two Riemannian spaces $\tilde{V}$ and V and ϕ is a real function of coordinates [see also Eq. (5.19)]. Moreover, it is known that a harmonic function is defined as a function whose Laplacian vanishes. In general, a harmonic function does not transform into a harmonic function. The conditions under which the harmonic functions remain invariant have been studied by Ishii (1975) who introduced the conharmonic transformation as a subgroup of the conformal transformation (5.148) satisfying the condition

$$\phi^i_{;i} + \phi_{;i}\phi^i_{;} = 0 \qquad (5.149)$$

A rank four tensor $L(X,Y,Z)$ that remain invariant under conharmonic transformation, for a n-dimensional Reimannian manifold V_n, is defined as (Mishra, 1984)

$$L(X,Y,Z) = R(X,Y,Z) - \frac{1}{n-2}[g(Y,Z)R(X) - g(X,Z)R(Y)$$

$$+ X\operatorname{Ric}(Y,Z) - Y\operatorname{Ric}(X,Z)] \qquad (5.150)$$

where $R(X,Y,Z) = D_X D_Y Z - D_Y D_X Z - D_{[X,Y]}Z$, ($D$ being the Riemannian connection) is the Riemann curvature tensor and $\operatorname{Ric}(X,Y) = g(R(X),Y)$, the Ricci tensor.

In local coordinates

$$L^t_{ijk} = R^t_{ijk} - \frac{1}{n-2}[g_{ij}R^t_k - \delta^t_j R_{ik} + \delta^t_k R_{ij} - g_{ik}R^t_j]$$ (5.150a)

Also

$$L(X,Y,Z,W) = R(X,Y,Z,W) - \frac{1}{n-2}[g(Y,Z)\mathrm{Ric}(X,W)$$

$$- g(X,Z)\mathrm{Ric}(Y,W) + g(X,W)\mathrm{Ric}(Y,Z) - g(Y,W)\mathrm{Ric}(X,Z)]$$ (5.151)

or in local coordinates

$$L_{hijk} = R_{hijk} - \frac{1}{n-2}(g_{ij}R_{hk} - g_{hj}R_{ik} + g_{hk}R_{ij} - g_{ik}R_{hj})$$ (5.151a)

where $R(X,Y,Z,W) = g(R(X,Y,Z),W)$ or in local coordinates, $R_{hijk} = g_{ht}R^t_{ijk}$. It may be noted that the contraction of Eq. (5.150a)

$$L_{ij} = -\frac{1}{n-1}Rg_{ij}$$ (5.152)

is also invariant under condition (5.149).

The curvature tensor defined by Eq. (5.150) or (5.151) is called *conharmonic curvature tensor*. A manifold whose conharmonic curvature tensor vanishes at every point is called the *conharmonically flat manifold*. A brief account of the relativistic significance of conharmonic curvature tensor has been discussed here (for further details, see Ahsan, 1998; Siddiqui and Ahsan, 2010).

Let V_4 be the spacetime of general relativity. Then from Eq. (5.150), we have

$$L(X,Y,Z) = R(X,Y,Z) - \frac{1}{2}[g(Y,Z)R(X) - g(X,Z)R(Y)$$

$$+X\,\mathrm{Ric}(Y,Z) - Y\,\mathrm{Ric}(X,Z)]$$

If $L(X,Y,Z) = 0$, then

$$R(X,Y,Z) = \frac{1}{2}[g(Y,Z)R(X) - g(X,Z)R(Y)$$

$$+ X\,\mathrm{Ric}(Y,Z) - Y\,\mathrm{Ric}(X,Z)]$$ (5.153)

or in local coordinates

$$R^t_{ijk} = \frac{1}{2}[g_{ij}R^t_k - \delta^t_j R_{ik} + \delta^t_k R_{ij} - g_{ik}R^t_j]$$ (5.154)

which on contraction yields

$$R_{ik} = -\frac{R}{4}g_{ik}$$ (5.155)

or in the index-free notation

$$\text{Ric}(X, Z) = -\frac{R}{4}g(X, Z) \qquad (5.156)$$

where R is the scalar curvature and thus, from Eq. (4.77), we have

Theorem 5.11   A conharmonically flat spacetime is an Einstein space. Moreover, from Eq. (5.154), we have

$$R_{hijk} = g_{ht}R^t_{ijk} = \frac{1}{2}(g_{ij}R_{hk} - g_{hj}R_{ik} + g_{hk}R_{ij} - g_{ik}R_{hj}) \qquad (5.157)$$

Using Eq. (5.155) in Eq. (5.157), we get

$$R_{hijk} = \frac{R}{4}(g_{hj}g_{ik} - g_{ij}g_{hk}) \qquad (5.158)$$

or

$$R(X, Y, Z, W) = \frac{R}{4}[g(X, Z)g(Y, W) - g(Y, Z)g(X, W)] \qquad (5.158a)$$

We thus have (cf., Section 4.13)

Theorem 5.12   A conharmonically flat spacetime is of constant curvature.

From this theorem, the conharmonic curvature tensor represents the deviation of the space time manifold from the spaces of constant curvature. The deviation from the conharmonical flatness is measured by the quantity

$$L = \sup_A \frac{|L_{abcd}A^{ab}A^{cd}|}{A_{bc}A^{bc}}$$

where $A^{ab} = Y^aX^b - Y^bX^a$, X, Y being two mutually orthogonal unit vectors. Also, $A_{bc} = -A_{cb}$.

(c) Concircular curvature tensor

In general, a geodesic circle (a curve whose first curvature is constant and second curvature is identically zero) does not transform into a geodesic circle by the conformal transformation

$$\tilde{g}_{ij} = \psi^2 g_{ij} \qquad (5.159)$$

of the fundamental tensor g_{ij}. The transformation which preserves geodesic circles was first introduced by Yano (1940). The conformal transformation (5.159) satisfying the partial differential equation

$$\psi_{;i;j} = \phi g_{ij} \qquad (5.160)$$

changes a geodesic circle into a geodesic circle. Such a transformation is known as concircular transformation and the geometry which deals with such transformation is called the concircular geometry (cf., Yano, 1940).

A $(1, 3)$ type tensor $M(X, Y, Z)$ which remain invariant under concircular transformation, for a n-dimensional Riemannian space V_n, is defined by Yano and Kon (1984) as

$$M(X, Y, Z) = R(X, Y, Z) - \frac{R}{n(n-1)}[Xg(Y, Z) - Yg(X, Z)] \qquad (5.161)$$

where $R(X, Y, Z) = D_X D_Y Z - D_Y D_X Z - D_{[X,Y]}Z$, ($D$ being the Riemannian connection) is the Riemann curvature tensor and R is the Ricci scalar. In local coordinates, Eq. (5.161) can be expressed as

$$M_{jih}^t = R_{jih}^t - \frac{R}{n(n-1)}(\delta_h^t g_{ji} - \delta_i^t g_{jh}) \qquad (5.162)$$

Also

$$M(X, Y, Z, W) = R(X, Y, Z, W)$$
$$- \frac{R}{n(n-1)}[g(X, W)g(Y, Z) - g(Y, W)g(X, Z)] \qquad (5.163)$$

or in local coordinates

$$M_{kjih} = R_{kjih} - \frac{R}{n(n-1)}(g_{kh}g_{ji} - g_{jh}g_{ki}) \qquad (5.164)$$

The curvature tensor $M(X, Y, Z)$ or $M(X, Y, Z, W)$ defined through Eqs. (5.161) and (5.163) is known as concircular curvature tensor. The contraction of Eq. (5.162) over t and h leads to

$$M_{ji} = R_{ji} - \frac{R}{n}g_{ji} \qquad (5.165)$$

which is also invariant under concircular transformation. Moreover

$$g^{ji}M_{ji} = 0$$

If the tensor $M(X, Y, Z)$ or $M(X, Y, Z, W)$ of a Riemannian manifold of dimension $n > 2$ vanishes, then the manifold is said to be concircularly flat. From Eqs. (5.161) and (5.163), it is evident that a concircularly flat space is a space of constant curvature. It can also be easily shown that a concircularly flat space is an Einstein space. Thus, the concircular curvature tensor represents the deviation of the space time manifold from the spaces of constant curvature. The deviation from the concircular flatness is measured by the quantity

$$M = \sup_A \frac{|M_{abcd}A^{ab}A^{cd}|}{A_{bc}A^{bc}}$$

where $A^{ab} = Y^a X^b - Y^b X^a$, X, Y being two mutually orthogonal unit vectors. Also, $A_{bc} = -A_{cb}$.

The importance of concircular transformation and concircular curvature tensor is very well known in the differential geometry of certain F-structures such as complex, almost complex, contact, almost contact, Hermitian and almost Hermitian structures, etc. While the relativistic significance of this tensor has been studied by Ahsan and Siddiqui (2009).

(d) Space-matter tensor

Petrov (1969) introduced a fourth rank tensor which satisfies all the algebraic properties of the Riemann curvature tensor and is more general than the Weyl conformal curvature tensor. This tensor is introduced as follows:

Let the Einstein's field equations be

$$R_{ab} - \frac{1}{2}Rg_{ab} = \lambda T_{ab} \tag{5.166}$$

where λ is a constant and T_{ab} is the energy-momentum tensor. On contraction (5.166) yields

$$\lambda T = -R \tag{5.167}$$

Introduce a fourth order tensor

$$A_{abcd} = \frac{\lambda}{2}(g_{ac}T_{bd} + g_{bd}T_{ac} - g_{ad}T_{bc} - g_{bc}T_{ad}) \tag{5.168}$$

From the definition this tensor has the properties that

$$A_{abcd} = -A_{bacd} = -A_{abdc} = A_{cdab} \tag{5.169}$$

$$A_{abcd} + A_{acbd} + A_{adbc} = 0 \tag{5.170}$$

Contraction of (5.168) over b and d yields

$$A_{ac} = \lambda T_{ac} + \frac{\lambda}{2}Tg_{ac} = \lambda T_{ac} - \frac{R}{2}g_{ac} \tag{5.171}$$

Define a new fourth order tensor (Petrov, 1969)

$$P_{abcd} = R_{abcd} - A_{abcd} + \sigma(g_{ac}g_{bd} - g_{ad}g_{bc}) \tag{5.172}$$

This tensor is known as *space-matter tensor*. First part of this tensor represents the curvature of the space and the second represents the distribution and motion of the matter. This tensor has the following properties:

(i) $P_{abcd} = -P_{bacd} = -P_{abdc} = P_{cdab}, \quad P_{abcd} + P_{acdb} + P_{adbc} = 0.$

(ii) $P_{ac} = R_{ac} - \lambda T_{ac} + \frac{R}{2}g_{ac} + 3\sigma g_{ac} = (R + 3\sigma)g_{ac}.$

(iii) If the distribution and the motion of the matter, i.e., T_{ab} and the space-matter tensor, P_{abcd} are given, then R_{abcd}, the curvature of the space is determined to within the scalar σ.

(iv) If $T_{ab} = 0$ and $\sigma = 0$, then P_{abcd} is the curvature of the empty spacetime.

(v) If g_{ab}, the metric tensor, σ the scalar and P_{abcd} are known, then T_{ab} can be determined uniquely.

From Eqs. (5.166) and (5.167), Eq. (5.168) may be expressed as

$$A_{abcd} = \frac{1}{2}(g_{ac}R_{bd} + g_{bd}R_{ac} - g_{ad}R_{bc} - g_{bc}R_{ad})$$

$$- \frac{R}{2}(g_{ac}g_{bd} - g_{ad}g_{bc}) \tag{5.173}$$

Thus, from Eqs. (5.14) and (5.173), the space-matter tensor defined through Eq. (5.172) may be expressed as

$$P_{abcd} = C_{abcd} + (g_{ad}R_{bc} + g_{bc}R_{ad} - g_{ac}R_{bd} - g_{bd}R_{ac})$$

$$+ \left(\frac{2}{3}R + \sigma\right)(g_{ac}g_{bd} - g_{ad}g_{bc}) \tag{5.174}$$

which can also be written as

$$P^h_{bcd} = C^h_{bcd} + (\delta^h_d R_{bc} - \delta^h_c R_{bd} + g_{bc}R^h_d - g_{bd}R^h_c) + \left(\frac{2}{3}R + \sigma\right)(\delta^h_c g_{bd} - \delta^h_d g_{bc}) \tag{5.175}$$

The algebraic properties, spinor equivalent and an algebraic classification of the space-matter tensor, defined by Eq. (5.174), along with some other interesting results have been obtained by Ahsan (for details, see Ahsan, 1977a, 1977b, 1978, 1996; Ahsan and Siddiqui, 2010).

EXERCISES

5.1 Show that the trace of the Weyl conformal tensor is zero.

5.2 If ξ_i is a Killing vector then show that $\mathcal{L}_\xi A^i = 0$ does not lead to $\mathcal{L}_\xi A_i = 0$.

5.3 Find all Killing vectors of the metric $ds^2 = x^2 dx + x dy$, where $x^a = (x^1, x^2) = (x, y)$.

5.4 Find all Killing vectors X^a of the three-dimensional Euclidean space $ds^2 = dx^2 + dy^2 + dz^2$.

5.5 Find the Killing vectors for the line-element $ds^2 = (dx^4)^2 + 2e^{x^1} dx^4 dx^2 - (dx^1)^2 + \frac{1}{2}e^{2x^1}(dx^2)^2 - (dx^3)^2$. This is the line element of Gödel universe.

CHAPTER 6

Applications

6.1 Introduction

In the previous chapters it is seen that the concept of tensors has not only played a vital role in the different fields of study but also has a wide range of applications. Keeping this applicational spirit, this chapter is completely devoted to the applications of tensors to the fields of differential geometry and relativity theory.

6.2 Maxwell's Equations

The phenomenon of electrodynamics is described by the Maxwell's equations which consist of two fundamental quantities, $\mathbf{E}$ and $\mathbf{H}$, representing the electric and magnetic field strengths, respectively. To know the electric state of the matter, two more quantities have to be introduced—the electric charge density ρ and the current density $\mathbf{J}$. If $\mathbf{v}$ is the velocity of the electric charge then the current and charge densities are related through the equation (in CGS units)

$$\mathbf{J} = \rho \mathbf{v} \tag{6.1}$$

In general, the quantities $\mathbf{E}$, $\mathbf{H}$, ρ and $\mathbf{J}$ are functions of the spacetime coordinates.

For a given distribution of charge and current, the electric and magnetic field strenghts are determined by the following set of Maxwell's Equations (in the absence of any pondermotive matter)

$$\nabla \cdot \mathbf{E} = 4\pi\rho \tag{6.2}$$

$$\nabla \cdot \mathbf{H} = 0 \tag{6.3}$$

$$\nabla \times \mathbf{E} = -\frac{1}{c}\frac{\partial \mathbf{H}}{\partial t} \tag{6.4}$$

$$\nabla \times \mathbf{H} = \frac{1}{c}\frac{\partial \mathbf{E}}{\partial t} + \frac{4\pi}{c}\mathbf{J} \tag{6.5}$$

Taking the divergence of Eq. (6.5), we get

$$\nabla \cdot (\nabla \times \mathbf{H}) = \frac{1}{c}\frac{\partial}{\partial t}(\nabla \cdot \mathbf{E}) + \frac{4\pi}{c}(\nabla \cdot \mathbf{J})$$

which on using Eq. (6.2) leads to

$$\frac{\partial \rho}{\partial t} + \nabla \cdot \mathbf{J} = 0 \tag{6.6}$$

This is the equation of continuity satisfied by the current and charge densities. Equation (6.6) is also known as the law of conservation of total charge.

The vectorial form of Maxwell's Eqs. (6.2)–(6.5) can also be solved for $\mathbf{E}$ and $\mathbf{H}$ in terms of a scalar function of position $\phi(x, y, z, t)$ and a vector field $\mathbf{A}(x, y, z, t)$ as follows:

Since $\nabla \cdot (\nabla \times \mathbf{A}) = 0$, taking the divergence of Eq. (6.3), we get

$$\mathbf{H} = \nabla \times \mathbf{A} \tag{6.7}$$

where $\mathbf{A}(x, y, z, t)$ is called the vector potential. Now using this value of $\mathbf{H}$ in Eq. (6.4), we get

$$0 = -\nabla \times \left(\frac{1}{c}\frac{\partial \mathbf{A}}{\partial t} + \mathbf{E}\right)$$

Since $\nabla \times (\nabla \phi) = 0$, this equation leads to

$$\mathbf{E} + \frac{1}{c}\frac{\partial \mathbf{A}}{\partial t} = -\nabla \phi \tag{6.8}$$

where $\phi(x, y, z, t)$ is known as the scalar potential. Thus, Maxwell's equations guarantee the existence of a scalar potential ϕ and a vector potential $\mathbf{A}$. For these potentials, we have following equations:

(a) *Equations of motion for scalar and vector potentials.* From Eq. (6.8), substitute the value of $\mathbf{E}$ into Eq. (6.2) we get

$$\nabla \cdot (-\nabla \phi) - \frac{1}{c}\nabla \cdot \left(\frac{\partial \mathbf{A}}{\partial t}\right) = 4\pi \rho$$

which may be expressed as

$$-\nabla^2 \phi - \frac{1}{c}\frac{\partial}{\partial t}(\nabla \cdot \mathbf{A}) = 4\pi \rho \tag{6.9}$$

While using Eqs. (6.7) and (6.8), Eq. (6.5) leads to

$$\nabla \times (\nabla \times \mathbf{A}) + \frac{1}{c}\frac{\partial}{\partial t}\left(\nabla \phi + \frac{1}{c}\frac{\partial \mathbf{A}}{\partial t}\right) = \frac{4\pi}{c}\mathbf{J}$$

or

$$\nabla(\nabla \cdot \mathbf{A}) - \nabla^2 \mathbf{A} + \frac{1}{c}\frac{\partial}{\partial t}\left(\nabla \phi + \frac{1}{c}\frac{\partial \mathbf{A}}{\partial t}\right) = \frac{4\pi}{c}\mathbf{J}$$

Since (grad div) is zero, the above equation reduces to

$$-\nabla^2 \mathbf{A} + \frac{1}{c}\frac{\partial}{\partial t}\left(\nabla\phi + \frac{1}{c}\frac{\partial \mathbf{A}}{\partial t}\right) = \frac{4\pi}{c}\mathbf{J} \tag{6.10}$$

Now introduce the d'Alembertian operator as

$$\Box^2 \equiv \nabla^2 - \frac{1}{c}\frac{\partial^2}{\partial t^2} \tag{6.11}$$

so that Eqs. (6.9) and (6.10) take the forms

$$\Box^2\phi - \frac{1}{c}\frac{\partial}{\partial t}\left(\nabla\cdot\mathbf{A} + \frac{1}{c}\frac{\partial\phi}{\partial t}\right) = 4\pi\rho \tag{6.12}$$

and

$$\Box^2\mathbf{A} + \frac{1}{c}\mathrm{grad}\left(\nabla\cdot\mathbf{A} + \frac{1}{c}\frac{\partial\phi}{\partial t}\right) = \frac{4\pi}{c}\mathbf{J} \tag{6.13}$$

Equations (6.12) and (6.13) are the equations of motion for the electromagnetic potentials $\mathbf{A}$ and ϕ, coupled with each other.

If we choose

$$\nabla\cdot\mathbf{A} + \frac{1}{c}\frac{\partial\phi}{\partial t} = 0 \tag{6.14}$$

then Eqs. (6:12) and (6.13), respectively, reduce to

$$\Box^2\phi = 4\pi\rho \tag{6.15}$$

$$\Box^2\mathbf{A} = \frac{4\pi}{c}\mathbf{J} \tag{6.16}$$

which are uncoupled symmetrical second order inhomogeneous partial differential equations satisfied by ϕ and $\mathbf{A}$. These equations are known as the equations of motion for the scalar potential ϕ and vector potential $\mathbf{A}$. It may be noted that Eq. (6.14) is the relation between the scalar and vector potentials. This relationship is known as *Lorentz condition*.

While for the electric and magnetic field strengths, we have

(b) *Equations of motion for* $\mathbf{E}$ *and* $\mathbf{H}$. We shall now find the equations of motion for the electric and magnetic field strengths as follows: Taking the curl of Eq. (6.4), we get

$$\nabla \times (\nabla \times \mathbf{E}) + \frac{1}{c}\nabla \times \left(\frac{\partial \mathbf{H}}{\partial t}\right) = 0$$

or

$$\nabla(\nabla\cdot\mathbf{E}) - \nabla^2\mathbf{E} + \frac{1}{c}\frac{\partial}{\partial t}(\nabla \times \mathbf{H}) = 0$$

which from Eq. (6.5) leads to

$$\nabla(\nabla \cdot \mathbf{E}) - \nabla^2 \mathbf{E} + \frac{1}{c}\frac{\partial}{\partial t}\left(\frac{1}{c}\frac{\partial \mathbf{E}}{\partial t} + \frac{4\pi}{c}\mathbf{J}\right) = 0 \qquad (6.17)$$

Also, in the absence of true charge, i.e., $\rho = 0$, Eq. (6.17) yields [using Eq. (6.2)]

$$\frac{1}{c^2}\frac{\partial^2 \mathbf{E}}{\partial t^2} - \nabla^2 \mathbf{E} = -\frac{4\pi}{c^2}\frac{\partial \mathbf{J}}{\partial t} \qquad (6.18)$$

Further, in the absence of external electromotive forces, the current $\mathbf{J}$ is given by the Ohm's law

$$\mathbf{J} = \sigma \mathbf{E} \qquad (6.19)$$

where σ is the electrical conductivity of the system and thus Eq. (6.18) reduces to

$$\frac{1}{c^2}\frac{\partial^2 \mathbf{E}}{\partial t^2} - \nabla^2 \mathbf{E} = -\frac{4\pi\sigma}{c^2}\frac{\partial \mathbf{E}}{\partial t} \qquad (6.20)$$

so that for the vacuum ($\sigma = 0$), we have

$$\frac{1}{c^2}\frac{\partial^2 \mathbf{E}}{\partial t^2} - \nabla^2 \mathbf{E} = 0 \qquad (6.21)$$

which is the equation of motion for the electric field strength.

Similarly, starting from Eq. (6.5), the equation of motion for the magnetic field strength $\mathbf{H}$ is found to be as

$$\frac{1}{c^2}\frac{\partial^2 \mathbf{H}}{\partial t^2} - \nabla^2 \mathbf{H} = 0 \qquad (6.22)$$

Moreover, in the absence of charge and current, Eqs. (6.15) and (6.16) reduce to

$$\Box^2 \phi = 0, \quad \Box^2 \mathbf{A} = 0 \qquad (6.23)$$

Therefore, from Eqs. (6.21)–(6.23), it is evident that the fields $\mathbf{E}$ and $\mathbf{H}$ and potentials $\mathbf{A}$ and ϕ satisfy the wave equation of the form

$$\left(\frac{1}{c^2}\frac{\partial^2}{\partial t^2} - \nabla^2\right)\Psi(x, t) = 0 \qquad (6.24)$$

where $\Psi(x, t)$ represent either of the four variables $\mathbf{E}, \mathbf{H}, \mathbf{A}$ and ϕ.

It can also be shown that Eq. (6.24) represents electromagnetic disturbances which propagates with the speed c. That is, in vacuum electromagnetic waves propagate with the speed of light.

(c) *Covariant form of Maxwell's equations.* In what follows we shall find the covariant form of the Maxwell's Eqs. (6.2)–(6.5). Let the covariant form of the four vector A^i be given as

$$A_i = g_{ij} A^j = (-\mathbf{A}, \phi) = (-A_x, -A_y, -A_z, \phi) \tag{6.25}$$

and the four-dimensional curl of A_i be defined as

$$F_{ij} = \frac{\partial A_i}{\partial x^j} - \frac{\partial A_j}{\partial x^i} = A_{i,j} - A_{j,i} \tag{6.26}$$

such that

$$F_{ij} = -F_{ji} \tag{6.27}$$

The second rank skew symmetric tensor F_{ij} defined by Eq. (6.26) is called electromagnetic field tensor. It has $\frac{1}{2} n(n-1)$ independent componenets in n-dimension. Thus in four-dimensions F_{ij} has only six independent components.

Since the electric and magnetic field strengths $\mathbf{E}$ and $\mathbf{H}$ are defined through Eqs. (6.8) and (6.7), respectively, thus the x-component of $\mathbf{E}$, from Eq. (6.8), is given by

$$E_x = -\frac{\partial \phi}{\partial x} - \frac{1}{c} \frac{\partial A_x}{\partial t} \tag{6.28}$$

which on using Eqs. (6.25) and (6.26) can be expressed as

$$E_x = -\frac{\partial A_4}{\partial x^1} + \frac{\partial A_1}{\partial x^4} = F_{14} \tag{6.29}$$

Similarly

$$E_y = -\frac{\partial \phi}{\partial y} - \frac{1}{c} \frac{\partial A_y}{\partial t} = \frac{\partial A_2}{\partial x^4} - \frac{\partial A_4}{\partial x^2} = F_{24} \tag{6.29a}$$

$$E_z = -\frac{\partial \phi}{\partial z} - \frac{1}{c} \frac{\partial A_z}{\partial t} = \frac{\partial A_3}{\partial x^4} - \frac{\partial A_4}{\partial x^3} = F_{34} \tag{6.29b}$$

In a similar way, using Eqs. (6.7), (6.25) and (6.26), we have

$$H_x = (\nabla \times \mathbf{A})_x = \frac{\partial A_z}{\partial y} - \frac{\partial A_y}{\partial z} = \frac{\partial A_3}{\partial x^2} - \frac{\partial A_2}{\partial x^3} = F_{23} \tag{6.30}$$

and

$$H_y = (\nabla \times \mathbf{A})_y = \frac{\partial A_x}{\partial z} - \frac{\partial A_z}{\partial x} = \frac{\partial A_1}{\partial x^3} - \frac{\partial A_3}{\partial x^1} = F_{31} \tag{6.30a}$$

$$H_z = (\nabla \times \mathbf{A})_z = \frac{\partial A_y}{\partial x} - \frac{\partial A_x}{\partial y} = \frac{\partial A_2}{\partial x^1} - \frac{\partial A_1}{\partial x^2} = F_{12} \tag{6.30b}$$

Equations (6.29) and (6.30) show that the six independent components $(F_{14}, F_{24}, F_{34}, F_{23}, F_{31}, F_{12})$ of the electromagnetic field tensor completely specify the electromagnetic field described by the electric and magnetic field strengths $\mathbf{E}$ and $\mathbf{H}$.

The electromagnetic field tensor F_{ij} can also be expressed as

$$F_{ij} = \begin{bmatrix} 0 & H_z & -H_y & E_x \\ -H_z & 0 & H_x & E_y \\ H_y & -H_x & 0 & E_z \\ -E_x & -E_y & -E_z & 0 \end{bmatrix} \tag{6.31}$$

Also $F^{ij} = g^{ik} g^{jl} F_{kl}$ and we have

$$F^{ij} = \begin{bmatrix} 0 & H_z & -H_y & -E_x \\ -H_z & 0 & H_x & -E_y \\ H_y & -H_x & 0 & -E_z \\ E_x & E_y & E_z & 0 \end{bmatrix} \tag{6.32}$$

Further, from Eq. (6.26) we have

$$\frac{\partial F_{ij}}{\partial x^k} = \frac{\partial^2 A_i}{\partial x^k \partial x^j} - \frac{\partial^2 A_j}{\partial x^k \partial x^i}$$

$$\frac{\partial F_{jk}}{\partial x^i} = \frac{\partial^2 A_j}{\partial x^i \partial x^k} - \frac{\partial^2 A_k}{\partial x^i \partial x^j}$$

$$\frac{\partial F_{ki}}{\partial x^j} = \frac{\partial^2 A_k}{\partial x^j \partial x^i} - \frac{\partial^2 A_i}{\partial x^j \partial x^k}$$

Adding these equations, we get

$$\frac{\partial F_{ij}}{\partial x^k} + \frac{\partial F_{jk}}{\partial x^i} + \frac{\partial F_{ki}}{\partial x^j} = 0 \tag{6.33}$$

Again, from Eq. (6.26) we have

$$F^{ij} = \frac{\partial A^i}{\partial x_j} - \frac{\partial A^j}{\partial x_i}$$

so that

$$\frac{\partial F^{ij}}{\partial x^j} = \frac{\partial^2 A^i}{\partial x^j \partial x_j} - \frac{\partial^2 A^j}{\partial x^j \partial x_i} = \left(\frac{\partial^2}{\partial x^j \partial x_j} \right) A^i - \frac{\partial}{\partial x_i} \left(\frac{\partial A^j}{\partial x^j} \right) \tag{6.34}$$

Since $\dfrac{\partial A^j}{\partial x^j} = 0$ and $\dfrac{\partial^2}{\partial x^j \partial x_j} \equiv \dfrac{1}{c^2} \dfrac{\partial^2}{\partial t^2} - \nabla^2 \equiv \Box^2$, Eq. (6.34) leads to

$$\frac{\partial F^{ij}}{\partial x^j} = \Box^2 A^i \tag{6.35}$$

which from Eq. (6.16) reduces to

$$\frac{\partial F^{ij}}{\partial x^j} = \frac{4\pi}{c} J^i \tag{6.36}$$

It can easily be shown that the set of Eqs. (6.33) and (6.36) are equivalent to Eqs. (6.2)–(6.5).

The covariant form of the Maxwell's equations (in curved spacetime) is given by

$$F_{ij;k} + F_{jk;i} + F_{ki;j} = 0 \tag{6.37}$$

$$F^{ij}_{;j} = \frac{4\pi}{c} J^i \tag{6.38}$$

Due to the skew symmetry of F_{ij}, this equation is only integrable (self-consistence) if the continuity equation

$$J^i_{;i} = \frac{1}{\sqrt{-g}} (\sqrt{-g} J^i)_{;i} = 0$$

is satisfied. Here a semicolon denotes the covariant differentiation and the electromagnetic field tensor F_{ij} is given by

$$F_{ij} = A_{i;j} - A_{j;i} \tag{6.39}$$

Also, we have

$$A^{i;j}_{;i} - A^{j;i}_{;i} = \frac{4\pi}{c} J^j \tag{6.40}$$

While for calculation purpose, it is sometime convenient to use partial derivatives instead of covariant derivatives; and thus using Eqs. (6.39) and (6.40), we have

$$[\sqrt{-g} g^{ik} g^{jl} (A_{l,k} - A_{k,l})]_{,j} = \frac{4\pi}{c} \sqrt{-g} J^i \tag{6.41}$$

Remarks

1. From Eq. (6.26)/(6.39), it may be noted that the electromagnetic field can be generated through a vector potential A_i. The potential A_i is determined upto a four-dimensional gradient. Moreover, the electromagnetic field has two invariants which can be constructed from F_{ij} and are given by

$$I_1 = F_{ij} F^{ij}, \quad I_2 = {}^*F^{ij} F_{ij} \tag{6.42}$$

where $*$ denotes the dual. In Minkowski space, these invariants are

$$I_1 = 2(\mathbf{H}^2 - \mathbf{E}^2), \quad I_2 = 4\mathbf{E} \cdot \mathbf{H} \tag{6.43}$$

It may further be noted that the vanishing of these two invariant is the criterion for the existence of electromagnetic waves [cf., [Zakharov, 1973)].

2. The source-free Maxwell's equations are conformally invariant. That is, a potential A_i which is a solution of Maxwell's equations in a Riemannian space with metric ds^2 is also a solution in a space where $\tilde{ds}^2 = \Omega^2 ds^2$. Since under a conformal change

$$\tilde{g}_{ij} = \Omega^2 g_{ij}, \quad \tilde{g}^{ij} = \Omega^{-2} g^{ij}, \quad \tilde{g} = \Omega^8 g \qquad (6.44)$$

$$\tilde{A}_i = A_i, \quad \tilde{A}_{i,j} = A_{i,j} \qquad (6.44a)$$

Now using Eqs. (6.44) and Eq. (6.41) with $J^i = 0$, it can easily be verified that source-free Maxwell's equations are conformally invariant.

6.3   Special Coordinate System

In general theory of relativity we are allowed to formulate the laws of physics using arbitrary coordinates and the principle of covariance states that the laws of physics are the same in any coordinates. Some of the coordinate choices are more natural and easier to work with than others. In this section, we shall discuss few of these choices.

Orthogonal coordinate system

In vector calculus we have been using almost exclusively the familiar Cartesian coordinate system and other coordinate systems such as cylindrical and spherical coordinates. These three coordinate systems (Cartesian, cylindrical, spherical) are actually only a subset of a larger group of coordinate systems—orthogonal coordinates. If in a coordinate system, the metric is of the form

$$ds^2 = g_{ii} dx^i dx^i, \quad i = 1, 2, 3, 4$$

i.e., the metric tensor has diagonal components only, then the coordinate system is said to be orthogonal coordinate system. In general, such coordinate system does not exist in four-dimensional Riemannian space. This is so because the system of differential equations

$$g'_{ij} \frac{dx'^i}{dx^k} \frac{dx'^j}{dx^l} = 0 \quad \text{for } i \neq j$$

has no solution satisfying the condition

$$x'^i = F^i(x^i), \quad \left| \frac{\partial x'^i}{\partial x^i} \right| \neq 0$$

Time-orthogonal coordinate system

In physics, we usually talk about events and events occur at a certain place (represented by three space coordinates) and time. So we choose time as the fourth coordinate and take $x^4 = ct$. If $g_{4\alpha} = 0, (\alpha = 1, 2, 3)$ then time-orthogonal coordinates exist. Moreover, if $g_{44} = \pm 1$, we then have Gaussian coordinates. In case of the time-orthogonal coordinates, the metric can be expressed as

$$ds^2 = g_{\alpha\beta}dx^\alpha dx^\beta + g_{44}(dx^4)^2$$

Minkowski coordinate system

Minkowski coordinates are Cartesian spacetime coordinates. In this coordinate system, the time component is multiplied by the speed of light c to give it the dimensions of length. These coordinates are commonly written as $(x^1, x^2, x^3, x^4) = (x, y, z, ct)$.

Fermi coordinate system

The local coordinates that can be introduced to a geodesic are called Fermi coordinates (named after the Italian physicist Enrico Fermi) and are defined as:

Let M be a n-dimensional Riemannian manifold, γ a geodesic on M, and p be a point on γ. Then there exists local coordinates $(t, x^2, \ldots, x^n)$ around p such that

(i) For small t, the coordinate $(t, 0, \ldots, 0)$ represents the geodesic near p,

(ii) On γ, the metric tensor is the Euclidean metric,

(iii) On γ, all Christoffel symbols vanish.

It may be noted that the Fermi coordinate system is valid only on the geodesic and thus, for example, if all Christoffel symbols vanish near p, then the geodesics are the straight lines and the manifold is flat near p.

Comoving coordinate system

Let $u'^i = \dfrac{dx'^i}{d\lambda}$ be the velocity field (of observers). Since λ is a parameter which is independent of the coordinate, the component of this velocity transforms as

$$u^j = \frac{\partial x^j}{\partial x'^k} u'^k$$

It is always possible to choose a coordinate system in which the spatial components of the velocity are zero, i.e., $u_1 = u_2 = u_3 = 0$. In this coordinate system the velocity is $u^i = (0, 0, 0, u^4)$, the particles do not change their position; the coordinates move with the time. Such a coordinate system is called comoving. Since the metric is time–dependent, the separation between two particles can vary although the coordinate difference between them never changes. In comoving coordinates the space is static, as most bodies on the scale of galaxies or larger are approximately comoving, and comoving bodies have static, unchanging comoving coordinates. So for a given pair of comoving galaxies, while the proper distance between them would have been smaller in the past and will become larger in the future due to the expansion of space, the comoving distance between them remains constant at all times. Comoving coordinates assign constant spatial coordinate values to observers who think that the universe looks like isotropic. Such observers are called *comoving observers* because they are moving in a universe which is expanding according to Hubble's law [Hubble's law states that "the speed v of recession of a galaxy (an astronomical object) is directly proportional to its distance D from us", i.e., $v = HD$, where H is known as the Hubble's constant]. The comoving time coordinate is the elapsed time since the Big Bang according to a clock of a comoving observer and is a measure of cosmological time. The comoving spatial coordinates tell us where an event occurs while cosmological time tells us when an event occurs. Together, they form a complete coordinate system, giving us both the location and time of an event.

6.4   Energy-momentum Tensors

The energy-momentum tensors (also known as stress-energy tensors) usually occur in dynamics, hydrodynamics, electromagnetic theory and in the field theories in general. But their role is not so important in these areas as it in general theory of relativity. When expressed in terms of the energy-momentum tensors, the conservation laws for energy and momentum take simpler form. In special theory of relativity (flat spacetime or Minkowski space), the energy E and linear momentum p are the two aspects of a single quantity—the 4-momentum. These two are connected through the equation

$$E^2 - c^2 p^2 = m^2 c^4$$

If ρ_0 is the proper density of the matter and $u^i = \dfrac{dx^i}{dt}$ denotes the motion of the matter, then energy-momentum tensor T^{ij} is defined by

$$T^{ij} = \rho_0 c^2 \frac{dx^i}{dt}\frac{dx^j}{dt} = \rho_0 c^2 u^i u^j \qquad (6.45)$$

If ρ is the coordinate density of matter, it can then easily be shown that the energy-momentum tensor defined by Eq. (6.45) takes the form

$$T^{ij} = \rho u^i u^j \qquad (6.46)$$

The energy-momentum tensor T^{ij} is the flow of the ith component of the 4-momentum along the jth direction. The different components of T^{ij} have their meanings as follows:

(i) T^{44} is the energy density.

(ii) cT^{4i} is the energy flow per unit area parallel to the ith direction.

(iii) T^{ii} is the flow of momentum component i per unit area in the ith direction, i.e., pressure across the ith plane.

(iv) T^{ij} is the flow of the ith component of momentum per unit area in the jth direction.

(v) $T^{i4}c$ is the density of the ith component of momentum.

The energy-momentum tensor T^{ij} also satisfies the equation

$$T^{ij}_{,j} = 0 \qquad (6.47)$$

which means that the energy-momentum tensor is divergence-free everywhere or conserved. This result of special theory of relativity can be converted to a form of general theory of relativity (curved spacetime), if the partial derivatives are replaced by covariant derivatives. Thus, for the curved spacetime, Eq. (6.47) takes the form

$$T^{ij}_{;j} = 0 \qquad (6.48)$$

which can also be expressed as

$$\frac{\partial T^{ij}}{\partial x^j} + \Gamma^j_{kj} T^{ik} + \Gamma^i_{kj} T^{kj} = 0 \qquad (6.49)$$

It may be noted that in the absence of matter, the energy-momentum tensor vanishes. Moreover, it is a second rank tensor whose divergence vanishes at all points.

Einstein identified the energy-momentum tensor as the source of the spacetime curvature and suggested the following simple but important relation

$$R_{ij} - \frac{1}{2} g_{ij} R = K T_{ij} \qquad (6.50)$$

between the energy-momentum tensor and curvature of the spacetime. Here $R_{ij} - \frac{1}{2} g_{ij} R = G_{ij}$ is the Einstein tensor (cf., Section 4.9) which describe the curvature of the spacetime, T_{ij}, the energy-momentum tensor describing the distribution of matter and K is some scalar constant whose magnitude determines the effectiveness of the energy density in warping the spacetime. Einstein himself derived these equations in 1915.

Energy-momentum tensor for electromagnetic field

The energy-momentum tensor for the electromagnetic field is defined by

$$T_{ij} = -\frac{1}{4\pi} \left(F^k_i F_{jk} - \frac{1}{4} g_{ij} F_{mn} F^{mn} \right) \qquad (6.51)$$

where F_{ij} is the skew symmetric electromagnetic field tensor satisfying Maxwell's equations [cf., Eqs. (6.33) and (6.36)]. T_{ij}, given by Eq. (6.51), is symmetric and trace free (see also Example 1.10) and in the absence of current J^i has zero divergence.

For the spacetime of special relativity, the electromagnetic field tensors F_{ij} and F^{ij} in terms of **E** and **H** are given by Eqs. (6.31) and (6.32), respectively; and thus the energy-momentum tensor T^i_j in terms of **E** and **H** is given by

$$8\pi T^i_j$$

$$= \begin{bmatrix}
2(E_x^2 + H_x^2) - E^2 - H^2 & -E_x E_y - H_x H_y & -E_x E_z - H_x H_z & H_y E_z - H_z E_y \\
-E_x E_y - H_x H_y & 2(E_y^2 + H_y^2) - E^2 - H^2 & -E_y E_z - H_y H_z & H_z E_x - H_x E_z \\
-E_x E_z - H_x H_z & -E_y E_z - H_y H_z & 2(E_z^2 + H_z^2) - E^2 - H^2 & H_x E_y - H_y E_x \\
H_y E_z - H_z E_y & H_z E_x - H_x E_z & H_x E_y - H_y E_x & E^2 + H^2
\end{bmatrix}$$

$$(6.52)$$

We have seen in Section 6.2 that the vanishing of the invariants of the electromagnetic field is the criterion for the existence of electromagnetic waves. That is

$$\mathbf{H}^2 - \mathbf{E}^2 = 0 \quad \text{and} \quad \mathbf{E} \cdot \mathbf{H} = 0$$

and for the electromagnetic radiation due to a plane wave in z-direction we have $E_x \neq 0, H_y \neq 0$ and $E_x = H_y$. Thus Eq. (6.52) becomes

$$8\pi T^i_j = \begin{bmatrix} 0 & 0 & 0 & 0 \\ 0 & 0 & 0 & 0 \\ 0 & 0 & -E^2 - H^2 & -H_y E_x \\ 0 & 0 & -H_y E_x & E^2 + H^2 \end{bmatrix} \tag{6.53}$$

Energy-momentum tensor for perfect fluid

The concept of perfect fluid is general enough to describe a wide variety of physical forms of matter. A mechanical medium which is incapable of sustaining any shearing stresses and in which the normal stresses are isotropic is said to define a perfect fluid. It is completely specified by two scalar quantities—the rest-frame energy density ρ and the isotropic rest-frame pressure p and one vector quantity—the 4-velocity of the fluid. The parameter p serves to specify the pressure in every direction.

The energy-momentum tensor for perfect fluid is defined as

$$T^{ij} = (\rho + p)u^i u^j \pm p g^{ij} \tag{6.54}$$

where ρ is the energy density, p is the pressure and u^i, the 4-velocity of the fluid such that $u_i u^i = \mp 1$.

As an example that how to calculate the components of T^{ij}, consider a spherically symmetric mass at rest with its centre at origin. The matter distribution in this object is assumed to be that of a perfect fluid. The metric of such object is given by (see also Example 4.6)

$$ds^2 = -e^\lambda dr^2 - r^2 d\theta^2 - r^2 \sin^2 \theta d\phi^2 + e^\nu dt^2 \tag{6.55}$$

where λ and ν are functions of r only. Since the mass is static, the velocity components are

$$\frac{dr}{ds} = \frac{d\theta}{ds} = \frac{d\phi}{ds} = 0 \tag{6.56}$$

and from Eq. (6.55), we have

$$\frac{dt}{ds} = e^{-\nu/2} \tag{6.57}$$

The components of T^{ij} as calculated from Eq. (6.54), using Eqs. (6.55) and (6.56), are given by (where u_i is such that $u_i u^i = -1$)

$$T^{ij} = \begin{bmatrix} p & 0 & 0 & 0 \\ 0 & p & 0 & 0 \\ 0 & 0 & p & 0 \\ 0 & 0 & 0 & -\rho \end{bmatrix} \tag{6.58}$$

In general, when we model some matter-energy distribution in general theory of relativity we need an equation which tells us that how the matter reacts with pressure and absolute temperature. This is known as the *equation of state* of the matter-energy system and may be of the form

$$p = p(\rho, T)$$

In most of the cases the physical system is in equilibrium and we can take $T = $ constant. The equation of state for an equilibrium situation now takes the form

$$p = p(\rho)$$

The form of the equation of state depends upon the situation under consideration. If we are finding the model of a star, we need an equation of state that depends upon the type of the star; or if we are obtaining a model of our universe then we require an equation of state that depends on what stage of the universe after Big Bang we are considering.

Consider now the evolution of the fluid that can be determined by an equation of state of the form

$$p = \omega\rho \tag{6.59}$$

where ω is some constant. Depending upon the values of this constant, there are three types of perfect fluids:

(i) *When $\omega = 0$.* In this case, Eq. (6.59) leads to $p = 0$, i.e., there is a stream of particles exerting no pressure. Such a system is known as *dust* whose energy-momentum tensor, from Eq. (6.54) is

$$T^{ij} = \rho u^i u^j \tag{6.60}$$

Now using this equation in Eq. (6.48), we get

$$(\rho u^i u^j)_{;j} = 0$$

which on using the product rule for covariant differentiation leads to

$$\rho u^i_{;j} u^j + \rho u^i u^j_{;j} = 0 \tag{6.61}$$

Multiply this equation by u_i, we get

$$\rho u_i u^i_{;j} u^j + \rho u_i u^i u^j_{;j} = 0 \tag{6.62}$$

Since $u_i u^i = -1$, Eq. (6.62) reduces to

$$\rho u^j_{;j} = 0 \qquad (6.63)$$

This is a continuity type equation. From this equation, Eq. (6.61) leads to

$$u^i_{;j} u^j = 0$$

which shows that the vector u^i is tangent to a geodesic [cf., Eq. (2.24a)]. Thus geodesic motion must apply for dust fluid particles.

(ii) *When $\omega = \frac{1}{3}$.* Here the pressure and density, from Eq. (6.59), are given by $3p = \rho$ which is equation of state for an isotropic gas of photons. A set of photons or other massless particles behave like *radiation*. For the radiative system, the energy momentum tensor, from Eq. (6.54) is given by

$$T^{ij} = p(4u^i u^j + g^{ij}) \qquad (6.64)$$

(iii) *When $\omega = -1$.* Such a system is known as *vacuum* and from Eqs. (6.54) and (6.59), the energy-momentum tensor is given by

$$T^{ij} = \rho_{vac} g^{ij} \qquad (6.65)$$

Thus, vacuum energy is a perfect fluid for which $p_{vac} = -\rho_{vac}$.

    The above considerations are important and play a vital role in the field of cosmology (for more details, see Stephani [1982]).

6.5   Kinematical Quantities—Raychaudhuri's Equation

In this section, we shall use x^i to denote the arbitrary coordinates $(i, j, \ldots = 1, 2, 3, 4)$ in four-dimensional spacetime with metric g_{ij}. Let there exist a unique vector field which represents the average matter velocity at each point of the spacetime of general relativity, and let this 4-velocity u^i be normalized so that

$$u_i u^i = -1 \qquad (6.66)$$

The vector fields defined by Eq. (6.66) are called time-like vector fields. One of the most important example is that of a velocity field of matter distribution: for example, that of matter inside a star or that of stars or galaxies (taken as continuous distribution of matter) in the universe. The properties of this time-like velocity field are best understood when we examine the behaviour of its covariant derivative and this is what we intend to do in this section.

    These vector fields can be expressed in a simpler manner if we use the normalized comoving coordinates (y^μ, s) which are defined locally as follows.

In some arbitrarily chosen space section of the spacetime, label the fluid particles by the coordinates $y^\mu(\mu, \nu, \ldots)$. Also at all later times, we label the same particle by the same coordinate values so that the fluid flowlines in spacetime are the curves $y^\mu = \text{constant}$. From the initial space section, the time coordinate can be determined by measuring the proper time along the flow lines. The velocity vector in terms of these coordinates is given by

$$u^i = \delta^i_4$$

while in terms of the general coordinates x^i, the velocity vectors are

$$u^i = \left(\frac{dx^i}{ds}\right)_{y^\mu = \text{constant}}$$

Now introduce, at each point, a *projection tensor* into the rest space of the observer moving with 4-velocity u^i as

$$h_{ij} = g_{ij} + u_i u_j \qquad (6.67)$$

It can easily be verified that this projection tensor satisfies the following properties:

$$h_{ij} = h_{ji}, \quad h_{ij}u^j = 0, \quad h^k_i h^j_k = h^j_i, \quad h^i_i = 3$$

In the instantaneous rest space of the comoving observers, the effective volume element is given by $\eta_{ijkl}u^l$ where the totally skew symmetric pseudotensor η is defined as (see also Section 2.6)

$$\eta^{ijkl} = \eta^{[ijkl]}, \quad \eta^{1234} = \frac{1}{\sqrt{-g}}, \quad g = \det(g_{ij})$$

The *time derivative* of a tensor X, as measured by an observer moving with velocity u^i, is denoted by $\dot{X}$ and is defined as

$$\dot{X}^{i\ldots j}_{k\ldots l} = X^{i\ldots j}_{k\ldots l;m}u^m \qquad (6.68)$$

The combined effects of the gravitational and inertial forces on the fluid are represented by the vector

$$\dot{u}^i = u^i_{;j}u^j \qquad (6.69)$$

which is known as the *acceleration vector*. While in comoving coordinates, $\dot{u}^i = \Gamma^i_{44}$. Consider the world lines (paths) of two neighbouring particles, labelled by the comoving coordinates y^μ and $y^\mu + \delta y^\mu$. The vector X^i, whose components are given in comoving coordinates, joins the same two world lines at all times. Such a vector is known as *connecting vector* and obeys the differential equation

$$\dot{X}_i = u_{i;j}X^j \qquad (6.70)$$

We shall now investigate the behaviour of the second rank tensor $u_{i;j}$. It is known that a rank two tensor can be decomposed into symmetric and skew symmetric parts, and the symmetric part can further be decomposed into a trace and trace-free part. Thus, we have

$$\dot{u}_i u_j + u_{i;j} = \dot{u}_{(i} u_{j)} + \dot{u}_{[i} u_{j]} + u_{(i;j)} + u_{[i;j]}$$

$$= u_{(i;j)} + u_{[i;j]} + \frac{1}{3} u^k_{;k} h_{ij} - \frac{1}{3} u^k_{;k} h_{ij} + \dot{u}_{(i} u_{j)} + \dot{u}_{[i} u_{j]}$$

This equation can be expressed as

$$u_{i;j} = \frac{1}{3} \theta h_{ij} + \sigma_{ij} + \omega_{ij} - \dot{u}_i u_j \tag{6.71}$$

which completely determines the first derivative of the velocity vector. Here

$$\theta = u^j_{;j}$$

$$\sigma_{ij} = u_{(i;j)} + \dot{u}_{(i} u_{j)} - \frac{1}{3} \theta h_{ij} \tag{6.72}$$

$$\omega_{ij} = u_{[i;j]} + \dot{u}_{[i} u_{j]}$$

$$\dot{u}_i = u_{i;j} u^j$$

From Eq. (6.72) it may be noted that

$$\omega_{ij} u^i = \omega_{ij} u^j = 0, \quad \sigma_{ij} u^j = 0, \quad \sigma^i_i = 0 \tag{6.73}$$

Moreover, from Eq. (6.69), we have

$$\dot{u}_i u^i = 0 \tag{6.73a}$$

The quantity θ defined in Eq. (6.72) is known as the *expansion* of the time-like fluid flow vector u^i. The second rank tensors σ_{ij} and ω_{ij} are, respectively, known as *shear* and *vorticity tensors*. The magnitude of σ_{ij} is known as the *shear* of u^i and is defined by

$$\sigma^2 = \frac{1}{2} \sigma^{ij} \sigma_{ij}, \quad \sigma^2 \geq 0 \tag{6.74}$$

and

$$\sigma = 0 \Leftrightarrow \sigma_{ij} = 0 \tag{6.75}$$

While from the definition of vorticity tensor ω_{ij}, we can define the *vorticity vector* ω_i as

$$\omega^i = \frac{1}{2} \eta^{ijkl} u_j \omega_{kl} \Leftrightarrow \omega_{ij} = \eta_{ijkl} \omega^k u^l \tag{6.76}$$

which satisfies the equations

$$\omega^i u_i = 0, \quad \omega^{ij} u_j = o, \quad \omega^i \omega_{ij} = 0 \qquad (6.77)$$

Since the vorticity tensor is skew symmetric, its diagonal component vanishes and thus it is traceless. The magnitude of the vorticity vector ω^i is called the *vorticity (rotation)* of the fluid velocity vector and is defined by

$$\omega = \sqrt{\omega^i \omega_i} = \sqrt{\frac{1}{2} \omega^{ij} \omega_{ij}} \qquad (6.78)$$

From Eq. (6.77), it follows that

$$\omega \geq 0 \quad \text{and} \quad \omega = 0 \Leftrightarrow \omega_i = 0 \Leftrightarrow \omega_{ij} = 0 \qquad (6.79)$$

If we consider $u^i = \dfrac{dx^i}{dt}$ as the time-like vector tangent to a geodesic then from Eq. (2.24) and (2.69) it follows that the acceleration vector $\dot{u}^i$ is zero and thus the decomposition (6.71) reduces to

$$u_{i;j} = \frac{1}{3} \theta h_{ij} + \sigma_{ij} + \omega_{ij} \qquad (6.80)$$

It may be noted, from Eqs. (6.73) and (6.77), that shear and vorticity tensors, acceleration and vorticity vectors are space-like.

Also, in general relativity by *congruence* we mean a set of curves in an open region of spacetime such that every point in the region lies precisely on one curve. A congruence generated by nowhere vanishing time-like, null or space-like vector fields are called *time-like, null* or *space-like congruence*, respectively. These congruences may be geodesic or non-geodesic, though the former is more useful in the context of gravity. A congruence is a *geodesic congruence* if $u_{i;j} u^j = 0$. In general relativity, a time-like congruence in a four-dimensional Lorentzian manifold can be interpreted as a family of world lines of observers in the spacetime. In particular, a time-like geodesic congruence can be interpreted as a family of free-falling test particles. Null congruences are also important, particularly null geodesic congruences, which can be interpreted as a family of freely propagating light rays.

For a time-like geodesic congruence, the quantities appearing in the decomposition (6.80) have the following physical meaning:

(i) The expansion scalar θ represents the fractional rate at which the volume of a small initially spherical cloud of test particles changes with respect to proper time of the particle at the centre of the cloud.

(ii) The shear tensor σ_{ij} represents any tendency of the initial sphere to become distorted into an ellipsoidal shape.

(iii) The vorticity tensor ω_{ij} represents any tendency of the initial sphere to rotate; the vorticity vanishes if and only if the world lines in the congruence are everywhere orthogonal to the spatial hypersurfaces in some foliation of the spacetime.

Raychadhuri's equation

Amal Kumar Raychaudhuri in his remarkable paper [Raychaudhari, A., "Relativistic cosmology", *Phys. Rev.*, **98**, 1123, 1955. Reprinted as a *Golden Oldie in GRG*, **32**, 749, 2000.] for the first time gave a general derivation of the fundamental equation of gravitational attraction for pressurefree matter, showing the repulsive nature of a positive cosmological constant, and underlying the basic singularity theorem. Fifty years hence, the Raychaudhuri equations have been discussed and analysed in a variety of contexts. Their rise to prominence was largely due to their use (through the notion of geodesic focusing) in the proofs of the seminal Hawking–Penrose singularity theorems of general relativity. Today, the importance of this set of equations, as well as their applicability in diverse scenarios, is a well-known fact.

We shall now investigate the behaviour of a congruence (collection) of particles having time-like 4-velocity u^i as they fall under their own gravity. From the Ricci identity, the Riemann curvature tensor is defined as

$$u^i_{;jk} - u^i_{;kj} = R^i_{ljk} u^l \tag{6.81}$$

Contracting this equation with i and j, we get

$$u^i_{;ik} - u^i_{;ki} = R^i_{lik} u^l$$

Multiplying this equation by u^k, we get

$$u^i_{;ik} u^k - u^i_{;ki} u^k = R^i_{lik} u^l u^k$$

which on using Eq. (6.72) reduces to

$$\theta_{;k} u^k - u^i_{;ki} u^k = R_{lk} u^l u^k \tag{6.82}$$

But

$$(u^i_{;k} u^k)_{;i} = u^i_{;ki} u^k + u^i_{;k} u^k_{;i}$$

so that

$$u^i_{;ki} u^k = (u^i_{;k} u^k)_{;i} - u^i_{;k} u^k_{;i} = \dot{u}^i_{;i} - u_{i;j} u^{j;i} \tag{6.83}$$

Also from Eqs. (6.71)–(6.74), (6.77) and (6.78), we have

$$u_{i;j} u^{i;j} = \frac{1}{3} \theta^2 + 2(\sigma^2 - \omega^2) \tag{6.84}$$

From Eqs. (6.83) and (6.84), Eq. (6.82) now reduces to

$$\theta_{;k} u^k - \dot{u}^i_{;i} + \frac{1}{3} \theta^2 + 2(\sigma^2 - \omega^2) = R_{lk} u^l u^k$$

which on using Eq. (6.68) can be expressed as

$$\dot{\theta} - \dot{u}^i_{;i} + \frac{1}{3} \theta^2 + 2(\sigma^2 - \omega^2) = R_{lk} u^l u^k \tag{6.85}$$

The Einstein field equations

$$R_{ij} - \frac{1}{2}g_{ij}R = -8\pi T_{ij}$$

can also be expressed as [cf., Eq. (5.37)]

$$R_{ij} = -8\pi\left(T_{ij} - \frac{1}{2}g_{ij}T\right) \tag{6.86}$$

where the distribution of matter is governed by the energy-momentum tensor of the perfect fluid defined as [cf., Eq. (6.54)]

$$T_{ij} = (\rho + p)u_i u_j + pg_{ij} \tag{6.87}$$

which leads to

$$T_{ij}u^i u^j = \rho, \quad T = g^{ij}T_{ij} = -\rho + 3p$$

Equation (6.86) now leads to

$$R_{ij}u^i u^j = -4\pi(\rho + 3p) \tag{6.88}$$

Substituting this value in Eq. (6.85), we get

$$\dot{\theta} - \dot{u}^i_{;i} + \frac{1}{3}\theta^2 + 2(\sigma^2 - \omega^2) = -4\pi(\rho + 3p)$$

which can also be expressed as

$$\dot{\theta} = \dot{u}^i_{;i} - \frac{1}{3}\theta^2 - 2(\sigma^2 - \omega^2) - 4\pi(\rho + 3p) \tag{6.89}$$

This is the propagation equation for the expansion scalar θ and is known as *Raychaudhuri's equation*. The quantity given by Eq. (6.88) is sometimes known as *Raychaudhuri's scalar*.

If we consider flow of the fluid along the time-like geodesic congruence then the full set of evolution equations for the expansion, shear and rotation along the flow, from the above considerations, are given as follows (cf., Kramer et al., 1980 and Stephani, 1982):

$$\dot{\theta} = -\frac{1}{3}\theta^2 - 2(\sigma^2 - \omega^2) + R_{lk}u^l u^k \tag{6.90}$$

$$\dot{\sigma}_{ij} = -\frac{2}{3}\theta\sigma_{ij} - \sigma_{ik}\sigma^k_j - \omega_{ik}\omega^k_j + \frac{2}{3}h_{ij}(\sigma^2 - \omega^2) + C_{kjil}u^k u^l + \frac{1}{2}\tilde{R}_{ij} \tag{6.91}$$

$$\dot{\omega}_{ij} = -\frac{2}{3}\theta\omega_{ij} - 2\sigma^k_{[j}\omega_{i]k} \tag{6.92}$$

where C_{kjil} is the Weyl conformal curvature tensor and $\tilde{R}_{ij} = h_{ik}h_{jl}R^{kl} - \frac{1}{3}h_{ij}h_{kl}R^{kl}$.

It is worth mentioning here that these evolution equations (and their generalisations) are essentially geometric statements and are independent of any reference to the Einstein field equations. There are a few points to note here. Firstly, one must realise that these are not equations but, essentially, identitites. The identities, however, become equations once we use the Einstein equations or any other geometric property (e.g. Einstein space, or vacuum, etc.) as an extra input. Moreover, the equations are coupled, nonlinear and first order. The equation for the expansion is of central interest (in the context of the singularity theorems) and it is rather straightforward to analyse. Its generalisation to the case of null geodesics (the null Raychaudhuri equation) plays a key role in geometrical optics in a curved spacetime.

As a simple example that how we can use Raychaudhuri's equation, consider the *strong energy condition* which demands that $(\rho + 3p) \geq 0$. It can easily be seen, from the spatial nature of ω_{ij}, that $\omega_{ij} = 0$ if and only if the vector field is orthogonal to family of hypersurfaces. Thus, if for a spacetime satisfying Einstein field equations and strong energy condition we have a congruence whose tangent vector is hypersurface orthogonal, then the Raychaudhuri Eq. (6.90) implies

$$\dot{\theta} \leq -\frac{1}{3}\theta^2 \qquad (6.93)$$

which on integration leads to

$$\theta^{-1}(\tau) \geq \frac{1}{3}\tau + \theta_0^{-1} \qquad (6.94)$$

where θ_0 is the initial value of θ and τ is the proper time.

Now consider a hypersurface-orthogonal congruence, which is initially converging ($\theta_0 < 0$) rather than expanding. In such case, Eq. (6.94) shows that the convergence will continue and we must reach at a place where geodesics cross in a finite proper time $\tau \leq -3\theta_0^{-1}$. In other words, we can say that the matter satisfying the condition that $(\rho + 3p) \geq 0$ can never begin to push geodesic apart, it can only increase the rate at which they are converging. Divergence of the expansion parameter by itself does not imply the singularity of the spacetime (geodesics crossing all the time, even in flat space). But most of the proofs of the singularity theorems take advantage of this property of Raychaudhuri equation to show that the spacetime must be geodesically incomplete in some way.

Some of the applications of Raychaudhuri's equation will be discussed in the next section.

6.6   Solutions of Einstein Field Equations

The theory of relativity was developed in two phases—Special Theory of Relativity and General Theory of Relativity. Special theory of relativity adapted the concept of inertial frame to the basic law of constancy of velocity of light dispensing with the concept of absolute space and time of

Galilean–Newtonian mechanics, while the general theory of relativity came into existence as an extension of special theory of relativity. The general theory of relativity proposed by Albert Einstein, almost a century ago, presented a new view of the spacetime we live in: instead of matter moving through a passive spacetime continuum the general theory of relativity asserts that the presence of matter should distort spacetime. This distortion causes the deflection of material particles and of light from their classical paths. On the basis of his general relativity, Einstein predicted that star light which passes the limb of the sun on its way to the earth should be deflected by *1.750 seconds of arc*. But this has to be verified experimentally only when there is total solar eclipse. Einstein was fortunate enough that a total solar eclipse occurred on May 29, 1919; Sir Arthur Stanley Eddington organised an expedition to the island of Principe' (lying off the west coast of Africa) and made a photograph of the star field around the sun during this event. The general relativistic deflection of light was confirmed when a comparison with night photograph was made. This curious property of the spacetime was turned into the news headlines of all the newspapers. On April 2, 1921 Einstein visited USA, and next day Times, New York put the headline of its newspaper as *"Einstein: Space and Time are Wedded, Matter and Energy Declared Interchangeable. Matter Curves Spacetime. Affecting all Objects Moving Therein."*

Since then the hold of Einstein's general relativity on rest of the physics strengthened as the theory successfully tested on each and every of its predictions. The general theory of relativity changed our perception of the universe in which we live and thus revolutionised the whole physics. In recent years, general relativity has become an integral and indispensible part of the modern physics. This theory links the gravitation and the structure of the spacetime. There are many appreciable connections between general relativity, particle physics and string theory and at the same time there are number of exciting astrophysical applications of general relativity such as black holes, gravitational lensing, the production and detection of gravitational waves, the big bang, the early universe, the late universe and the cosmological constant, etc.

As stated earlier, the basic idea of Einstein's theory of gravitation consists in geometrizing the gravitational force, that is mapping all the properties of the gravitational force and its influence upon the physical processes onto the properties of a Riemannian space. Gravitational fields are produced by the masses and so one may ask that how the properties of the Riemannian space are calculated from the distribution of matter. Here "matter" means every thing that can produce a gravitational field (i.e., that contributes to the energy-momentum tensor), for example, atomic nuclei, electron and electromagnetic field.

The Einstein field equations, in the presence of matter, are given by

$$R_{ij} - \frac{1}{2} R g_{ij} = -k T_{ij} \qquad (6.95)$$

while in the absence of matter (or in empty spacetime), the field equations are

$$R_{ij} = 0 \qquad (6.96)$$

[cf., Eqs. (5.36)–(5.38)].

The field Eqs. (6.95) constitute a system of ten differential equations to determine ten metric functions g_{ij} [since both sides of Eq. (6.95) have second rank symmetric tensors]. However, the contracted Bianchi identities $G^{ij}_{;j} = 0$ [cf., Eq. (4.65)] represent four constraints on the function g_{ij} and there are only six independent equations in (6.95). This is appropriate because if a metric is a solution of Einstein equations in one coordinate system x^i, it should also be solution in any other coordinate system x'^i. This means that there are four unphysical degrees of freedom in g_{ij} represented by the four functions $x'^i(x^i)$ and we expect that Einstein field equation only constraints the six coordinate independent degrees of freedom.

Equation (6.95) is very complicated differential equation. The left-hand side of this equation contains the Ricci scalar R and the Ricci tensor R_{ij} which are the contractions of the Riemann curvature tensor R^h_{ijk}; the Riemann tensor involves the derivatives and products of the Christoffel symbols, which in turn involve the conjugate metric tensor and the derivatives of the metric tensor. Moreover, the right-hand side of Eq. (6.95) consists of energy-momentum tensor which generally involves metric tensor. The Einstein field equations are also non-linear and thus it is impossible to superpose the two known solutions to get the third solution. Thus, in general, it is very difficult to solve Einstein field equations and to overcome such difficulty it is necessary to make some simplifying assumptions. Even in its simplest form $R_{ij} = 0$ it is not an easy job to find a general solution. The most easier and popular simplifying assumption is that the metric has significant degree of symmetry.

Apart from being complicated and non-linear, Einstein field equations are important in themselves as mathematically they relate the energy-momentum distribution to the components of the curvature tensor; while physically these equations tell us about the nature of the gravitational field which is generated by a given source. Thus the source for the gravitational field is the energy-momentum tensor. The physical justification can also be explained by considering the evolution of the expansion θ of a family of neighbouring time-like geodesics and as we have seen in the previous section that such evolution is given by the Raychaudhuri equation [Eq. (6.90)] which encodes the effect of gravity.

After finishing his general theory of relativity, Einstein worked on a static cosmological model and the result was a static universe. In order to get a model of the universe, Einstein modified his field equations by adding a new term Λ, known as *cosmological constant;* and now Einstein field equations read as

$$R_{ij} - \frac{1}{2}Rg_{ij} + \Lambda g_{ij} = -kT_{ij} \qquad (6.97)$$

In this section, we shall discuss some important solutions of the field Eqs. (6.95)–(6.96) which played an important role in the development of general relativity and we have

The Schwarzchild solutions

This is one of the simplest and most useful solution of Einstein equations [Eq. (6.96)]. This solution has played a key role in the early development of general relativity and even today is considered to be a solution of fundamental importance. Einstein himself has obtained this solution using the method of successive approximation, but it was Karl Schwarzschild who obtained a simple solution in 1916, a month after Albert Einstein gave his general theory of relativity. Karl Schwarzschild (October 9, 1873–May 11, 1916) was a German physicist and is best known for providing the first exact solution to the Einstein field equations of general relativity. At the outbreak of World War I in 1914 he joined the German army and served on both the western and eastern fronts, rising to the rank of lieutenant in the artillery. While serving on the front in Russia in 1915, he began to suffer from a rare and painful skin disease called pemphigus. But somehow, he managed to write three outstanding papers—two on relativity theory and one on quantum theory. His papers on relativity produced the first exact solutions to the Einstein field equations that now bear his name—the Schwarzschild metric. He died on May 11, 1916 from the painful autoimmune disease pemphigus. *Asteroid 837 Schwarzschilda* is named in his honour. Schwarzschild has obtained two solutions—exterior and inetrior.

The gravitational fields that are most important to us in our daily life (that of the earth and the sun) are produced by slowly rotating and nearly spherical mass distribution so we shall first deal with exterior solution (empty space surrounding a gravitating body), since it is easy to get the motion of the test particles outside an object. In our later discussion we shall also deal with the interior solution.

Exterior solution describes the geometry of the spacetime in the empty space outside a static spherically symmetric distribution of matter and the metric, in spherical coordinates (r, θ, ϕ, t), is

$$ds^2 = -\left(1 - \frac{2m}{r}\right)^{-1} dr^2 - r^2 d\theta^2 - r^2 \sin^2 \theta d\phi^2 + \left(1 - \frac{2m}{r}\right) dt^2 \quad (6.98)$$

where m is interpreted as the mass of the gravitating objcet and r is the radial coordinate (sometimes known as Schwarzschild coordinate). This solution can easily be obtained by taking $R_{ij} = 0$ in Example 4.6 and then solving the resulting equations to get the values of λ and ν. Equation (6.98) is known as *Schwarzschild exterior solution*. In the list of important spacetimes, Schwarzschild exterior solution is second only to Minkowski spacetime. Equation (6.98) also gives us the important result: "The empty spacetime outside a spherically symmetric distribution of matter is described by a static metric". This is known as *Birkhoff's Theorem*.

In CGS units, the Schwarzschild exterior solution (6.98) can also be expressed as

$$ds^2 = -\left(1 - \frac{2mG}{rc^2}\right)^{-1} dr^2 - r^2 d\theta^2 - r^2 \sin^2 \theta d\phi^2 + \left(1 - \frac{2mG}{rc^2}\right) dt^2$$

(6.99)

In Eq. (6.98), the metric coefficient becomes infinite at $r = 0$ and $r = 2m$. It is known that if any of the scalars $R, R_{ij}R^{ij}, R_{ijkl}R^{ijkl}, R_{ijkl}R^{klmn}R^{ij}_{mn}$ and so on approaches to infinity as we move to some point then that point is regarded as the singularity of the curvature (it must be checked that this point can be reached by travelling a finite distance along a curve). From Eq. (6.98), it can be shown that

$$R_{ijkl}R^{ijkl} = \frac{48m^2}{r^6}$$

(6.100)

Thus, $r = 0$ is the real singularity. The other singularity occurs at $r = 2$ m and is known as *Schwarzschild singularity*. Here $r = r_s$ is called the *Schwarzschild radius*. In CGS units, it is given by

$$r = r_s = \frac{2Gm}{c^2}$$

(6.101)

The Schwarzschild solution describes a black hole if the radius of the object is smaller than a certain critical value. For sun, this critical radius (the Schwarzschild radius) is $r_s = 2.956$ km while the actual radius of the sun is 6.96×10^5 km, which is much larger for sun not to be a black hole. If the radius of the sun would have been less than three kilometre, the sun would have been a black hole. But in this case, the sun would not be radiating and there would be no life on earth. Black holes are the objects whose gravity is so strong that even light cannot escape from it. A black hole has a number of unusual properties. In the beginning black holes were described in a static framework, but it is now realised that the stars evolve into black holes by collapse. Moreover, most of the time black holes attract and swallow the matter around them; and thus a time dependent solution of Einstein equations is needed to describe the evolution of black holes. Such time dependent solutions have also been discussed in this section.

The singularity at $r = 2m$ can be removed if we use the transformation $r - 2m = u^2$ and the exterior solution (6.98) becomes

$$ds^2 = -4(u^2 + 2m)du^2 - (u^2 + 2m)(d\theta^2 + \sin^2 \theta d\phi^2) + \frac{u^2}{u^2 + 2m}dt^2 \quad (6.102)$$

This line element is free from singularity and thus $r = 2m$ is a removable singularity. The solution (6.102) is valid only for positive values of the mass m.

To know the gravitational field inside a celestial object, we have to find the model of this object; and to model such situation we assume that the matter inside this celestial object is that of a perfect fluid. That is, we have to consider the energy-momentum tensor of the form given by Eq. (6.54). Also assume that the matter inside the object is at rest and $u_i = (0, 0, 0, e^{-\nu/2})$. Here, for the metric (6.55), the Einstein field Eqs. (6.95) with energy-momentum tensor given by Eq. (6.54) have to be solved to get the values of λ and ν.

The spherically symmetric gravitational field inside an object (star) of mass m and radius r is given by the metric

$$ds^2 = -\left(1 - \frac{r^2}{R_0^2}\right)^{-1} dr^2 - r^2 d\theta^2 - r^2 \sin^2\theta d\phi^2 + \left[A - B\left(1 - \frac{r^2}{R_0^2}\right)^{1/2}\right]^2 dt^2$$

(6.103)

where $R_0^2 = \dfrac{3}{8\pi\rho}$ and constants A and B can be fixed by demanding that the solutions given by Eqs. (6.98) and (6.103) should match at the boundary $r = r_1$ of the sphere and are given by

$$A = \frac{3}{2}\left(1 - \frac{r_1^2}{R_0^2}\right)^{1/2}, \quad B = \frac{1}{2}, \quad m = \frac{4\pi}{3}\rho r_1^3$$

For solution (6.103) to be real, we must have

$$r_1^2 < R_0^2, \quad r_1^2 < \frac{3}{8\pi\rho}, \quad 2m < r_1 \tag{6.104}$$

Equation (6.104) provides an upper limit on the possible size of a sphere of given density and on the mass of a sphere for a given radius. The solution given by Eq. (6.103) is known as *Schwarzschild interior solution.*

The Reissner-Nordström solution

This spherically symmetric solution of the Einstein-Maxwell equations was derived independently by H. Reissner in 1916, H. Weyl in 1917, and G. Nordström in 1918. It represents a spacetime with no matter sources except for a radial electric field, the energy of which has to be included on the right-hand side of the Einstein equations. Since Birkhoff's theorem, mentioned above in connection with the Schwarzschild solution, can be generalized to the electrovacuum case, the Reissner-Nordström solution is the unique spherical electrovacuum solution. Similar to the Schwarzschild solution, it thus describes the exterior gravitational and electromagnetic fields of an arbitrary static, spherically symmetric, charged body of mass m and charge Q. The metric is given by

$$ds^2 = -\left(1 - \frac{2m}{r} + \frac{Q^2}{r^2}\right)^{-1} dr^2 - r^2(d\theta^2 + \sin^2\theta d\phi^2) + \left(1 - \frac{2m}{r} + \frac{Q^2}{r^2}\right) dt^2$$

(6.105)

The electromagnetic field in these spherical coordinates is described by the "classical" expressions for the time component of the electromagnetic potential and the (only non-zero) component of the electromagnetic field tensor is

$$A_4 = -\frac{Q}{r}, \quad F_{41} = -F_{14} = -\frac{Q}{r^2} \tag{6.106}$$

This solution, known as the *Reissner–Nordström solution* has been obtained by solving the Einstein–Maxwell field equations $R_{ij} = kT_{ij}$ for the metric (6.55) where T_{ij} is the energy-momentum tensor of the electromagnetic field given by Eq. (6.51). This solution has a real singularity at $r = 0$ and in the absence of charge reduces to Schwarzschild exterior solution (6.98).

The Vaidya solution

In general relativity, the Vaidya solution describes the non-empty external spacetime of a spherically symmetric and nonrotating star which is either emitting or absorbing null dusts. It is named after the Indian physicist Prahalad Chunnilal Vaidya and constitutes a simplest non-static generalization of the non-radiative Schwarzschild solution to Einstein's field equation, and therefore is also called the "radiating Schwarzschild metric" or "the metric of radiating star".

Prahalad Chunnilal Vaidya (May 23, 1918–March 12, 2010) was an Indian physicist and mathematician, renowned for his original work in general theory of relativity. Professor Vaidya's research on general theory of relativity was started when he went to Banaras Hindu University in 1942, where he joined the school of relativity started by Professor V.V. Narlikar. It was only ten months that he spent with Professor Narlikar (the father of famous Indian astrophysicist Jayant Vishnu Narlikar), the revolutionary idea of developing a spacetime geometry was born within him, which would describe the gravitational field in the exterior of a radiating star. There was pioneering work done around the same area, but it was helpful only up to some extent. The well-known Schwarzschild solution (6.98) describes the geometry around a spherical star. However, it necessarily assumes the exterior of the star to be empty. Vaidya generalized this case to incorporate the radiation from the star, and the resulting solution was the famous *Vaidya metric*. Till date, Professor Vaidya is known to be one of the pioneers of the golden age of general relativity. The invention of the metric of a radiating star gave Professor Vaidya worldwide recognition at the age of twenty-four, even before the beginning of his professional career.

The Vaidya metric pioneered the key idea of using the light rays as a coordinate frame. In other words, the idea of a null coordinate was born, which has played extremely significant role in subsequent research in gravitation theory of next many decades, and helped generate several significant results and insights. The Vaidya metric has by now found a number of applications in gravitation theory and it is widely used and internationally cited to study many problems in gravitation and general relativity. The classic Vaidya metric is a spherically symmetric Petrov type D solution of the Einstein equations in the presence of pure radiation matter field which propagates at the speed of light. In various contexts this "null dust" may be interpreted as high-frequency electromagnetic or gravitational waves, incoherent superposition of aligned waves with random phases and polarisations, or as massless scalar particles or neutrinos. The Vaidya solution depends on an arbitrary "mass function" $m(u)$ of the retarded time u which characterizes the profile of the pure radiation (it is a "retarded mass" measured at conformal infinity). Various sandwiches and shells of null matter can thus be constructed that are bounded either by flat ($m = 0$) or Schwarzschild-like vacuum regions. Due to this property such solutions have been extensively used as models of spherically symmetric gravitational collapse of a star, as an exterior solution describing objects consisting of heat-conducting matter, as an interesting toy model for investigation of singularities and their possible removal by quantum effects, for studies of various formulations of the cosmic censorship conjecture on both classical and quantum level, process of black-hole evaporation, and for other purposes.

A spherically symmetric star of mass m and radius r_0 is supposed to start radiating at time t_0. As the star continues to radiate the zone of radiation increases in thickness, its outer surface at a later instant $t = t_1$ being $r = r_1$. For $r_0 \leq r \leq r_1, t_0 \leq t \leq t_1$ let the line element be of the form

$$ds^2 = -e^\lambda dr^2 - r^2 d\theta^2 - r^2 \sin^2\theta d\phi^2 + e^\nu dt^2 \tag{6.107}$$

where $\lambda = \lambda(r,t), \nu = \nu(r,t)$. For the nature of radiation, the energy-momentum tensor T_{ij} is taken to be of the form

$$T_{ij} = \rho u_i u_j \tag{6.108}$$

where ρ is the density of radiation and the lines of flow are null geodesics. That is

$$u_i u^i = 0, \quad u^i_{;j} u^j = 0 \tag{6.109}$$

Now solving the Einstein field equations $R_{ij} = 8\pi T_{ij}$ with T_{ij} given by Eq. (6.108), the line element (6.107) becomes

$$ds^2 = -\left(1 - \frac{2m}{r}\right)^{-1} dr^2 - r^2 d\theta^2 - r^2 \sin^2\theta d\phi^2 + \frac{\dot{m}^2}{f^2}\left(1 - \frac{2m}{r}\right) dt^2 \tag{6.110}$$

with

$$m'\left(1 - \frac{2m}{r}\right) = f(m), \quad m = m(r.t)$$

for $r_0 \leq r \leq r_1$, $t_0 \leq t \leq t_1$. The non-zero components of the energy-momentum tensor T_{ij} are given by

$$-T^1_1 = T^4_4 = \frac{m'}{4\pi r^2}, \quad T^4_1 = \frac{m'^2}{4\pi \dot{m} r^2}, \quad T^1_4 = -\frac{\dot{m}}{4\pi r^2}$$

where an overhead dash and dot denote the differentiation with respect to r and t, respectively.

Using the null coordinates, the Vaidya metric (6.110) can be expressed as

$$ds^2 = \left[1 - \frac{2m(u)}{r}\right] du^2 + 2dudr - r^2 \left(d\theta^2 + \sin^2\theta d\phi^2\right) \qquad (6.111)$$

where u is the retarded time coordinate in the Schwarzschild exterior solution (6.98) and is related to the Schwarzschild time coordinate t through the relation

$$u = t - r - 2m \log(r - 2m)$$

and this transformation can be used only when $\dfrac{dm}{du} = 0$.

Since the Vaidya metric (6.110) is a natural and simplest extension of the Schwarzschild metric (6.98), there is a common feature between them—both the metrics are of Petrov type D. However, three clear differences between the Schwarzschild and Vaidya metrics are:

(i) the mass parameter m for Schwarzschild metric is a constant, while for Vaidya metric $m(u)$ is a u-dependent function.

(ii) the Schwarzschild metric is a solution to the vacuum Einstein equation $R_{ij} = 0$, while Vaidya metric is solution is to the trace-free Einstein equation $R_{ij} = 8\pi T_{ij}$ with a nontrivial pure radiation energy field.

(iii) the Schwarzschild solution (6.98) has four independent Killing vector fields, including a timelike one, and thus is a static metric; while Vaidya solution (6.110) has only three independent Killing vector fields regarding the spherical symmetry, and consequently is nonstatic.

It may be interesting to note that the evolution of the Vaidya metric took almost ten years. The first paper was published in the Indian journal "Current Science" in 1943 [Vaidya, P.C., *Current Science*, **12**, 12, 1943] which was followed by a paper by V.V. Narlikar and P.C. Vaidya in the journal "Nature" in 1947 [Narlikar, V.V. and Vaidya, P.C., *Nature*, **159**, 642, 1947]. In 1951, a complete version of Vaidya metric was appeared in "Proceedings of Indian Academy of Sciences" [Vaidya, P.C., *Proc. Indian Acad. Sci.*, **33**, 264, 1951]. Finally, the solution given by Eq. (6.111) was published in "Nature" in 1953 [Vaidya, P.C., *Nature*, **171**, 260, 1953].

The Kerr solution

It is known that most of the stars are rotating relative to the fixed stars (local inertial system) and consequently are not spherically symmetric. Thus their gravitational field cannot be described by Schwarzschild exterior solution. In Newtonian gravitation theory due to the rotational flattering of the star although the field definitely changes, it still remains static. On the other hand in Einstein theory the field is produced due to the flow of matter. The metric will still be time independent (for a time-independent rotation of the star) but not invariant under time reversal. Moreover, from the weak-field asymptotic result it is known that angular momentum destroys spherical symmetry, and this lack of spherical symmetry makes the calculations much more difficult. It is therefore expected that the gravitational field of a rotating star can be described by an axially symmetric and stationary vacuum metric. Like Schwarzchild solution, this new metric should be asymptotically flat, i.e., at large distance from the source it reduces to flat space. Such a solution was found by Roy P. Kerr in 1963 (47 years after the discovery of Schwarzschild exterior solution).

The Kerr metric was discovered rather accidentally, in the course of formal mathematical investigations not obviously related to physics, and only afterwards it was found to describe the exterior gravitational field of a rotating body or black hole. In fact, no explicit solution of Einstein field equations with a perfect fluid source has been found until today that could be matched to the Kerr metric. Its main application is to the description of rotating black holes, which earned it great importance in relativistic astrophysics. The metric given by Kerr is

$$ds^2 = (r^2 + a^2 \cos^2 \theta)(d\theta^2 + \sin^2 \theta d\phi^2) + 2(du + a\sin^2 \theta d\phi)$$
$$\times (dr + a\sin^2 \theta d\phi) - \left(1 - \frac{2mr}{r^2 + a^2 \cos^2 \theta}\right)(du + a\sin^2 \theta d\phi)^2 \quad (6.112)$$

where a is a real constant. Using the transformation

$$(r - ia)e^{i\phi} \sin \theta = x + iy, \quad r\cos \theta = z, \quad u = t + r \quad (6.113)$$

the Kerr metric (6.112) takes the form

$$ds^2 = dx^2 + dy^2 + dz^2 - dt^2 + \frac{2mr^3}{r^4 + a^2 z^2}(k)^2 \quad (6.114)$$

where

$$(r^2 + a^2)rk = r^2(xdx + ydy) + ar(xdy - ydx) + (r^2 + a^2)(zdz + rdt) \quad (6.115)$$

The function r is defined by

$$r^4 - (R^2 - a^2)r^2 - a^2 z^2 = 0, \quad R^2 = x^2 + y^2 + z^2 \quad (6.116)$$

so that asymptotically $r = R + O(R^{-1})$.

The form in which the Kerr metric first appeared in the literature is given by Eq. (6.112), but Kerr [Kerr, R.P., *Phys. Rev. Lett.*, **11**, 5, 237, 1963] did not give any hint that how it had been derived. The Kerr solution turned out to be extremely important from the point of view of physics. It is still the simplest exact solution of Einstein's equations that describes the exterior field of a rotating body and the spacetime around a stationary rotating black hole. Because of this, it became a basis of hundreds of research papers discussing astrophysical aspects of black holes. Another useful form of the Kerr metric, in Boyer–Lindquist coordinates, is given by

$$ds^2 = \left(\frac{r^2 + a^2 \cos^2\theta}{r^2 + a^2 - 2mr}\right) dr^2 + (r^2 + a^2 \cos^2\theta)d\theta^2$$

$$+ \sin^2\theta \left[r^2 + a^2 + \frac{2mra^2 \sin^2\theta}{r^2 + a^2 \cos^2\theta}\right] d\phi^2$$

$$- \left(\frac{4mra \sin^2\theta}{r^2 + a^2 \cos^2\theta}\right) d\phi dt - \left(1 - \frac{2mr}{r^2 + a^2 \cos^2\theta}\right) dt^2 \qquad (6.117)$$

where Boyer–Lindquist coordinates in comparison with spherical coordinates are

$$x = \sqrt{r^2 + a^2} \sin\theta \cos\phi, \quad x = r \sin\theta \cos\phi$$

$$x = \sqrt{r^2 + a^2} \sin\theta \sin\phi, \quad x = r \sin\theta \sin\phi$$

$$z = r \cos\theta, \quad z = r \cos\theta$$

It may be noted that the Kerr metric (6.112) is Ricci flat, i.e., $R_{ij} = 0$. Here, m is the mass and $J = ma$ is the angular momentum of the body. However, the main features of the Kerr geometry (6.112) are:

(i) There are three off-diagonal terms in the metric—which is one of the features that makes calculations difficult.

(ii) By considering the g_{44} component of the metric, it is evident that for $m \neq 0$ there is a coordinate singularity located at $r^2 + a^2 \cos^2\theta = 0$, i.e.,

$$r = 0, \theta = \frac{\pi}{2} \qquad (6.118)$$

(iii) Since the line element is independent of both u and ϕ, the Kerr solution admits two Killing vectors. Labelling the coordinates as (u, r, θ, ϕ), the two Killing vectors are $(1, 0, 0, 0)$ and $(0, 0, 0, 1)$. Any constant-coefficient linear combination of these Killing vectors will again be a Killing vector.

(iv) For $a = 0$, Eq. (6.112) reduces to

$$ds^2 = r^2(d\theta^2 + \sin^2\theta d\phi^2) + 2dudr - \left(1 - \frac{2m}{r}\right) du^2 \qquad (6.119)$$

which is the Schwarzschild exterior solution in the so-called "advanced Eddington-Finkelstein coordinates." Based on this analogy, the line element (6.112) is sometimes known as the advanced Eddington–Finkelstein form of the Kerr spacetime. Also, since we know that $r = 0$ is a curvature singularity in the Schwarzschild solution, this strongly suggests that the singularity in the Kerr spacetime at $r = 0$ and $\theta = \pi/2$ is a curvature singularity.

(v) For $m = 0$, the Kerr solution (6.112) reduces to

$$ds^2 = (r^2 + a^2 \cos^2 \theta)(d\theta^2 + \sin^2 \theta d\phi^2) + 2(du + a \sin^2 \theta d\phi)$$
$$\times (dr + a \sin^2 \theta d\phi) - (du + a \sin^2 \theta d\phi)^2 \qquad (6.120)$$

which is actually flat Minkowski spacetime. For this metric it can be verified that the Riemann tensor is identically zero.

(vi) When $m \neq 0$ and $a \neq 0$, all the non-zero components of the Riemann tensor contain at least one factor of m.

(vii) For the metric (6.112), we have

$$R_{ijkl}R^{ijkl} = \frac{48m^2(r^2 - a^2 \cos^2 \theta)[(r^2 + a^2 \cos^2 \theta)^2 - (16r^2a^2 \cos^2 \theta)]}{(r^2 + a^2 \cos^2 \theta)^6}$$
$$(6.121)$$

which again shows that the singularity located at $r = 0, \theta = \pi/2$ is actually a curvature singularity.

(viii) The Kerr metric (6.117) is expressed in terms of Boyer-Lindquist coordinates so that the number of off-diagonal components of the metric are minimized. There is now only one off-diagonal component which will be helpful in analysing the asymptotic behaviour.

The Kerr-Newman solution

Soon after the discovery of the metric of a rotating black holes, Newman and his co-workers obtained the metric of a charged rotating black hole. The field outside a charged rotating object is given by

$$ds^2 = \left(\frac{r^2 + a^2 \cos^2 \theta}{r^2 + a^2 + e^2 - 2mr}\right) dr^2 + (r^2 + a^2 \cos^2 \theta)d\theta^2$$

$$+ \sin^2 \theta \left[r^2 + a^2 + \frac{a^2 \sin^2 \theta(2mr - e^2)}{r^2 + a^2 \cos^2 \theta}\right] d\phi^2$$

$$- \left(\frac{2a \sin^2 \theta(2mr - e^2)}{r^2 + a^2 \cos^2 \theta}\right) d\phi dt - \left(1 - \frac{2mr - e^2}{r^2 + a^2 \cos^2 \theta}\right) dt^2 \quad (6.122)$$

The line element (6.122) is commonly known as the Kerr–Newman solution. It contains three real parameters: m (mass), e (charge) and a (angular momentum per unit mass). It is now known that a black hole is completely characterized by these three parameters. This is known as *no hair theorem*. Thus super massive black holes, with masses several billion times that of sun, can be described by just three parameters. If the quantum effects are taken into account, then it was shown by Stephen Hawking in 1974 that a black hole will emit thermal black body radiation. This is now called *Hawking radiation*. Accordingly, the laws describing the thermodynamics of black holes were formulated soon. The Kerr–Newman solution (6.122) is of Petrov type D with non-null electromagnetic field and reduces to

(i) the Kerr metric if the charge is zero.

(ii) the Reissner-Nordström solution if the angular momentum is zero.

(iii) the Schwarzschild solution if both the charge and the angular momentum are zero.

6.7 Some Important Tensors

Here we shall discuss some more tensors which have their applications in differential geometry and relativity theory.

Killing tensor

Let M denote a four-dimensional spacetime manifold with Lorentzian metric g_{ab} and metric connection Γ^a_{bc}. A vector field ξ^i on M which satisfies

$$\mathcal{L}_\xi g_{ij} = \xi_{i;j} + \xi_{j;i} = 0 \tag{6.123}$$

is referred to as a Killing vector field. The concept of a Killing vector can be generalized in a variety of ways. A totally symmetric tensor field K of order r on M satisfying

$$K_{(a_1...a_r;a_{r+1})} = 0 \tag{6.124}$$

is referred to as a Killing tensor field [named after Wilhelm Karl Joseph Killing (1847–1923)—a German mathematician]. Here symmetrization of index pairs of a tensor field on M is indicated by round brackets, i.e., $T_{(ab)} = \frac{1}{2}(T_{ab} + T_{ba})$. A Killing tensor with $r = 1$ is a Killing vector. Killing tensors are of interest principally because of their association with polynomial first integrals of the geodesic equation: if t is the geodesic tangent vector, then the quantity $K_{a_1...a_r} t^{a_1}...t^{a_r}$ is a first integral of the geodesic motion. The second order Killing tensors are those which satisfy

$$K_{(ab;c)} = 0, \quad K_{ab} = K_{ba} \tag{6.125}$$

The metric tensor itself and all symmetrized products of Killing vectors are Killing tensors. The maximum number of independent Killing tensors admitted by a four-dimensional spacetime is 50 and this maximum number is attained if and only if the spacetime is of constant curvature. Killing tensors are known to be useful in general theory of relativity because, like Killing vectors, they provide conserved quantities for geodesic motion. The Kerr solution (6.112) (the rotating black hole) is the most famous example of a manifold possessing a Killing tensor (for more details about the applications of Killing tensors, the reader is referred to [Keane and Tapper, 2010] and the references therein).

Codazzi tensor

Codazzi tensors arise very naturally in the study of Riemannian manifolds with harmonic Riemann curvature or harmonic Weyl tensor. A symmetric

(0, 2) type tensor field T on a Riemannian manifold (M, g) is said to be a Codazzi tensor if it satisfies the equation

$$(\nabla_X T)(Y, Z) = (\nabla_Y T)(X, Z) \tag{6.126}$$

for arbitrary vector fields X, Y and Z. This equation is known as Codazzi equation. In local coordinates, this equation can be expressed as

$$T_{ij;k} = T_{ik;j} \tag{6.126a}$$

The Codazzi tensor T_{ij} is called non-trivial if it is not a constant multiple of the metric. The geometrical and topological consequences of the existence of a non-trivial Codazzi tensor on a Riemannian manifold have been studied by Derdzinski and Shen (1983). Codazzi tensors appear in a natural way in many geometric situations. Some of the examples are given below

1. The simplest Codazzi tensors are parallel ones; non-trivial (i.e., not proportional to the metric) tensors of this type exist only in locally reducible manifolds.

2. For a space (M, g) of constant sectional curvature k and any function f on M, the formula $b = \nabla df + kfg$ defines a Codazzi tensor.

3. The second fundamental form of any hypersurface (M, g) in a space of constant curvature is a Codazzi tensor (non-trivial, unless M is totally umbilic).

4. Let (M, g) be a conformally flat manifold, and let $n = \dim M \geq 3$. Then the tensor

$$b_{ij} = R_{ij} - \frac{1}{2(n-1)} R g_{ij} \tag{6.127}$$

   is a Codazzi tensor [non-trivial, unless (M, g) is of constant curvature]. In fact, for $n = 3$, the Codazzi equation for b_{ij} is equivalent to the conformal flatness of g_{ij}, while, for $n \geq 4$, the Weyl conformal tensor C_{ijkl} of any Riemannian manifold satisfies the well-known divergence formula

$$(n - 2)\nabla^j C_{jklm} = (n - 2)(\nabla_l b_{km} - \nabla_m b_{kl}) \tag{6.128}$$

5. A Riemannian manifold is said to have *harmonic curvature* if $\delta R = 0$ (in local coordinates, $\nabla^j R_{jklm} = 0$). This happens if and only if the Ricci tensor R_{ij} satisfies the Codazzi equation [Eq. (6.126a)]. For further details about Codazzi tensor, the reader is referred to [Derdzinski and Shen, (1983)].

Schouten tensor

In Riemannian geometry, the Schouten tensor is a second-order tensor introduced by Jan Arnoldus Schouten. It is defined, for $n \geq 3$, by

$$P_{ij} = \frac{1}{n-2}\left[R_{ij} - \frac{1}{2(n-1)} R g_{ij}\right] \tag{6.129}$$

where R_{ij} is the Ricci tensor, R is the scalar curvature, g_{ij} is the Riemannian metric and n is the dimension of the manifold. This equation, on multiplication with g^{ik} leads to

$$g^{ik}P_{ij} = P_j^k = \frac{1}{n-2}\left[g^{ik}R_{ij} - \frac{1}{2(n-1)}Rg^{ik}g_{ij}\right]$$

or

$$P_j^k = \frac{1}{n-2}\left[R_j^k - \frac{1}{2(n-1)}R\delta_j^k\right] \tag{6.130}$$

Contracting this equation with k and j, we get

$$P = \frac{R}{2(n-1)}, \quad R = 2(n-1)P \tag{6.131}$$

The Weyl tensor C_{ijkl} can also be expressed in terms of Riemann tensor R_{ijkl} and Schouten tensor through the equation

$$R_{ijkl} = C_{ijkl} + g_{ik}P_{jl} - g_{jk}P_{il} - g_{il}P_{jk} + g_{jl}P_{ik} \tag{6.132}$$

While the Ricci tensor, in terms of Schouten tensor, can be expressed as

$$R_{ij} = (n-2)P_{ij} + g_{ij}P_k^k \tag{6.133}$$

The Schouten tensor often appears in conformal geometry because of its relatively simple conformal transformation law

$$g_{ij} \to \Omega^2 g_{ij}, \quad P_{ij} \to P_{ij} - \nabla_i\gamma_j + \gamma_i\gamma_j - \frac{1}{2}\gamma_k\gamma^k g_{ij}$$

where $\gamma_i = \Omega^{-1}\partial_i\Omega$. Since the Weyl tensor is conformally invariant, to study the conformal deformation of the metric, we only need to understand the Schouten tensor. Thus, if g_{ij} is locally conformally flat (i.e., $C_{ijkl} = 0$ relative to the Reimannian metric g_{ij}), then Riemann curvature tensor is determined by Schouten tensor. We also have

Weyl–Schouten theorem. A Riemannian manifold of dimension n with $n \geq 3$ is conformally flat if and only if the Schouten tensor is a Codazzi tensor for $n \geq 3$, or the Weyl tensor vanishes for $n > 3$.

Cotton tensor

In differential geometry, the Cotton tensor on a (pseudo)-Riemannian manifold of dimension n is a third order tensor concomitant of the metric, like the Weyl tensor. The vanishing of the Cotton tensor for $n = 3$ is necessary and sufficient condition for the manifold to be conformally flat, as with the Weyl tensor for $n \geq 4$. For $n < 3$ the Cotton tensor is identically zero. The concept is named after Emile Cotton. The proof of the classical result that for $n = 3$ the vanishing of the Cotton tensor is equivalent to the metric being conformally flat is given by Eisenhart using a standard integrability argument. This tensor density is uniquely characterized by its conformal properties coupled with the demand that it can be differentiable for arbitrary metrics. Recently, the study of three-dimensional spaces is becoming of great interest, because the Cotton tensor restricts the relation between the Ricci tensor and the energy-momentum tensor of matter in the Einstein equations and plays an important role in the Hamiltonian formulation of general relativity.

Denoting the Ricci tensor by R_{ij} and the scalar curvature by R, the components of the Cotton tensor are (in local coordinates)

$$C_{ijk} = \nabla_k R_{ij} - \nabla_j R_{ik} + \frac{1}{2(n-1)}[\nabla_j R g_{ik} - \nabla_k R g_{ij}] \tag{6.134}$$

The Cotton tensor can be regarded as a vector valued 2-form, and for $n = 3$ one can use the Hodge star operator to convert this into a second-order trace-free tensor density

$$C_i^j = \nabla_k \left(R_{li} - \frac{1}{4} R g_{li} \right) \epsilon^{klj} \tag{6.135}$$

which is sometimes called the *Cotton–York tensor*.

Some of the properties of the Cotton tensor are:

(i) *Conformal rescaling*: Under conformal rescaling of the metric $\tilde{g} = e^{2\phi} g$ for some scalar function ϕ, it may be noted that the Christoffel symbols transform as (see also Section 5.3)

$$\tilde{\Gamma}_{bc}^a = \Gamma_{bc}^a + S_{bc}^a$$

where S_{bc}^a is given by the equation

$$S_{bc}^a = \delta_c^a \partial_b \phi + \delta_b^a \partial_c \phi - g_{bc} \partial^a \phi, \quad \partial_b \phi = \frac{\partial \phi}{\partial x^b}$$

The Riemann curvature tensor transforms as

$$\tilde{R}_{bcd}^a = R_{bcd}^a + \nabla_c S_{db}^a - \nabla_d S_{cb}^a + S_{ce}^a S_{db}^e + S_{de}^a S_{cb}^e$$

In n-dimensional manifolds, the Ricci tensor, obtained by contracting the transformed Riemann tensor, transforms as

$$\tilde{R}_{bc} = R_{bc} - g_{bc} \nabla^a \partial_a \phi - (n-2)\nabla_c \partial_b \phi + (n-2)(\partial_c \phi \partial_b \phi - g_{bc} \partial^a \phi \partial_a \phi)$$

Similarly the Ricci scalar R transforms as

$$\tilde{R} = e^{-2\phi} R - 2e^{-2\phi}(n-1)\nabla^a \partial_a \phi - (n-2)(n-1)e^{-2\phi} \partial^a \phi \partial_a \phi$$

Using the above equations, the Cotton tensor transforms as

$$\tilde{C}_{abc} = C_{abc} + (n-2)\partial_d \phi C_{bca}^d \tag{6.136}$$

where C_{bca}^d is the Weyl conformal tensor.

(ii) *Symmetries*: The Cotton tensor has the following symmetries:

$$C_{abc} = -C_{acb}$$

and therefore

$$C_{[abc]} = 0$$

Moreover, the Bianchi formula for the Weyl tensor can be rewritten as

$$C^a_{bcd;a} = (3 - n)C_{bcd}$$

Bach tensor

The origin of the Bach tensor is in an integrability condition for a four-dimensional space to be conformal to an Einstein space. The Bach tensor is a tensor built up from pure geometry, and thereby captures necessary features of a space being conformally Einstein in an intrinsic way. In differential geometry and general relativity, the Bach tensor is a tensor of rank two which is conformally invariant in dimension $n = 4$. It is the only known conformally invariant tensor that is algebraically independent of the Weyl tensor. In general relativity, conformally invariant features of a metric are usually described by the Weyl and the Bach tensors, and in three-dimensions (where the Weyl tensor identically vanishes) by the Cotton-York tensor. The Bach tensor was first discussed by Bach [1921] and is defined through the equation

$$B_{ab} = P^{cd}C_{acbd} + \nabla^c\nabla_a P_{bc} - \nabla^c\nabla_c P_{ab} \tag{6.137}$$

where C_{abcd} is the Weyl tensor and P_{ab} the Schouten tensor [cf., Eq. (6.129)] given in terms of the Ricci tensor R_{ab} and scalar curvature R. It can be shown that

$$B_{ab} = \nabla^c\nabla^d C_{acbd} + \frac{1}{2}R^{cd}C_{acbd} \tag{6.138}$$

where B_{ab} is the Bach tensor, a symmetric, divergence-free, trace-free, conformally covariant tensor (cf., Kozameh et al., 1985; Penrose and Rindler, 1986; and Szekeres; 1968). Moreover, $B_{ab} = 0$ for spacetimes which are conformally flat, or vacuum, or conformal to an Einstein space (for further details about the Bach, Schouten and Cotton tensors, the reader is referred to Bergman, 2004).

Bibliography

Ahsan, Z., "Algebraic classification of space-matter tensor in general relativity", *Indian J. Pure Appl. Math.*, **8**, 231–7, 1977a.

Ahsan, Z., "Algebra of space-matter tensor in general relativity", *Indian J. Pure Appl. Math.*, **8**, 1055–61, 1977b.

Ahsan, Z., "A note on the space-matter spinor in general relativity", *Indian J. Pure Appl. Math.*, **9**, 1154–7, 1978.

Ahsan, Z., "A symmetry property of the spacetime of general relativity in terms of the space-matter tensor", *Brazilian J. Phys.*, **26**, 3, 572–6, 1996.

Ahsan, Z., "Relativistic significance of conharmonic curvature tensor", *Math. Today*, **16A**, 23–8, 1998.

Ahsan, Z., "Electric and magnetic Weyl tensors", *Indian J. Pure Appl. Math.*, **30**, 863–9, 1999.

Ahsan, Z., *Differential Equations and Their Applications*, 2nd ed., PHI Learning, New Delhi, 2013.

Ahsan, Z. and Husain, S.I., "Invariants of curvature tensor and gravitational radiation in general relativity", *Indian J. Pure Appl. Math.*, **8**, 656–62, 1977.

Ahsan, Z. and Siddiqui, S.A., "Concircular curvature tensor and fluid spacetimes", *Int. J. Theor. Phys.*, **48**, 3202–12, 2009.

Ahsan, Z. and Siddiqui, S.A., "On the divergence of space-matter tensor in general relativity", *Adv. Stud. Theor. Phys.*, **4**, 11, 543–56, 2010.

Bach, R., "Zur Weylschen Relativitastheorie und der Weylschen Erweierung des Krummungstensorbergis", *Math. Z.*, **9**, 110–35, 1921.

Bergman, J., *Conformal Einstein spaces and Bach tensor generalizations in n dimensions*, Linköping Studies in Science and Technology. Thesis No. 1113, Matematiska institutionen, Linköpings universitet, SE-581 83 Linköping, Sweden, Linköping, 2004.

Derdzinski, A. and Shen, C.-L., "Codazzi tensor fields, curvature and Pontryagin forms", *Proc. Lond. Math. Soc.*, **47**, 3, 15–26, 1983.

Greenberg, P.J., "Algebra of Riemann curvature tensor in general relativity", *Stud. Appl. Math.*, **51**, 3, 277, 1972.

Ishii, Y., "On conharmonic transformations," *Tensor (N.S.)*, **7**, 73–80, 1957.

Keane, A.J. and Tupper, B.O.J., "Killing tensors in pp-wave spacetimes", *Classical Quantum Gravity*, **27**, 245011, 2010.

Kozameh, C.N., Newman, E.T. and Tod, K.P., "Conformal Einstein spaces", *Gen. Relativ. Gravitation*, **17**, 343, 1985.

Kramer, D., Stephani, H., MacCallum, M.A.H. and Herlt, E., *Exact Solutions of Einstein's Field Equations*, Cambridge University Press, 1980.

Ludvigsen, M., *General Relativity: A Geometric Approach*, Cambridge University Press, 1999.

Mishra, R.S., *Structures on a Differentiable Manifold and Their Applications*, Chandrama Prakashan, Allahabad, 1984.

Narlikar, J.V., *General Relativity and Cosmology*, Macmillan Company of India Ltd., 1978.

Penrose, R. and Rindler, W., *Spinors and Space-Time*, Vol. 2, Cambridge University Press, Cambridge, 1986.

Petrov, A.Z., Dissertation, Moscow State University, 1957.

Petrov, A.Z., *Einstein Space*, Pergamon Press, 1969.

Pirani, F.A.E., *Lectures on General Relativity*, Brandies Summer Institute, 1964, Prentice-Hall, NJ, 1965.

Sachs, R.K., In *Relativity, Groups and Topology*, de Witt, C. and de Witt, B. (Eds.), Gordon and Breach, New York, 1964.

Sharma, D.N. and Husain, S.I., "Algebraic classification of curvature tensor in general relativity", *Proc. Natl. Acad. Sci.*, **39(A)**, 405, 1969.

Siddiqui, S.A. and Ahsan, Z., "Conharmonic curvature tensor and the spacetime of general relativity", *Differ. Geom. Dyn. Syst.*, **12**, 213–20, 2010.

Stephani, H., *General Relativity: An Introduction to the Theory of the Gravitational Field*, Cambridge University Press, Cambridge, 1982.

Szekeres, P., "Conformal tensors", *Proc. R. Soc. London, Ser. A*, **304**, 113–22, 1968.

Weinberg, S., *Gravitation and Cosmology: Principles and Applications of the General Theory of Relativity*, John Wiley & Sons, Inc., New York, 1972.

Yano, K., "Concircular geometry I. Concircular transformation", *Proc. Imp. Acad. Tokyo*, **16**, 195–200, 1940.

Yano, K., *Integral Formulas in Riemannian Geometry*, Marcel Dekker, Inc., New York, 1970.

Yano, K. and Kon, M., *Structures on Manifolds*, World Scientific Publishing Co., Singapore, 1984.

Zakharov, V.D., *Gravitational Waves in Einstein's Theory*, Halsted Press, John Wiley & Sons, Inc., New York, 1973.

Answers and Hints to Exercises

Chapter 1

8. As $B_{ij}A^iA^j$ is an invariant, $B'_{ij}A'^iA'^j = B_{ij}A^iA^j$. Using the transformation law for tensors

$$\left[B'_{ij} - B_{lm}\frac{\partial x^l}{\partial x'^l}\frac{\partial x^j}{\partial x'^m}A(kl)\right]A'^iA'^j = 0$$

which shows that B_{ij} is a rank two tensor as A^i is arbitrary.

9. Use quotient law.

11. Put $B = B_{ijk}u^iu^ju^k = 0$ and differentiate partially to obtain $\dfrac{\partial^3 B}{\partial u^k\partial u^j\partial u^i}$.

12. Use symmetry of B_{ijk} and above exercise.

13. Find $\dfrac{\partial^4 B}{\partial v^l\partial u^k\partial v^j\partial u^i}$, where $B = B_{ijkl}u^iu^jv^kv^l = 0$.

14. Simplify the left-hand side and use $A_{ik} = -A_{ki}$.

15. Given that $\phi b_{ij} + \psi b_{ji} = 0$. Changing the dummy indices, we get $\phi b_{ji} + \psi b_{ij} = 0$ and thus $(\phi + \psi)(b_{ij} + b_{ji}) = 0$ and b_{ij} is skew symmetric.

16. Put $X_{ijk} = A_{ij}B_k$, then X_{ijk} is symmetric with respect to i and j. Similarly, $X_{jki} = A_{jk}B_i$, $X_{kij} = A_{ki}B_j$ which on adding and using the given condition leads to $X_{ijk} + X_{jki} + X_{kij} = 0$. Thus $X_{ijk} = 0$ which means that $A_{ij}B_k = 0$. Therefore, either $A_{ij} = 0$ or $B_k = 0$.

17. We have $\psi = P_{ij}A^iA^j$, then $\psi = P_{ji}A^jA^i$. Adding these two equations leads to $2\psi = (P_{ij} + P_{ji})A^iA^j$ or, $\psi = Q_{ij}A^iA^j$, where $Q_{ij} = P_{ij} + P_{ji}$ showing that Q_{ij} is symmetric.

221

Chapter 2

1. Use the transformation law for g_{ij} so that

$$g' = \det(g'_{ij})$$

$$= \det\left(\frac{\partial x^k}{\partial x'^i}\frac{\partial x^l}{\partial x'^j}g_{kl}\right)$$

$$= \det\left(\frac{\partial x^k}{\partial x'^i}\right)\det\left(\frac{\partial x^l}{\partial x'^j}\right)\det g_{kl}$$

$$= \left[\det\left(\frac{\partial x^k}{\partial x'^i}\right)\right]^2 g$$

which shows that $g' \neq g$.

2.

$$(g_{ij}) = \begin{bmatrix} 5 & -3 & 0 \\ -3 & 3 & 2 \\ 0 & 2 & 4 \end{bmatrix}, (g^{ij}) = \begin{bmatrix} 2 & 3 & -3/2 \\ 3 & 5 & -5/2 \\ -3/2 & -5/2 & 3/2 \end{bmatrix}, g = 4$$

4. (a) $g_{11} = g_{22} = u^2 + v^2, g_{33} = 1, g^{11} = g^{22} = (u^2 + v^2)^{-1}, g^{33} = 1$

   (b) $g_{11} = g_{22} = a^2(\sinh^2 u + \sin^2 v), g_{33} = 1,$

   $g^{11} = g^{22} = [a^2(\sinh^2 u + \sin^2 v)]^{-1}, g^{33} = 1.$

5. The coordinates of this problem are known as *paraboloidal coordinates*. Here

$$g'_{11} = \frac{\partial x^i}{\partial x'^1}\frac{\partial x^j}{\partial x'^1}g_{ij}$$

$$= \left(\frac{\partial x^1}{\partial x'^1}\right)^2 g_{11} + \left(\frac{\partial x^2}{\partial x'^1}\right)^2 g_{22} + \left(\frac{\partial x^3}{\partial x'^1}\right)^2 g_{33}$$

$$= (x'^2)^2(\cos x'^3)^2 + (x'^2)^2(\sin x'^3)^2 + (x'^1)^2$$

$$= (x'^2)^2 + (x'^1)^2$$

Similarly $g'_{11} = (x'^1)^2 + (x'^2)^2, g_{33} = (x'^1 x'^2)^2, g_{ij} = 0, i \neq j$. Use these values in $ds^2 = g'_{11}(dx'^1)^2 + g'_{22}(dx'^2)^2 + g'_{33}(dx'^3)^2$ to get the required result.

6. Find volume spanned by $dxdydz$, that is, $dV = \sqrt{g}dxdydz$ which in fact is zero and all the three coordinates x, y, z are linearly independent.

The space is thus either two-dimensional or one-dimensional. Take $z = $ constant, then $ds^2 = dx^2 + dy^2 - (\frac{3}{13}dx + \frac{4}{13}dy)^2$ and here $g \neq 0$. Thus, the given metric is two-dimensional instead of one-dimensional.

7. Simplify left-hand side and use $\delta_i^i = n$.

8. Multiply the given equation by g^{ij}, then use $\delta_k^k = n, a^{ij}a_{ij} = a$ and $\alpha = \frac{a}{n}$ to get $a_{ij} = \alpha g_{ij}$.

9. For null vectors $g_{ij} A^i A^j = 0$.

10. Use Eq. (2.32).

11. Use Eq. (2.32).

14. In an orthonormal frame, $\epsilon^{ijkl} = \eta^{ip}\eta^{jm}\eta^{kn}\eta^{lo}\epsilon_{pmno}$. For non-zero components of ϵ^{ijkl}, exactly one of the indices i, j, k, l must equal to zero. Since $\eta^{44} = -1. \eta^{ii} = 1$. this gives one minus sign. Thus $\epsilon_{ijkl} = -\epsilon^{ijkl}$. When the metric g_{ij} is considered, this equation becomes

$$[-\det g_{ab}]^{-1/2}\epsilon_{ijkl} = -[-\det g_{ab}]^{1/2}\epsilon^{ijkl}$$

In general $\epsilon_{ijkl} = [\det g_{ab}]^{1/2}\epsilon^{ijkl}$.

15. Use Eq. (2.42) with $\delta_b^a = g_b^a, \delta_a^a = g_a^a = 4$.

Chapter 3

1. As ϕ is a scalar, $\frac{\partial \phi}{\partial x^l}$ are the components of a covariant vector. Put $\phi_l = \frac{\partial \phi}{\partial x^l}$ and simplify the left-hand side.

2. Differentiate $g_{ij}g^{ij} = \delta_i^i$ with respect to x^k partially.

4. Differentiate $A_i' = \frac{\partial x^l}{\partial x'^i}A^l$ to show that $\frac{\partial A_i}{\partial x^k}$ is a tensor. Use the definition of $A_{i;j}$ and $A_{j;i}$ and form the difference $A_{i;j} - A_{j;i}$ to get the other part.

6. From the properties of Christoffel symbols, $\Gamma_{ljk} + \Gamma_{jlk} = \frac{\partial g_{jl}}{\partial x^k}$. Multiply both sides of this equation by $A^{jk}/2$ to get the result.

7. (i) $\frac{d^2 x^1}{ds^2} + x^1 \left(\frac{dx^2}{ds}\right)^2 = 0,$

$$\frac{d^2 x^2}{ds^2} + \frac{2x^1}{(x^1)^2 - (x^2)^2}\frac{dx^1}{ds}\frac{dx^2}{ds} + \frac{x^2}{(x^2)^2 - (x^1)^2}\left(\frac{dx^2}{ds}\right)^2 = 0$$

(ii) $\dfrac{d^2x}{ds^2} + \dfrac{1}{2f}\dfrac{\partial f}{\partial x}\left[\left(\dfrac{dx}{ds}\right)^2 + \dfrac{1}{f}\left(\dfrac{dt}{ds}\right)^2\right] = 0,$

$\dfrac{d^2y}{ds^2} = \dfrac{d^2z}{ds^2} = 0, \dfrac{dt}{ds} = kf(x)$

(iii) $\dfrac{d^2x}{ds^2} + \dfrac{a^2}{2f^2}\dfrac{\partial f}{\partial x} = 0, \dfrac{d^2y}{ds^2} + \dfrac{a^2}{2f^2}\dfrac{\partial f}{\partial y} = 0,$

$\dfrac{d^2z}{ds^2} + \dfrac{a^2}{2f^2}\dfrac{\partial f}{\partial z} = 0, \dfrac{dt}{ds} = \dfrac{a}{f}$

8. (i) From the given metric, calculate Γ^i_{jk} and use them in the equation of geodesic to get

$$\dfrac{d^2r}{ds^2} = r\left(\dfrac{d\theta}{ds}\right)^2, \dfrac{d^2\theta}{ds^2} + \dfrac{2}{r}\left(\dfrac{dr}{ds}\right)\left(\dfrac{d\theta}{ds}\right) = 0$$

While $ds^2 = dr^2 + r^2 d\theta^2$ leads to $1 = \left(\dfrac{dr}{ds}\right)^2 + r^2\left(\dfrac{d\theta}{ds}\right)^2 = 0,$

which when used in above equation gives

$$R_0 = r^2\dfrac{d\theta}{ds} = \text{constant}$$

(ii) Use $\dfrac{d\theta}{ds} = \dfrac{R_0}{r^2}$ in $1 = \left(\dfrac{dr}{ds}\right)^2 + r^2\left(\dfrac{d\theta}{ds}\right)^2 = 0$ to get the first order

differential equation $\left(\dfrac{dr}{d\theta}\right)^2 + r^2 = \dfrac{r^4}{R_0^4}.$

9. See Examples 1.10 and 3.14. Also use the definition of $F_{ij;k}$ to write the value of $F_{ij;k} + F_{jk;i} + F_{ki;j}$.

15. Let the hypersurfaces be characterized by $f = $ constant. Since the vector A_i is orthogonal to the hypersurface $f = $ constant, therefore, $A_i = af_{,i}$, where a is the constant of proportionality. Thus, $A_{i;j} = (af_{,i})_{;j} = a_{,j}f_{,i} + af_{,i;j}$. Now compute $A_{[i;j}A_{k]}$ and use $f_{,i;j} = f_{,j;i}$ to get required result.

16. Since $e^{ijkl}_{;m} = 0$, the covariant differentiation of both sides of Eq. (2.35) leads to the desired result.

17. The given coordinates are cylindrical and thus the metric is $ds^2 = d\rho^2 + \rho^2 d\phi^2 + dz^2$. Use $A^1 = g^{1j}A_j = g^{11}A_1 = A_1, A^2 = g^{22}A_2 = \dfrac{1}{\rho^2}z\sin\phi, A^3 = g^{33}A_3 = e^\phi\cos z$, in the definition of $\text{div}A^i = \text{div}A_i = \dfrac{1}{\sqrt{g}}\dfrac{\partial}{\partial x^l}(\sqrt{g}A^l)$ to get the required result.

19. Given condition curl $A_i = 0$ means that $\dfrac{\partial A_i}{\partial x^j} - \dfrac{\partial A_j}{\partial x^i} = 0$ which shows that $A_i dx^i$ is an exact differential. Let $A_i dx^i = d\phi$, where ϕ is a scalar. But $d\phi = \dfrac{\partial \phi}{\partial x^i} dx^i$ which means $A_i dx^i = \dfrac{\partial \phi}{\partial x^i} dx^i$ so that $A_i = \dfrac{\partial \phi}{\partial x^i}$, that is A_i is gradient.

20. In cylindrical coordinates

$$\nabla^2 \phi = \frac{\partial^2 \phi}{\partial r^2} + \frac{1}{r}\frac{\partial^2 \phi}{\partial \theta^2} + \frac{\partial^2 \phi}{\partial z^2} + \frac{1}{r}\frac{\partial \phi}{\partial r}$$

21. Use equations

$$g_{ij}\frac{dx^i}{ds}\frac{dx^j}{ds} = 0 \quad \text{and} \quad \frac{d^2 x^i}{ds^2} + \Gamma^i_{jk}\frac{dx^j}{ds}\frac{dx^k}{ds} = 0$$

22. Find $\dfrac{dx}{ds}, \dfrac{dy}{ds}, \dfrac{dz}{ds}, \dfrac{dt}{ds}$ and substitute them in the given metric to get $ds^2 = 0$.

Chapter 4

1. (i) -2, (ii) Yes, since g_{ij} are constant.

2. (i) $(x^1, x^2, x^3) = (r, \theta, \phi)$, (ii) Yes. Calculate R^h_{ijk}, it should be zero.

3. Write $S^{kl}_{ij} = T^{kl}; ij - T^{kl}; ji$. Use the Ricci identity $S^{kl}_{ij} = -T^{ml}R^k_{mij} - T^{km}R^l_{mij}$ so that

$$S^{ij}_{ij} = -T^{mj}R^i_{mij} - T^{im}R^j_{mij} = -T^{mj}R_{mj} + T^{im}R_{mi} = 0$$

5. Here $x^1 = \phi, x^2 = \theta, g_{11} = a^2, g_{22} = (b + a\sin\phi)^2$

$$\Gamma^1_{22} = -\frac{1}{a}(b + a\sin\phi)\cos\phi, \Gamma^2_{21} = \Gamma^2_{12} = a(b + a\sin\phi)^{-1}\cos\phi$$

$$R_{1212} = a(b + a\sin\phi)\sin\phi$$

7. Since $R_{ij} = g^{lm}R_{limj}$, find R_{ij} for $i = j$ and take $R_{ij} = 0$ to prove the condition $\phi'' - \theta'\phi' + \phi'^2 = 0$.

8. Here $g^{ij}R_{ij} = \dfrac{1}{2}Rg^{ij}g_{ij}$ which means that $R = \dfrac{n}{2}R$ so that $\left(1 - \dfrac{n}{2}\right)R = 0$ leads to $R = 0$. Thus $R_{ij} = 0$.

9. Multiply the given identity by g^{ij} to get $R_{;k} = 0$ which means that $\dfrac{\partial R}{\partial x^k} = 0$ and thus R is constant.

14. Here $(x^1)^2 + (x^2)^2 + (x^3)^2 + (x^4)^2 = c^2$ which means that the space is a hypersurface in Euclidean space V_4. In such a space $g_{ij} = 1$ for $i = j$ and $g_{ij} = 0$ for $i \neq j$. Let $x'^1 = \theta, x'^2 = \phi, x'^3 = \psi$, then $g'_{11} = c^2, g'_{22} = c^2 \sin^2 \theta, g'_{33} = c^2 \sin^2 \theta \sin^2 \phi, g'_{ij} = 0, i \neq j$ and $ds^2 = c^2(d\theta^2 + \sin^2 \theta d\phi^2 + \sin^2 \theta d\psi^2)$ which is a V_3. Now find the non-vanishing components of R'_{ijkl} and then verify $R'_{ijkl} = K(g'_{ik}g'_{jl} - g'_{il}g'_{jk})$ for $K = 1/c^2 = $ constant.

15. Here $T^i_{j;i} = R^i_{j;i} + (\alpha R_{;i})$ as $\delta^i_{j;i} = 0$. If $T^i_{j;i} = 0$ then $R^i_{j,i} + \alpha R_{,i}\delta^i_j = 0$ which means that $\frac{1}{2}R_{,j} + \alpha R_{,j} = 0$ and this leads to $\left(\alpha + \frac{1}{2}\right)R_{,j} = 0$. But since $R_{,j}$ is not identically zero, therefore $\alpha = -1/2$.

17. Here

$$R_{1212} = -\frac{1}{2}\left[\frac{\partial^2 f}{(\partial x^1)^2} + \frac{\partial^2 f}{(\partial x^2)^2}\right] + \frac{1}{2f}\left[\left(\frac{\partial f}{\partial x^1}\right)^2 + \left(\frac{\partial f}{\partial x^2}\right)^2\right] \quad \text{(i)}$$

Also for a V_2, $K = \dfrac{R_{1212}}{g}$. Given that V_2 is flat, that is, $K = 0$ which means that $R_{1212} = 0$ and Eq. (i) leads to

$$\frac{\partial^2 f}{(\partial x^1)^2} + \frac{\partial^2 f}{(\partial x^2)^2} = \frac{1}{f}\left[\left(\frac{\partial f}{\partial x^1}\right)^2 + \left(\frac{\partial f}{\partial x^2}\right)^2\right] \quad \text{(ii)}$$

But $f = f(r), r^2 = (x^1)^2 + (x^2)^2$, Eq. (ii) can now be written as

$$\frac{d^2 f}{dr^2} + \frac{1}{r}\frac{df}{dr} = \frac{1}{f}\left(\frac{df}{dr}\right)^2 \quad \text{(iii)}$$

Put $P = \log f(r)$, then Eq. (iii) becomes

$$\frac{d^2 P}{dr^2} + \frac{1}{r}\frac{dP}{dr} = 0$$

This equation can be expressed as

$$\frac{d}{dr}\left(r\frac{dP}{dr}\right) = 0$$

which means that

$$r\frac{dP}{dr} = \text{constant} = k$$

Solving this equation, we get $P = \log \dfrac{r}{a}$. Combine it with $P = \log f(r)$ to get $f(r) = c(r)^k$.

Chapter 5

1. We have $C^m_{imj} = g^{mn}C_{nimj}$. Use the definition of C_{hijk} [i.e., Eq. (5.13)] and $\delta^i_i = n$.

2. From the definition $\mathcal{L}_\xi A_i = \mathcal{L}_\xi(g_{ij}A^j) = (\mathcal{L}_\xi(g_{ij})A^j + g_{ij}\mathcal{L}_\xi A^i)$. If $\mathcal{L}_\xi A^i = 0$, then $\mathcal{L}_\xi A_i = A^j\mathcal{L}_\xi g_{ij}$ which is zero only when ξ_i is a Killing vector.

3. $\dfrac{\partial}{\partial y}$.

4. From Killing equation deduce that $\dfrac{\partial X^a}{\partial x^b} + \dfrac{\partial X^b}{\partial x^a} = 0$. Differentiate this equation with respect to x^c and permute the indices to show that $\dfrac{\partial^2 X^a}{\partial x^b \partial x^c} = 0$. Now integrate it to get $X^a = \omega^a_b x^b + t^a$, where $\omega_{ab} = -\omega_{ba}$ and t^a are constants of integration, usually termed as *parameters*. The Killing vectors are $X^1 = \dfrac{\partial}{\partial x}$, $X^2 = \dfrac{\partial}{\partial y}$, $X^3 = \dfrac{\partial}{\partial z}$,

$$X^4 = y\frac{\partial}{\partial z} - z\frac{\partial}{\partial y}, X^5 = z\frac{\partial}{\partial x} - x\frac{\partial}{\partial z}, X^6 = x\frac{\partial}{\partial y} - y\frac{\partial}{\partial x}.$$

5. The Killing vectors are $(0,0,0,1), (0,0,1,0), (0,1,0,0), (1,-x^2,0,0)$, $(2x^2, -(x^2)^2 + 2e^{-2x^1}, 0, -4e^{-x^1})$.

Index